A MANUAL ON METHODS FOR MEASURING PRIMARY PRODUCTION IN AQUATIC ENVIRONMENTS

IBP HANDBOOK No. 12

A Manual on Methods for Measuring Primary Production in Aquatic Environments

INCLUDING A CHAPTER ON BACTERIA

Edited by

RICHARD A. VOLLENWEIDER

with the collaboration of

J. F. TALLING and D. F. WESTLAKE

SECOND PRINTING

INTERNATIONAL BIOLOGICAL PROGRAMME
7 MARYLEBONE ROAD, LONDON NW1

BLACKWELL SCIENTIFIC PUBLICATIONS
OXFORD AND EDINBURGH

ISBN 0 632 05700 9

FIRST PUBLISHED 1969
REPRINTED 1971

Distributed in the U.S.A. by
F. A. DAVIS COMPANY, 1915 ARCH STREET,
Philadelphia, Pennsylvania

Printed and bound in Great Britain by
BURGESS & SON (ABINGDON) LTD

Contents

List of Contributors

Cassie R.M. Zoology Department, University of Auckland, New Zealand

Edmondson W.T. Department of Zoology, University of Washington, Seattle, Washington 98105, U.S.A.

Findenegg I. Rosentalerstrasse 62, Klagenfurt, Austria

Fogg G.E. Botany Department, Westfield College, London NW3, Great Britain

Goldman C.R. Zoology Department, University of California, Davis, California 95616, U.S.A.

Hobbie J.E. Zoology Department, North Carolina State University, Raleigh, North Carolina, U.S.A.

Jitts H.R. CSIRO, Division of Fisheries and Oceanography, Cronulla, N.S.W., Australia

Margalef R. Instituto de Investigaciones Pesqueras, Paseo Nacional, Barcelona 3, Spain

Owens M. Water Pollution Research Laboratory, Elder Way, Stevenage, Hertfordshire, Great Britain

Ruggiu D. and Saraceni C. Istituto Italiano di Idrobiologia, Verbania-Pallanza, (Novara), Italy

Soeder C.J. Limnologisches Institut der Universität Freiburg, Falkau, (Federal Republic of Germany)

Sorokin Yu.I. Institute of Freshwater Biology, U.S.S.R. Academy of Science, Borok, Jaroslav, Nekouz, U.S.S.R.

Steemann Nielsen E. Royal Danish School of Pharmacy, Copenhagen, Denmark

Talling J.F. Freshwater Biological Association, The Ferry House, Ambleside, Westmorland, Great Britain

Vollenweider R.A. Fisheries Research Board, Canada Centre for Inland Waters, Burlington, Ontario

Westlake D.F. Freshwater Biological Association, The River Laboratory, East Stoke, Wareham, Dorset, Great Britain

Wetzel R.G. Department of Botany and Plant Pathology, Kellogg Gull Lake Biological Station, Michigan State University, Hickory Corners, Michigan, U.S.A.

Foreword

The International Biological Programme is a worldwide plan of co-ordinated research concerned with 'the biological basis of productivity and human welfare'. The handbook series of IBP consists of volumes which are needed by biologists who are participating in the programme around the world.

The PF section of IBP deals with the processes of production in aquatic ecosystems. Its aim at the outset was to produce four manuals of methods for the investigation of the major trophic levels and of water as a nutrient solution. Of these handbooks planned the *Methods for Assessment of Fish Production in Fresh Waters* edited by W.E.Ricker has appeared in 1968 as IBP Handbook No. 3; *Methods for Chemical Analysis of Fresh Waters* edited by H.Golterman with the assistance of R.S.Clymo is published as IBP Handbook No. 8.

The present handbook deals with the fundamental issue of primary production. Like the previous volumes, this manual is based on an intensive working meeting which in this case was held in May 1965 at the Istituto Italiano di Idrobiologia, Verbania-Pallanza. A companion volume to the present book containing the papers read at the meeting was first published in the Memorie dell'Istituto Italiano di Idrobiologia and was later also reprinted in the U.S.A.

The editor of this volume, Dr R.A.Vollenweider, was until recently at the Istituto Italiano and is now in a leading position at the Canada Centre for Inland Waters in Burlington, Ontario. Dr Vollenweider has published extensively on the subject and his authority on primary production of freshwaters is widely recognised.

E.B.WORTHINGTON
IBP Central Office
7 Marylebone Road
London NW1

December 1968

Preface

The present Manual on Methods for Measuring Primary Production in Aquatic Environments is one of a series of IBP Handbooks. The general outline was decided during the first IBP Symposium on Primary Productivity held at Pallanza (Italy), 26 April–1 May 1965. Although most of it is devoted to freshwater environments, it is not restricted to these, but includes many references to marine environments.

A manual can be written on the basis of different concepts. The present book is the result of a combined effort from many authors, but it is not a sequence of individual contributions. Although the basic idea has been to produce a simple outline of techniques already established for primary productivity studies, it is also more than a simple presentation of methods. Much emphasis has been given to a critical review of techniques, rather than to a set of standard procedures to be used in all situations. Science develops continually. The methods in a field as young as primary productivity, although satisfactory today, may need revision tomorrow.

For this reason it has not been possible to create a uniform entity; the primary task of the editor has been to balance, adjust and redistribute some of the individual contributions. Some repetitions have been unavoidable and, vice versa, not all gaps have been filled. Some of the sections originally planned have proved to be impractical at this stage, and publication has proceeded in the hope that these points may be included in a later edition. The editor apologises for not attempting the whole task by himself. As a compensation the reader will find an extensive literature index at the end of the book, from which he may obtain useful additional information.

One of the editor's tasks is to thank his colleagues who have contributed to this Manual. He does this with great pleasure, for many of them have really generously dedicated their time to the none-too-easy task. Their contributions are inserted as complete as possible, and credit is given to their work by appropriate reference after the title of the section or sub-section. Where it has been necessary to make cuts and transfers, this could not always be done, but as far as possible even small insertions are acknowledged. Four contributions from individuals not present at the Symposium are acknowledged with thanks. The first—which is a masterpiece of clarity and should be perused by every reader—is on the use of statistics by Professor R.M.Cassie. The others are by Professor W.T.Edmondson on a simple method of counting plankton, by Dr H.R.Jitts on the use of scintillation counting techniques, and by Drs C.Saraceni and D.Ruggiu on sampling techniques.

The editor wishes to thank Dr J.Rzoska, Scientific Co-ordinator of the IBP/PF Section, for his encouragement and infinite patience during the final editing of the Manual. At this stage further editorial assistance was received from Dr J.F.Talling and Mr D.F.Westlake, who revised the English and made a number of small changes, at the same time preserving the original version. They are grateful for assistance received from their colleague Dr A.Marker.

The editor and contributors also wish to thank Dr Livia Tonolli and the late Professor V.Tonolli of the Istituto Italiano di Idrobiologia, Verbania Pallanza, for their hospitality and support.

The papers read at the Pallanza Symposium have been collected and published under the title *Productivity in Aquatic Environments: Proceedings of an IBP/PF Symposium,* C.R.Goldman, Editor. They appeared as Volume XVIII (Supplement) 1965 in the *Memorie dell'Istituto Italiano di Idrobiologia* and have also been reprinted under an identical title and published by the University of California Press, 1966.

There are many references to the Proceedings in our Manual and they form a companion volume to the present work.

R.A.VOLLENWEIDER

Verbania-Suna

NOTE ON SECOND PRINTING

A revision of this book is in preparation. It has involved a considerable amount of work and a number of collaborators and is not yet completely finished.

Owing to the demand for the existing version and the exhaustion of stock, the book is reprinted, herewith, in an unchanged form.

Attention is drawn to a forthcoming handbook on the assessment of microbial production in inland waters which will largely supersede chapter 4 of this handbook.

1

Objectives

R A VOLLENWEIDER

Primary production studies are concerned with (a) the evaluation of the capacity of an ecosystem to build up, at the expense of external energy, both radiant and chemical, primary organic compounds of high chemical potentials for further transformation and flow to higher system levels; (b) the composition, properties and fate of the structural elements of the system which act as carriers of the primary production processes. Accordingly, the measurement problems involved are threefold: (a) problems related to establishing and quantitatively measuring those system components which are capable of maintaining, at any moment, the flow of matter and energy through the system; (b) problems concerned with assessing the sum of these flows at a given moment, and during a certain period of time; (c) problems concerned with defining the energies involved in biosynthesis at the primary production level.

This definition attempts to indicate that photosynthesis is a fundamental process of primary production, but also that primary production is not identical with photosynthesis; the concept comprises chemo-autotrophic processes as well. Further, emphasis is given to all important structural elements involved in biosynthesis at the primary production level (not only carbon), and to the biological units (the systematic groups *sensu stricto*) of the system, as well as to their dynamics. The problem areas indicated are identical for all self-contained ecosystems, both terrestrial and aquatic.

At the practical level, considering the present stage of research, primary production studies in aquatic environments are, however, restricted to, or centred round, some of the above-defined aspects. Particular attention is paid to the flow of carbon, whereas the fate of other chemical components is still almost unknown. In the past many investigations were concerned with the analysis of primary producer communities, their composition and dynamics, but at present there prevails a certain tendency to neglect these aspects in favour of rate measurements. In consequence still little is known, and our understanding is rudimentary regarding the production process as a whole. In fact, although a considerable analytical material is now at our disposal, as yet no real attempt has been made to integrate the structural and dynamic properties of plant communities, except for some aspects. This is, of course, in part due to limited man-power, in part to uncertainties which arise from the fact that we still lack an appropriate theoretical frame-work, on the basis of which such integration becomes possible. In this connexion it is worthwhile to mention that the energy concept applied to specific results—although of high theoretical interest—in most instances is interpretative, not based on direct measurements of energy content and flow. Accordingly, there is a large open field for both experimental and theoretical studies.

The particular aim of the present Manual does not allow us to fill in or even outline these gaps. The contents of the book have been balanced along the lines of current research in aquatic primary production. Here, some words must be said about the particular properties of aquatic systems. They differ from terrestrial systems which, in general, are relatively easy to define as sociological units (forests of a particular type, shrub vegetations, prairies, etc.), the structure of which is given by a few dominating species which persist on the same place over a longer period of time. The character of aquatic systems, at least at the primary producer level, is much more ephemeral and dependent upon a variety of changing environmental factors, such as meteorological, hydrological, nutritional, but also on biological factors (e.g. grazing). In addition to this it must be remembered that the recruitment of the various subsystems (littoral, benthic and pelagic in lakes; niches of different flow characteristics in flowing waters) comes from biological units of quite different organizational level: macrophytes on one side, and algae (and bacteria) on the other. The biological cycles, life duration, space occupancy of these are of quite different order. Looking at the whole system, it is often difficult to single out their functional characteristics, in as far as they may compete simultaneously for the same factors available, *i.e.* light and nutrients. They may also contribute at the same time and in comparable proportions to the overall efficiency of the whole system. Accordingly, and in some contrast to many terrestrial problems, primary production analyses of aquatic systems can hardly be done on the basis of some fairly uniform standard procedures and, in particular, it is almost impossible to isolate them from appropriate analyses of the environment itself.

For the present Manual an attempt has been made to account for these various aspects. Starting from methods used to assess standing crops of phytoplankton, periphyton and higher aquatics (chapter 2), it proceeds to techniques of rate measurement currently available for these three groups with direct as well as indirect methods. In addition, some particular aspects such as bioassay techniques, extracellular products, community respiration, etc. are discussed (chapter 3). No attempt has been made to include methods concerning flow rates of elements other than carbon, or problems regarding the nutrient availability-efficiency relationship, etc. A short-coming is also to be noted with regard to the problem area of energy exchanges.

It was felt that two additional chapters should complete the Manual. One is considering the basic methods needed to assess bacterial production, particularly the chemo-autotrophic one (chapter 4); it should be mentioned that a special IBP–PF meeting is devoted to bacterial production. The other chapter gives an introduction to environmental analyses (chapter 5). Both these chapters, of course, do not exhaust the subjects and readers are invited to consult other handbooks on these. Nevertheless it is hoped that these chapters may be useful for guiding beginners in the field.

2

Sampling Techniques and Methods for Estimating Quantity and Quality of Biomass

GENERAL PRINCIPLES

R A VOLLENWEIDER

One of the basic requirements of a quantitative science is the development and adoption of sound sampling techniques. There are no general rules as to how this can be done. Ingenuity is necessary to devise new apparatus but imagination and criticism are needed to use it in a natural environment. Only then will it be possible to collect what has been called a 'representative sample' of a community. If the research does not reach this stage, then the best apparatus will be unsuitable, and, *vice versa*, an imaginative research worker will often find means and ways to adapt even primitive devices to his particular problem. As an example, in a shallow water, a simple glass tube may be as efficient as a costly water sampler, and may be even better if the microstratification is to be studied, which a sampler would not reveal. To keep one's eye on the whole is therefore the first principle in sample techniques, and the next is to adapt the apparatus selected to the particular properties of the biocoenosis to be studied.

If these two points are observed, then a third principle will be more or less self-evident: As counting is a time-consuming operation, the effort spent to obtain a certain counting precision for an individual sample should be relative to its representative value. Often, it is far better to collect a number of samples from the same locality, varying the sampling place slightly for every individual sample and counting them at a lower precision level, than to put too much effort into counting a single sample with high accuracy.

One has to look at methods with critical eyes, and the best way to achieve this view, besides experience, is a sufficient acquaintance with elementary statistics. This is a positive recommendation, but also a warning: formulae are less important than concepts! Many biologists restrict their knowledge to Gaussian distributions, variance calculation and some other linear problems. But often biological statistics are not Gaussian, i.e. their basic model is not the normal (random) distribution, but some model of over or underdispersion, and in many cases the sampling itself is not random, but stratified; and for such cases, even statisticians do not have ready-made solutions, as yet.

This should be borne in mind in presenting numerical data. Readers often like to re-check them in connection with their own findings. So, they should be published with all information needed, to retrieve the original estimations; this is particularly indicated if the final figures result from calculations based on the use of any arbitrary conversion factor.

2.1 PHYTOPLANKTON

2.11 Techniques for sampling water and phytoplankton
C SARACENI and D RUGGIU

(a) Closing samplers and multiple-chamber water samplers
Samples of water or phytoplankton may be collected using bottles fitted with a closing device, which can be lowered open to the desired depth and then closed automatically by various means. Closure is usually activated by a drop-weight ('messenger') which slides down the supporting wire or cord. The bottles most commonly used are the 'FRIEDINGER', 'RUTTNER' and 'VAN DORN' (Schwoerbel 1966). Their sampling capacity usually varies from $\frac{1}{2}$ to 5 litres. One in particular, a multiple-chamber sampler ('Hydra', Stepanek 1961), permits the rapid collection of already concentrated material. Depending upon the investigation, it may be preferable to use bottles of chemically neutral plastic material (polyethylene) or glass, rather than metal, which, by liberating metallic ions into solution, often contaminates the sample. A winch fitted with a meter or, in its absence, a cord (e.g. nylon) marked at suitable intervals, allows the sampler to be lowered to the desired depth.

(b) Integrating samplers (pumps and tubes)
The use of a suction-pump with a tube to the desired depth is recommended if a large quantity of organisms are to be collected quickly and concentrated

directly by filtering the pumped water. Further, a pump is advisable in those experiments requiring a rapid, abundant supply of water. A pump is also advantageous because it can supply a homogeneous collection of organisms (any particular stratum) or gradually collect all the organisms in a complete column of water down to a desired depth.

(c) Special techniques (microstratifications, sampling
near bottom, shallow waters)
For collecting sediments and their overlying waters, one may use Plexiglass tubes, mounted on suitable frames and fitted with an opening-closing device, such as the 'Jenkin surface mud sampler' (Mortimer 1942) and 'Züllig' sampler (Züllig 1953). Water, 20–30 cms from the sediment can be collected using the modification of 'Friedinger's' bottle employed by Züllig (Züllig 1953). Jaag *et al.* (Jaag, Ambühl & Zimmermann 1956) used a modified Friedinger bottle mounted on a rigid pole and held horizontally, to collect water near the bottom in running water. These are also convenient for collecting in shallow water. Joeris (1964) described another type of bottle which can also be used for collecting both in a shallow water and in water near the bottom. In shallow, muddy and very productive waters, one can use open pipes about one metre long, which one immerses vertically, seals and finally withdraws (a technique used to study several Egyptian waters by M.Salah & R.A.Vollenweider).

(d) Suitability of net samples
The use of nets for collecting phytoplankton permits only qualitative, and not quantitative, studies, as the volume of water filtered off is not normally measured. Using nets with an attachment for registering the volume of filtered off water would overcome this difficulty, but plankton is collected selectively because of the mesh size of net (the fishnet mesh normally used, No.25, has openings of 60 μ). All the nanno- and ultra-plankton is lost from the sample, so the investigation would be limited to net plankton of dimensions greater than 60 μ (e.g. *Tabellaria, Asterionella, Fragilaria, Ceratium, Peridinium*, etc.). Elongated forms whose minor axis is less than 60 μ could escape from the net. For work on Primary Production, then, nets are not recommended and bottles with a closing device are preferable.

(e) Preservation and transportation of samples
A simple, convenient method for transporting the collected material alive is to place the samples in small portable refrigerators in which the phyto-

plankton can be maintained for several hours without deterioration. Double-walled, spacious boxes of insulating plastic material are used. Their internal temperature is kept consistently low for the necessary time by special freezing units, which are usually fixed to the inside of the lid having been frozen in a freezing chamber in advance.

For fixing and preserving the collected samples one can use a 10% formalin solution or better still 'Lugol's' solution (made up of 10 gm of pure iodine, 20 gm of KI, 200 cc of distilled water and 20 gm of glacial acetic acid added a few days prior to using; store the solution in dark glass bottles). This is added to the samples in a 1:100 ratio. This solution is the best preservative and facilitates sedimentation (maximum time 4 hours per cc for nanno-plankton; Rodhe, Vollenweider & Nauwerck 1958) and shows flagella and cilia well and permits counting of the phytoplankton under Utermöhl's microscope. The following solution also proved to be a good preservative: 1 part *o*-fluorotoluene; 1 part 1-2-dichloroethanol; 3 parts chlorobutanol; the solution is added to samples in a 1:100 ratio.

2.12   Counting
R MARGALEF

(a) Direct methods
Direct microscopical examination is necessary both for taxonomic work and for the quantitative assessment of phytoplankton in terms of cell numbers and volume. Ideally, the total content of algae, in an aliquot volume of a water sample, is counted; the smaller organisms, which sometimes form a considerable part of the biomass, are included.

For this purpose, the algae have to be concentrated. Since delicate cells such as small flagellates are almost unrecognisable in the fixed state, one has to examine part of the water sample in fresh condition, or, if necessary, after centrifugation.

(i) *Kolkwitz chamber and Utermöhl's method*
For fixation, a sufficient volume of the sample (about 100 ml) is treated with a few drops of Lugol's solution. The fixed sample should be of light-yellow colour; it may be kept for months if well stopped and sheltered from light. The fixative is excellent but can produce some damage to the Coccolitho-phoridaceae; in waters rich in such organisms it is advisable to take a duplicate

sample and fix it with neutral formalin, to a final concentration of formol of about 4%.

In absence of an inverted microscope, algae can be counted in a simple shallow Kolkwitz chamber. In this case, sedimentation must be carried out in a suitable glass tube or cylinder. The supernatant water is decanted down to a few milliliters, the rest is subsequently centrifuged and the concentrate transferred to the chamber. After enumeration of the larger forms, the cover-glass of the chamber is removed with care to prevent agitation; nanno-plankters are then counted using a water immersion objective. When bulky plankton or tripton (=non-living particulate matter) is present, a sufficient number (at least 20) of visual fields should be enumerated rather than two transects, because of the sweeping effect of the objective, when carried close to the chamber bottom. The same applies to other types of counting cells (Palmer & Maloney 1954; Serfling 1949). Haemocytometers can be used in place of any of these as plankton counting chambers, but because of their very shallow depth are unsuitable for the larger plankters.

Nowadays, most cell counts are done with Utermöhl's 'inverted' microscope (Utermöhl 1958). According to the abundance or scarcity of plankton, a few (up to 25) ml of the sample are poured into the sedimentation chamber. For larger quantities, up to 100 ml, the concentration by sedimentation can be carried out in two stages or 'combined chambers' are used. Such 'combined chambers' consist of two parts, a bottom plate chamber and a chamber cylinder. After a suitable sedimentation time, this latter can be removed transversely, and counting of the sediment collected in the bottom plate chamber is done in the usual way. As some nannoplankters sink slowly (about 1 cm in 3 hours) sedimentation time in hours must be at least three times the height of the sedimentation chamber in centimeters.

Enumeration of cells can be carried on in two stages: First, the whole bottom area of the chamber is scanned under a low magnification to count the large forms which generally occur in small numbers. After this, the nannoplankton individuals of two crossed diameter transects are enumerated using a high power objective. The total number of cells is found by multiplying the number of individuals, counted in the transects with the ratio of the whole chamber area to the area of the inspected transects.

The volume of water prepared for sedimentation depends on the density of natural algal populations. In lakes poor in phytoplankton and in oceanic water at least 100 ml should be used. In fertile lakes and in coastal marine waters 25 ml or less are sufficient. Dilution may even be required. Technical difficulties may arise during the process of sedimentation. In order to prevent convection currents in the cylinder, temperature should be kept fairly constant during sedimentation. The formation of bubbles on the walls can be avoided if the sample is brought to room temperature first. Before being filled into the chamber the sample should be thoroughly shaken. In general algae do not stick to the walls, and losses by non-sedimentation are small. If this should happen, lengthening of the sedimentation time does not help.

Buoyant Cyanophyceae fixed with iodide sink down within the time mentioned above. Only very thin filamentous forms, such as *Lyngbya limnetica*, colonies of *Botryococcus* or some other delicate cells are sometimes not precipitated within a reasonable time. In such cases, 1 ml of the fresh sample should be enumerated in a shallow Kolkwitz chamber under medium magnification, in addition to the sedimented sample. This is also recommended for delicate and easily disintegrating colonies (e.g. *Uroglena*) which may be counted as colonies with more ease than as scattered individuals after fixation. When high cylinders, or combined chambers, are used, it is almost impossible to have the plankton settled homogeneously, even when the filling chamber (Utermöhl's 'Füllkammer') is used (Nauwerck 1963). Therefore, counts of crossed transects, or of visual fields in different parts of the chamber, are indispensable when the entire chamber is not counted.

If extreme accuracy is required the counting of several samples in chambers of different sizes is recommended. Thus, errors that may arise from the low density of certain species can be diminished. Generally, at least 100 individuals of every important species should be enumerated. The sediment of every sample ought to be counted at different magnifications; this is because part of the smaller cells may be overlooked at low magnification. Utermöhl (1958) expresses the opinion that in counting the phytoplankton of eutrophic lakes, chambers of at least three different sizes (50, 10 and 1 ml) should be used.

On the other hand, the sampling error may far exceed the accuracy of counting. So, e.g. the vertical and horizontal distribution of phytoplankton may be changed considerably within short intervals by wind action. Therefore, more will usually be gained if one collects and counts several vertical series and does not insist on a too intense treatment of the individual samples.

(ii) *Concentration by centrifugation or filtration*

A convenient procedure to concentrate phytoplankton is to have samples of 10 to 20 ml centrifuged for 15 to 30 minutes at about 1500 rpm. The supernatant water is removed until the volume of the sample is reduced to a $^1/_{10}$–$^1/_{40}$ of the initial. This is conveniently done with a glass tube connected to a water aspirator, or filter pump, with a rubber pipe; the end of the tube is bent with the opening directed upwards. The plankton is resuspended in the remaining volume of water, and the suspension is examined in a Kolkwitz chamber or in a hemocytometer. Centrifugation is applied, in general, to living plankton; dead plankton is more easily sedimented. Centrifugation makes observations on living flagellates and other elements of nannoplankton possible. Precipitation of organisms may be facilitated by adding a small amount of a coagulant, for instance 0·5 ml of a 1% solution of potassium aluminium sulphate per 4 ml of each tube (Ballantine 1953). The buoyancy of certain components of phytoplankton limits the applicability of centrifugation.

Continuous centrifugation has been used to separate the seston from large volumes of water. In the most common types, a cup of metal or plastic (with the walls tapering outwards toward the base) spins around its vertical axis; the water is fed in at the top, the seston accumulates along the lower edge, and the clear water overflows. Kimball & Ferguson Wood (1964) describe a simple and cheap model; only the cup (diameters: 3·6 cm up, 4·5 cm down) has to be machined and can be adapted to any commercial mixer or chopper. At a flow rate of half a liter per minute, it removes from 80 to 90% of the algae. The collected seston can be re-suspended in a few ml of water, or be used for pigment extraction.

Partial filtration and resuspension of the retained material in a small volume of water is a frequently used method, but it is rather difficult to separate all the organisms from the filter.

A volume of water can be passed through a membrane or molecular filter; then, after eventual staining, the filter is dehydrated, cleared and mounted in a slide and the organisms identified and counted (Holmes 1962; Cole & Knight-Jones 1949). The amount of filtered water (1 to 200 ml per cm^2 of filter) depends on plankton density. Sometimes a great amount of fine particulate material clogs the filter before enough phytoplankton for accurate counts has been collected. In such cases filters with pores of about 1 μ or more can be used. Best results are obtained if the phytoplankton is previously killed with formalin or iodide, and if the applied suction is only $^1/_3$–$^1/_2$ atm. It is necessary to avoid salt crystals and be sure that the mounting medium evenly fills the pores. For desalting of freshwater samples, a few ml of distilled water are passed through the sample. For marine samples a series of progressively diluted volumes of sea water is used. Dehydration is obtained by passing volumes of 10–15 ml of progressively more concentrated ethanol (ethyl alcohol). After dehydration, Holmes recommends staining with alcoholic Fast Green (0·1 % in 95 % ethanol); this solution stands for 20 minutes over the filter, suction is then restarted and the filter is washed again with ethanol. The filter is cleared with creosote, methoxybenzene (anisole), or immersion oil. Then it may be mounted on a slide, using Canada balsam dissolved in toluene or xylol. The procedure can be shortened by applying immersion oil to the membrane-filter after washing with distilled water, but the shape of the organisms deteriorates (Moore 1963).

The enumeration of organisms on the filter is subject to the same statistical requirements as the scanning of sedimented organisms with Utermöhl's microscope. All the filter has to be scanned looking for big organisms, and then several transects or visual fields are examined under higher magnification. Holmes recommends taking separate samples, one on filters of 1–2 cm diameter for the big and scarce organisms, another on a small filter (0·5 cm) for the more abundant elements of nannoplankton. The preparation of good dehydrated and mounted slides is time consuming but allows for a delay of examination; the filters can be kept for at least several years.

(b) Incomplete and indirect methods
(i) *Net samples*
Nets for concentration of phytoplankton are still in use. Only the finest mesh nets, with holes of 50 μ down can be considered. The net operates selectively on the plankton community. Only a fraction of the population of each species is retained, and this fraction varies according to the species. Comparison of the enumeration of phytoplankton samples collected with a net, with the results of examination of water samples obtained in the same places and studied with Utermöhl's technique, is very instructive. Retention of nets has been estimated from 94 % for *Ceratocorys horrida* and 11 % in *Peridinium crassipes* to less than 0·1 % in genera as important in marine plankton as *Cyclococcolithus*, *Dinoporella*, *Gyrodinium*, *Platymonas* and *Rhodomonas*. One can assume that only about 8–12 % of cells are retained by meshes of 40 μ. Thus any detailed discussions about the most convenient shape of nets, use of flowmeters and evaluation of filtered water, are immaterial (see also 2.11). Nevertheless, net sampling may be useful. It concentrates species of large size that may have indicator value and supplements estimations of the species diversity in the community.

(ii) *Cultures*

As in bacteriology, it is possible to successively dilute samples in culture media and wait for the growth of cultures. One obtains an estimate of minimal densities of small flagellates. But very often the success of the cultures is rather a function of the offered nutrients than of the real distribution of organisms.

(iii) *Electronic dimensional particle counter*

Recently there has been some interest in the application of electronic dimensional particle counters used for counting blood cells and different organisms in pure cultures, for the study of plankton (Hastings, Sweeney & Mullin 1962; El-Sayed & Lee 1963; Maloney, Donoval & Robinson 1962). Electric current flows between two electrodes, separated by a wall with a small hole; any particle, as it passes the hole (effected by an appropriate suction device), produces a current pulse, which is suitably filtered, amplified and counted. In this manner, the number of particles suspended in a volume of liquid (e.g. 1 ml) can be counted or recorded very rapidly.

Such equipment may be useful on condition that one does not ask too much of it, i.e. it has to be considered like any scanner furnishing information that needs interpretation. Thus the electronic dimensional particle counter can give information about the total density and characteristics of the whole seston, and may be particularly useful for continuous operation, in order to detect gradients or discontinuities in the distributions of suspended matter of any kind, living or dead. The samples to be studied may be collected with water bottles or through a tube and pumping system (peristaltic pumps). The electrical isolation of the sample, as well as a good stabilized current supply and good earth connection, are essential. Temperature and the water level in the sample should be kept approximately constant. A small hole allows more counts and higher precision, but since there are always some big particles or big organisms in the seston, it seems difficult in practical work to use holes below 175 µ if one does not want to have repeated obstructions of the hole. Also air bubbles may be a nuisance. There is a coincidence effect; small particles passing simultaneously give the same signal as one big particle, and moreover, cells of the same volume, but of different nature, such as diatoms and blue-greens, give different signals. Continuous stirring of the sample is necessary; nevertheless, there is always a certain amount of agglutination and sedimentation. There is also electronic noise and, of course, everything is counted, dead or alive. In most instances the number of detritus particles is much higher than of living cells.

In axenic (one-organism) cultures, it is possible to select threshold, sensitivity and hole size, in order to get numbers that come close to real densities. But this approximation comes more from mutual compensation between different sources of error than from honest counting. The illusion is dissipated when we try to analyse mixed populations. (This opinion of Dr Margalef is not fully shared by the editor. Counting possibilities depend on the type of the apparatus used). Nevertheless, the method is worthy of further development and application, and with some practice it gives figures of indisputable relative value.

(iv) *Echosounders* can detect layers rich in plankton. Phytoplankton does not contribute to the scattering, except in the case of dense growth of blue-greens with gas vacuoles. Often, the layers of dense plankton are visible in the echograms only if they coincide, or where they intersect, with strong gradients in water density (pycnoclines).

(v) *Optical methods—nephelometry*—offer the possibility of assaying rapidly a great number of cultures, in the laboratory, or aboard ship, for instance in enrichment experiments. But in natural waters these methods are practical only for dense blooms.

(c) Procedures for evaluation of detritus
A great part of the particulate material suspended in natural waters, both freshwater and marine, is lifeless. There are many sorts of fragments of organisms, fibres and other material coming from land and the atmosphere, as well as organic aggregates possibly formed by condensation of dissolved organic matter. All this material is important as food and for its surface effect; often it acts as a support for the growth of organisms.

The amount of detritus relative to plankton can be ascertained using Utermöhl's microscope. Sometimes it is convenient to have a more precise estimate. Krey (1961) recommends sedimentation in Utermöhl's microscope, followed by photographing and statistical analysis of numbers and sizes of lifeless particles on the photographs. Riley, van Hemert & Wangersky (1965) estimate the surface of organic aggregates and other material from mounts on molecular filters.

Fluorescence can help in the distinction between living and non-living material. E.J.Wood (1955) uses an ordinary microscope for this purpose, so it is possible to switch to ordinary observation. A powerful light source sends light through a substage filter BG 12 (passing light around 450 mμ), and an OG 1 (yellow) filter is used in the eye-piece. Chlorophyll in living and recently dead material fluoresces bright red. Staining an aliquot with acridine orange (concentration below 1 part per 5000) may be very helpful in the recognition of living photosynthetic organisms that adhere to masses of detritus.

(d) A simplified method for counting phytoplankton
W T EDMONDSON

The method described below has the great advantage of requiring no specialized equipment. When used with care it is capable of giving nearly as precise results as those obtained with more complicated methods. Probably the weakest point is the method of subsampling; this can be compensated for by increasing the number of drops counted.

(i) A microtransect method as described by Lackey (1938) is used. The microtransect is the area seen through the microscope when the slide is moved so that a path is explored from one side of a square coverglass to the other. If a measured amount of water has been put under the coverglass, the transect represents a known amount of water, and the number of organisms per ml of water can be calculated.

(ii) The subsample must be small enough to fit under an unsupported 22 mm coverglass; such a volume is one drop from a medicine dropper of ordinary diameter. The sizes of drops which fall freely from a clean pipette held vertically are fairly uniform in size. It is important that the dropper be held vertically and that the drop be given time to form fully. Too much delay results in concentration of material in the drop. A standard chemical volumetric pipette is unsuitable for this purpose because of the narrow opening. The dropper must be calibrated. In the original Lackey method, total volume of the sample was measured as number of drops. One drop represents a definite fraction of the total, and it is unnecessary to make any other measurement of the sample. Greater precision can be achieved by weighing with a sensitive one-pan balance.

(iii) Measure the width of the high power field with a stage micrometer. Each transect will represent a definite fraction of the area under the coverglass, hence a definite volume of the sample.

(iv) To make a count, agitate the sample to distribute organisms evenly and carefully deliver one drop to a clean slide. Carefully cover with a 22 mm square coverglass and examine. The liquid should not run beyond the edge of the coverglass. Now place the slide so that the middle of one edge is in view with the high power. Move the slide so that a transect is examined across the middle of the coverglass, counting the number of cells seen. This part of the operation must be carried out rapidly so that evaporation does not cause large air spaces under the coverglass. Record the number and repeat, counting another transect well separated from the first.

(v) Count another drop in the same way. If the results are very different from the first, count a third drop.

Since this method is subject to considerable sampling variation, it is necessary to count several drops for a relatively precise count. Accuracy is increased by having the original sample very large, but the subsampling must be done carefully.

(vi) Calculate the total number per drop by using the formula

$$\text{Total number/drop} = \frac{\text{Area of the coverglass}}{\text{Area of 1 transect}} \times \frac{\text{Individual counts}}{\text{recorded per transect}}$$

(vii) (Example from the Limnology class of Professor W.T.Edmondson). A fixed sample of *Euglena* was counted using the drop transect method which has an inherently high variance, by the inverted microscope method which is better, and by the Coulter electronic particle counter.

Class results:
Thousands of cells/ml
(each based on 4 transects)

80–100	1	
101–120	3	Mean *138·5*
121–140	8	Standard deviation 24·5
141–160	5	Coefficient of variation 17·7
161–180	3	
181–200	1	

The individual counts rounded to the nearest thousand were:
92, 104, 107, 111, 121, 125, 132, 133, 137, 138, 138, 140, 141, 142, 146, 146, 148, 163, 176, 178, 191.

The count with the inverted microscope was *133*, which is in good agreement with the class count.

The count with the Coulter counter was somewhat higher, *160* when adjusted for coincident counts but in essential agreement. The Coulter counter registers all particles including partly disintegrated cells, which would not be recorded in an optical count.

2.13   Expressions of populations
I FINDENEGG

A population can be evaluated in many ways and it seems wise to select the way most appropriate to the problems faced. Evaluation of numbers of individuals is appropriate for studies considering population dynamics, diversity and structure of the ecosystem. Since production is usually computed and expressed as amount of carbon fixed per unit of time, the appropriate way of evaluating populations in productivity studies, on the other hand, is carbon content. It is dangerous to be content to pass from one to another form of expression simply by applying conventional conversion factors. However, it is worthwhile to consider that ratios between different entities, or measures, far from being constants ('conversion factors'), are extremely interesting indices of dynamic properties of populations. Dry weight per unit volume, chlorophyll content per cell, surface volume ratio, etc., change in one and the same species according to temperature, nutrient supply and age of the population.

(a) Numbers
Numbers are perhaps the best quantitative expression of phytoplankton populations. Sometimes it is easier to count colonies, and this may have also some statistical advantage from the point of view of colony distribution in several visual fields. But the average number of cells per colony is different in time and space, depending upon vitality, rate of increase, tenacity of connecting pads, etc., and can also be changed according to the treatment (e.g. intensity of shaking, storage, etc.) to which the sample has been subjected.

Length of filaments is a convenient form for recording populations in filamentous forms like *Oscillatoria, Mougeotia*, etc. In dense populations this can be done approximately by counting the number of intersections of filaments with the lines of a rectangular grid or reticulum of known distance between the lines.

(b) Sedimentation volume
Sedimentation volume used in connection with net sampling is almost valueless as an estimate of phytoplankton biomass, and in no case should be considered more than a rough approximation only.

(c) Volumes and size

Since phytoplankton organisms differ greatly in size, cell numbers do not give a true picture of the actual biomass. Therefore, the number of individuals of each species must be multiplied by the average cell volume. The volume can be calculated from the mean dimensions of the cell, assuming that its form corresponds roughly to simple geometrical solids (Sphere: $(4r^3\pi)/3$ or simplified $4r^3$; Cone: $(r^2\pi h)/3$ or r^2h; Cylinder: $r^2\pi h$ or $3r^2h$, etc.). The volume may also be obtained by measuring the displacement of scaled plastic or clay models. Note that the scale factor is cubic, not linear!

Some examples: The cell volume of *Peridinium willei*, e.g., may be compared to a hemisphere. Assuming the mean radius to be 27 μ; then $4r^3 = 78,732$, or in round figures, 80,000 μ^3, and the volume of the hemisphere is 40,000 μ^3. Filamentous forms and belt-shaped colonies are reckoned as μ^3 per 1 mm length. *Oscillatoria rubescens*, e.g., has a diameter of 6 μ, $r = 3$ μ, $h = 1000$ μ, $3r^2h = 27,000$ μ^3, or approximately, 30,000 μ^3/mm. Nauwerck (1963) gives a detailed list of cell volumes for the phytoplankton of Lake Erken in Sweden. Paasche (1960) and other authors have published similar data on marine phytoplankton.

The surface of the cells may be computed in the same way. As the surface development controls absorption phenomena estimates of a population in terms of cell surface may be interesting from the point of view of its production capacity (Paasche 1960).

Table 1 gives some informative data about cell volumes of some freshwater phytoplankton species (Nauwerck 1963; Findenegg, unpublished). It must be emphasized, however, that cell dimensions in one species may differ from lake to lake; therefore, the cell volume of the important forms should be determined in every particular case.

TABLE 1. Calculated volumes of some species of freshwater plankton organisms acc. to Nauwerck (1963) and Findenegg (unpublished)

	μ^3		μ^3
Microcystis aeruginosa (col.) ...	100,000	Pandorina morum (col.) ...	4,000
Gomphosphaeria lacustris (col.)	2,000	Gloeococcus schroeteri (col.) ...	5,000
Anabaena flos-aquae (col.) ...	80,000	Oocystis solitaria	400
Oscillatoria rubescens (1 mm) ...	30,000	Scenedesmus quadricauda ...	1,000
Uroglena americana (col.) ...	90,000	Ankistrodesmus falcatus ...	250
Mallomonas caudata	10,000	Botryococcus braunii (col.) ...	10,000
Dinobryon divergens & D. sociale	800	Tetraedron minimum	40
Kephyrion sp. pl.	50	Chlorella vulgaris	200
Melosira granulata (1 mm) ...	60,000	Closterium aciculare	4,000
Melosira islandica (1 mm) ...	80,000	Cosmarium phaseolus	3,000
Cyclotella bodanica	10,000	Cosmarium reniforme	30,000
Cyclotella comensis	400	Staurastrum paradoxum ...	20,000
Stephanodiscus astraea	2,000	Gymnodinium helveticum ...	20,000
Stephanodiscus hantzschii var.			
pusillus	200	Peridinium willei	40,000
Asterionella formosa	700	Ceratium hirundinella ...	70,000
Tabellaria fenestrata	4,000	Rhodomonas lacustris	200
Fragilaria crotonensis (1 mm) ...	200,000	Cryptomonas ovata	2,500
Synedra acus angustissima ...	1,000	Cryptomonas erosa	2,500
Cymatopleura solea	80,000		

2.14 Chemical components

(a) General remarks

R A VOLLENWEIDER

The chemical approach to the standing crop question considers mass rather than the species composition. In many respects, knowledge about the total mass and the chemical and biochemical components per unit of lake surface and volume, is as important as species enumeration and total plankton volume.

Substances to be considered may be either unspecified totals such as dry weight and ash, or specific elements such as carbon, nitrogen, phosphorus, silica, etc., or biochemical products, such as proteins, carbohydrates, fats, photosynthetic and other pigments, and even enzymes.

The outline of methods for such analyses is beyond the direct scope of the present manual, except for dry weight and photosynthetic pigments.

For the rest, the reader should consult any one of the text books on the subject, e.g. *Moderne Methoden der Pflanzenanalyse* (*Modern Methods of*

Plant Analysis), edited by K.Paech & M.V.Tracey, Springer Verlag, Berlin-Göttingen-Heidelberg, Volumes 1–7 (1956–1964). A selected number of methods may also be found in the IBP Handbook No.8: *Methods for Chemical Analysis of Fresh Waters* edited by Golterman & Clymo.

(b) Dry weight and ash content
C J SOEDER and J F TALLING

The methods used to separate planktonic material for these determinations will depend on the quantities present and degree of purity, as well as the type of algae and objective in mind. A sensitive procedure based upon membrane filtration is described by Strickland & Parsons (1968).

Dry weight is one of the most frequently used bases of reference in productivity studies and all kinds of physiological investigations. Although more reliable than fresh weight (e.g. Stocker 1960; Myers 1962), dry weight is far from being an absolute unit, since the biological object in the dried status will always retain a variable amount of residual water.

Provided that the dried samples are transferred to the balance with all the necessary precautions, several factors are likely to make the results more or less uncertain. There is a considerable influence of the drying procedure. Freeze drying or desiccation over agents like phosphopentoxide, etc., are certainly superior to drying in the oven. The latter technique is often preferred for convenience, but it implies the loss of volatile substances from the samples. Naturally, the final weight of oven dried material depends on drying temperature (see below). This may mainly be due to differences in the percentage of residual water: the loss of volatile substances or heat decomposition products will increase with temperature.

Most authorities dry their samples at 105°C, but many other drying temperatures between 60 and 110°C have been used. Where we lack information on the amount of substance that was lost, it is almost impossible to convert one type of dry weight into another.

A very instructive finding was published by D'Alconteres *et al.* (1960) who determined the total N-content of algae after freeze drying and oven drying. The respective nitrogen contents were 6·28 and 5·18%. Thus close to 20% of total N was lost during the drying process in the oven.

Some data may be given here:

Dry weight of *Chlorella* at different drying temperatures (autospores from synchronized cultures of strain 211/8b Göttingen). Mean values of 6 samples each.

Drying temperature: 60°C   80°C   102°C
% of weight at 60°C: 100   93   90

After predrying of samples at 80°C for 24 hours and subsequent drying at 102°C for 8 hours an additional loss of $3 \pm 0.1\%$ was found.

Ash content. Although this is a small percentage of the dry weight ($\sim 5\%$) in many planktonic algae, it may form 50% or more of the dry weight in algae with massive inorganic skeletal structures, especially the silica walls of diatoms. Freshwater plankton diatoms are generally more heavily silicified than their marine counterparts; Einsele & Grim (1938) provide useful tabulated data for many important freshwater species. Consequently the *ash-free dry weight* is often preferable to dry weight as a measure of algal quantity, when comparisons are being made which involve mixed assemblages of species. Another important measure, the carbon content, is normally between 40 and 60% of the ash-free dry weight.

2.15 'Conversion factors' between different criteria
R A VOLLENWEIDER

In the absence of specific analyses it is often necessary, or at least desirable, to estimate particular components indirectly from available data using certain 'conversion factors'. For example: the carbon content of an individually enumerated phytoplankton population is often considered to be about 10% (by weight) of the total volume (calculated according to 2.13, and assuming the specific weight of phytoplankton be equal to unity). Crude protein is calculated from total nitrogen analyses by multiplying the analytical values by 6.25.

For marine environments, a general conversion table was elaborated and proposed by a sub-committee of the Bergen Symposium 1957 on Primary Productivity (Rapp. Cons. Int. Explor. Mer 1958).

Although not entirely useless, such conversion tables, and conversion factors as a whole, must be used with utmost caution. Unlike physical and chemical conversion factors, those used in biology are only rough estimates, even under most favourable conditions, since the relative chemical composition of biological samples depends on a large number of biological, environmental and historical factors and conditions. The carbon/nitrogen ratio in phytoplankton may vary as much as from 5 to 25 (Redfield, Ketchum & Richards 1963) depending on luxury or starvation conditions of the external medium. The nitrogen/phosphorus ratio is often of the order of 10—15, but can be as low as 1, or as high as 60.

Therefore, in reporting results which were obtained indirectly, the conversion factors used should be referred to clearly, and it is recommended that the original values be given as well.

It should be mentioned here that a more systematic approach to these questions is urgently needed (*cf.* Lund 1964). Some components probably do follow relatively simple laws. It was recently shown that the carbon/volume relationship is allometric (Mullin, Sloan & Eppley 1966). The relationships between other components may be more complex, or dependent on external conditions. Moreover knowledge of the actual chemical composition of different biological samples may be an independent source of information on the biochemical status of a population, and the preceding environmental conditions can be deduced. The importance of these aspects cannot be overestimated in view of any biodynamic interpretation of the production processes as a whole, and is one of the central problems of future research in productivity.

2.16 Photosynthetic pigments
R A VOLLENWEIDER

Introduction

Because of their importance in photosynthesis, measurements of photosynthetic pigments have received considerable attention for a long time. In 1934 Harvey introduced a method that employed visual standards, and since that time numerous workers have used either such colorimetric, or more sophisticated spectrophotometric and fluorimetric techniques (Kozminski 1938; Manning & Juday 1941; Gessner 1944, 1949; Kalle 1949, 1959; Berardi & Tonolli 1952; Richards with Thompson 1952; Vollenweider 1956; Rodhe, Vollenweider & Nauwerck 1958; Parsons & Strickland 1963; Holm-Hansen *et al.* 1965; Sakamoto 1966; a.o.).

The simultaneous determination of chlorophyll *a*, *b* and *c* (as well as astacin and non-astacin type carotenoids) by the polychromatic spectrophotometric method of Richards with Thompson has been widely used. However, discrepancies and inconsistent results were often observed, leading to revisions by Parsons (1963), Parsons & Strickland (1963) and Talling & Driver (1963). Accordingly, chlorophyll *a* values calculated on the basis of the earlier Richards with Thompson equations are probably affected by an error of about $+25\%$, and estimates of other pigments appear to be un-reliable.

The editor considered it advisable to pay most attention to methods for chlorophyll *a* because this is normally the most abundant and important pigment in living material, and there is more information on this pigment than on the others. Chlorophyll degradation products interfere with the spectrophotometric determinations and this problem is discussed where necessary. Each section (phytoplankton, periphyton and macrophytes) differs in approach and emphasis because the problems usually encountered are different. In view of the considerable potential of pigment estimates (including both photosynthetic and non-photosynthetic) as subsidiary parameters of biological communities, and of their status (*cf.* also Margalef 1965), a more thorough approach to this problem area in future research would be highly desirable (*cf.* also 2.15).

(a) General outline of spectrophotometric methods
J F TALLING
(i) *Volume of water sample*
0·5 to 2 litres is often convenient for sampling and appropriate for the commonly encountered concentration range of 1–20 mg chlorophyll a/m^3 ($=\mu g/l$). In order to obtain extracts of suitable optical density, smaller sample volumes can be used with denser populations. Larger volumes (e.g. 5 l) may be desirable for unproductive waters, but may be also inconvenient to obtain or to filter. Consequently a more sensitive fluorimetric method has been developed for work on oceanic waters, in which concentrations are usually below 1 mg/m^3 (for details, see Yentsch & Menzel 1963; Holm-Hansen *et al.* 1965).

(ii) *Filtration*
Both membrane filters and the finer porosity grades of glass fibre filters are now commonly used. The latter are cheaper and filter more rapidly, but their retention of the smallest particles is inferior to that of the finer grades of membrane filters. During filtration, the filter is held clamped in a suitable support, and connected to a source of reduced pressure. The pressure reduction should probably not exceed 2/3 atmosphere during filtration, to minimize the possible loss by fragmentation of delicate organisms. Filters of large diameter (e.g. 7 cm glass fibre) are useful if rapid filtration is desirable or if clogging by suspended solids is likely, as with silty river water or hypolimnion water samples containing ferric hydroxide. The addition of a small quantity

of magnesium carbonate suspension to the filter is often recommended, as an aid to retention and as a precaution against the development of acidity—and hence pigment degradation—in the extract. After filtration is complete, the filter should preferably not be dried but used immediately for extraction. Dried filters have often been stored for several days or weeks, but are then liable to yield less pigment. If necessary, as with glass fibre filters, the average content of water retained by the filter should be found by weighing and allowed for when calculating the % composition of the solvent to be added.

(iii) *Extraction*
Either acetone (80% or 90% aqueous mixture) or methanol (90% or 100%) can be used as the solvent. The former is less efficient in extraction for some algae, but absorption characteristics of the principal photosynthetic pigments in it are better known (comparative tabulation in Talling & Driver 1963). Originally most work with phytoplankton utilized an extraction period in cool dark conditions (refrigerator) of about 24 hours. This may give good results, but because of possible changes in the extracted pigments a much shorter period is now often recommended, combined with some additional means for accelerating the extraction. Exposure to ultrasonic vibration ('sonification') is one such means, but is often inconvenient to apply and sometimes not very efficient. Grinding the filter and algae can be an effective method; practical details of one procedure are given in the IBP/PF Chemical Handbook. With methanol, a brief (e.g. 30 seconds) exposure of the cells to the boiling solvent greatly accelerates the extraction, which can often be completed within 30 minutes.

After the extraction period, the extract is centrifuged and the clear supernatant solution used to fill a spectrophotometer cell (cuvette).

(iv) *Spectrophotometric estimation*
Used in the normal way, the spectrophotometer enables measurements of optical density ($^{10}\log I_0/_I$) to be made at specified wavelengths for the pigment extract in a cell of known thickness (path length). A thickness of about 4 cm is generally most useful, as shorter cells (e.g. 1 cm) involve a loss of sensitivity, and longer cells (e.g. 10 cm) are less convenient, require more solvent, but can give increased sensitivity which may be of value for unproductive waters.

The optical density measured at 750 mμ can be taken as an approximate measure of non-selective 'background' absorption by other materials (also scattering and cell-to-cell differences), and is subtracted from measurements of optical density in the red spectral region (600–700 mμ) from which concentrations of chlorophyll *a* and its degradation products are calculated; it should normally be less than 0·005 units per cm of cell thickness.

The procedure used to calculate the concentration of chlorophyll *a* from values of optical density depends upon two pairs of alternatives.

First (1a), one may disregard the possible contributions from degradation products, and express the result as the concentration of chlorophyll *a* equivalent to the optical density (-ies) measured. Or (1b), a differentiation may be attempted between the concentrations of chlorophyll *a* and its degradation product(s) (e.g. as phaeophytin). This differentiation can be based upon the relative changes of optical density (or of fluorescence) at the red absorption maximum induced by acidification, or upon a shift in the blue absorption maximum which accompanies the degradation of chlorophyll *a* (see Moss 1967a, b). It can be calculated either in terms of the proportions (%) of chlorophyll *a* and phaeophytin *a*, or, by simple mathematical manipulation, in terms of concentrations of these pigments. Examples are given in Section 2.32c, and by Yentsch & Menzel (1963), Holm-Hansen *et al.* (1965), Yentsch (1966), Lorenzen (1967), and Moss (1967b).

Second (2a), the estimation of chlorophyll *a* concentration can be based upon the optical density measured at one wavelength near the red absorption maximum, or (2b) upon measurements at several wavelengths (e.g. 3-'trichromatic' methods). All such measurements are normally corrected by subtraction of the optical density at 750 mμ, as outlined earlier. Examples of 'trichromatic' methods include the much-used early procedure of Richards & Thompson (1952) and later modifications—involving the same wavelengths of 630, 645, and 665 mμ—outlined by Strickland & Parsons (1968). Such methods were developed with the aim of distinguishing the contributions, in an extract mixture, of several pigments with overlapping absorption spectra. However, the dominance of absorption due to chlorophyll *a* in the region of its red absorption peak (663–665 mμ) makes it doubtful whether the accuracy of estimation of this pigment is improved by adopting a calculation based on three wavelengths rather than one. The latter (alternative 2a) is also more easily combined with the procedures intended to differentiate between chlorophyll *a* and its phaeophytin (alternative 1b).

(b) Examples of specific procedures

Two examples are described in detail in the IBP/PF Chemical Handbook (edit. Golterman & Clymo 1969) and in the manual by Strickland & Parsons

(1968), and need not be repeated here. Their relationship to the methods and alternatives generally available can be found by reference to the preceding section. Both involve 90% acetone as solvent. Absorption characteristics of chlorophyll *a* in methanol are less well known, but relevant data are listed by Talling & Driver (1963) who propose the following simple approximate relationship for the concentration of chlorophyll *a* (Chl. *a*, in µg/ml solvent) in 90% methanol which yields an optical density at 665 mµ of D_{665} measured with a path length of 1 cm:

$$Chl.\ a = 13 \cdot 9\ D_{665}$$

In terms of the classification of procedures given above, this is a combination of alternatives 1a and 2a. For acetone as solvent, see sections 2.22 and 2.32. The reader is also referred to the UNESCO Monograph on Oceanographic Methodology No. 1 (1966).

2.2 MACROPHYTES
D F WESTLAKE

Aquatic macrophyte communities range from completely submerged stands of large algae (e.g. *Chara, Cladophora*), mosses (e.g. *Fontinalis*), pteridophytes (e.g. *Isoetes*) and angiosperms (e.g. *Elodea, Ranunculus* spp.), through stands of rooted plants with floating leaves (e.g. *Nymphaea*) and mats of floating plants with emergent leaves (e.g. *Eichhornia, Lemna*) to wet-lands with plants with little except their underground parts submerged (e.g. *Equisetum, Phragmites, Rhizophora*). Most techniques required for use with emergent plants will either be similar to those used for submerged plants or to those used for terrestrial plants. In the latter case it is recommended that the appropriate PT techniques should be adapted (see PT Grasslands Manual, Milner & Hughes 1968). The methods described here are therefore primarily intended for application to submerged plants.

2.21 Sampling

As the biomass of higher plants is very variable in time and space careful thought must be given to the design of sampling programmes in relation to the aims of the experiment, the man-power available and the accuracy required (Grieg-Smith 1964). The general aim will be to remove and weigh the vegetation from enough known areas to obtain a mean biomass sufficiently accurate to show significant differences between different sampling periods and sites. The spatial variation is often non-random, being both contagious and related to gradients such as increasing depth, which means that normal statistical methods must be applied with caution. It is often possible to select the size and shape of the sampling area to reduce the variability, e.g. large quadrats, rectangular quadrats in contagious (clumped) communities, summed quadrats along transects parallel to gradients. Otherwise samples should be taken by random numbers on rectangular co-ordinates. Sampling, or experiments, in areas previously disturbed must be avoided.

Biomass will vary with time, and if only one determination is to be made in a year it should be made near the time of the seasonal maximum biomass, which is often near the time of flowering (cf. 3.52).

It is often particularly important to sample the underground parts of the plants (Westlake 1965b), even if this can be done only in a portion of the quadrats. Also it is often useful to collect the dead material as well as the live plant.

If the production of the whole site is required, map the shore and outer limits of the vegetation and find the area between by planimetry. Bare areas included will give bare or partly bare quadrats which will be included in the mean biomass per unit area populated. For comparisons between different habitats, or species, sampling may be limited to typical areas.

(a) General techniques

According to the depth of the water the sampling areas may be approached by wading, in boats or by diving. Removal of the plants may be direct, by hand from a quadrat, or indirect, by a sampling apparatus, and this choice is influenced by the method of approach and the nature of the substratum.

Mark off areas for direct sampling with stakes and string if large, or quadrat frames if smaller. Make light metal or floating wooden frames in four pieces so that they can be slid horizontally into the vegetation and subsequently fitted together (e.g. two pieces of pipe with right angle bends and two pieces with male joints to fit the bends). It is often necessary to decide on a convention for the weed that is to be considered to be in the quadrat, e.g. all plants *rooted* within the quadrat, or all plant material *within* the up-ward projection of the quadrat. This depends largely on the habit of the plant and it may even be necessary to change the convention at different times of year or in different habitats, though this should be only as a last resort.

If the plants are rooted in soft mud or silt, whole plants may often be pulled out by loosening the mud but if the shoots are cut off at ground level by shears, scythes or similar tools the roots must be sampled separately. In shallow or flowing water the roots may be dug out but in deep lakes divers will probably need some type of corer to avoid reducing visibility.

Most submerged plants, when cut, float to the surface. In rivers they may be collected in a net downstream of the sampling area. In lakes it is best to keep hold of the cut shoots but if it can be shown that they all reach the surface they may be collected there. After removal keep the plants in polythene bags in the shade, or in a cold store (5°C) if they cannot be dealt with the same day. If chemical components are to be analysed sub-samples should be deep-frozen or freeze-dried.

(b) Special equipment

Self-contained underwater breathing apparatus (SCUBA) is recommended for divers, with either wet or dry suits (e.g. used by Nygaard 1958; Kosicka & Kosicki 1959; Raspopov 1962; Wood 1963; Fager *et al.* 1966). In deep turbid rivers visibility may be very poor, although there is enough light for plants to grow, and this presents special problems for divers.

Grabs provide an alternative to the use of divers for sampling in deep water but none is entirely satisfactory. They all sample small areas, remove the roots inadequately, are prone to errors arising from the wrongful inclusion or exclusion of weed at the edges and rarely succeed when stones are present. If they have to be used, one suited to the type of plant and bottom should be selected (Table 2).

TABLE 2. Sampling apparatus for macrophytes

Type of apparatus	Suggested application	Reference
Scoop; diver operated	important root systems	Nygaard 1958
Ekman dredge	mud; small root systems	Welch 1948
Petersen dredge	hard bottom; poor sampling	Welch 1948
Petersen dredge, modified	hard bottom; better sampling	Potzger & Engel 1942
Cylindrical sampler	soft bottom; upright plants, small root system	Grøntved 1957
Quadrat frame sampler	soft bottom; tall plants, small root systems	Forsberg, 1959
Pronged grab	luxuriant vegetation; roots only from soft bottom	Bernatowicz 1960 Lipin & Lipina 1939

In mud, sand or small gravel a tube 5–10 cm in diameter and 50 cm long, with a sharp edge and a bung, will often be sufficient for root cores, although numerous samples must be taken because the area sampled is so small.

(c) Treatment of samples

Wash in a shallow sloping trough with a jet of water (approx. 2·5 atm.) to remove soil, epiphytes and animals. The total weight of such material may exceed the weight of the plants and the weight of epiphytes alone may sometimes be of the same order as the plant weight (estimated from Odum 1957; Edwards & Owens 1965). Pass the water through a $\frac{1}{2}$ inch mesh net and recover the plant fragments by flotation or sorting of sub-samples.

Sorting into different species and for productivity studies (see 3.52) is best done at this stage. If the other species form less than 10% of the total, separation is generally unnecessary. Species should be identified and published papers should cite the taxonomic keys and sources of nomenclature used.

It is usual to determine the wet (fresh) weight and then sub-sample to determine the percentage dry weight. From this the total dry weight may be estimated. Consistent fresh weights are best obtained by using a domestic spin-drier to remove adherent water (Edwards & Owens 1960). In the absence of a spin-drier hang the weed on lines and turn frequently until water almost ceases to drip from it (Westlake 1965b), but this is less accurate and more laborious. Balances capable of holding bulky samples, weighing up to 5 or 10 kg, will be needed for samples from 1 square metre.

The weed should be chopped and well mixed before taking sub-samples by some suitable techniques; at least by taking numerous smaller samples taken from different parts of the heap. Drying at 105°C takes about 24 hours if the weed is spread loosely and thinly on drying trays. Cool the dry weed in a desiccator or sealed polythene bags before weighing as it can take up to 10% moisture from the atmosphere. Balances weighing up to 1 kg in 0·1 g are most convenient.

Further reduction in particle size with a star beater mill is needed before making other analyses. It is possible to reduce small samples with a pestle and mortar, but this can be extremely laborious.

2.22   Chemical components

(a) General analyses

Most analyses will be made adapting appropriate techniques described in the P F Chemical Methods Manual (Golterman & Clymo 1969) or recommended in the PT Grassland Manual (Milner & Hughes 1968) and higher aquatic plants raise few special problems. As carbonates are often an important part of the dry weight, sometimes over 50%, precautions must be taken to prevent their decomposition during ashing. This can be done by ensuring that the temperature does not exceed 550°C (Westlake 1965b) but if this is not possible, or if bicarbonates or magnesium carbonate are significant components, decompose the carbonates by acetic acid before ashing and determine the carbon dioxide to correct the ash value. The high ash content of most submerged macrophytes (15–25% dry weight in freshwater, 20–35% in sea-water, c. 75% if very calcareous) means that it is important to know the biomass in terms of dry organic weight (Westlake 1965a & b; Straškraba 1968).

For most macrophytes it may be assumed that the organic carbon content lies between 44–48% of the organic weight but exceptions may be found (e.g. plants especially rich in reducing sugars, fats or lignins; Straškraba 1967; Westlake 1965b). Determinations should be made by dry combustion (e.g. Belcher & Ingram 1950) after removing carbonate with sulphur dioxide, not by wet combustion.

Similarly the energy contents are likely to be between 4·3 and 4·8 Kcal/g organic matter (Straškraba 1967; Westlake 1965b). Standard bomb calorimetry (see Grassland Research Institute Staff 1961) or a micro-calorimeter (Phillipson 1964) may be used for determinations. Excessive carbonates may interfere (Paine 1966) and a correction of 0·14–0·43 gcal/mg $CaCO_3$ is needed.

Proximate analyses may be made using normal agricultural techniques (Association of Official Agricultural Chemists 1965). Lignin is not likely to be an important constituent in most aquatic macrophytes.

(b) Chlorophyll determinations

Sub-samples of fresh shoots are extracted with pure acetone rendered basic with magnesium carbonate. It will usually be necessary to grind or homogenise the material to ensure thorough extraction. A mechanical homogeniser is best, but clean washed sand in a pestle and mortar can be used as a laborious alternative. Centrifuge at 2,500 r.p.m. for 10–15 minutes or filter under low vacuum through a No.4 sintered glass filter. Wash the residues and add the filtered or centrifuged washing to the extract. Dry overnight over anhydrous sodium sulphate and dilute to 90% with water. Alternatively, assume that the water in the fresh material dilutes the acetone, calculate this water as an appropriate percentage of the fresh weight and adjust the dilution of the acetone accordingly. Discussions of pigment extraction from macrophytes may be found in Smith & Benitez (1955), Bruinsma (1963) and Wetzel (1964). All operations should be carried out at low temperatures in the dark or shade, without delay.

Normally only chlorophylls *a* and *b* need be considered for spectrophotometric analysis (see also 2.16 & 2.32c). Chlorophyll *c* will be found only when epiphytic diatoms are abundant and chlorophyll *d* when Rhodophyceae are present. If dead and moribund material is included in the sample chlorophyll degradation products will interfere and the method of Lorenzen (1967) for chlorophyll *a* and phaeopigments should be used (see 2.32c). Chlorophyll *a* in the absence of degradation products may be determined using the approximate equation derived from Talling & Driver (1963):

$$\mu\text{g Chl. } a \text{ per sample} = 11 \cdot 9 \, D_{665} \cdot (v/l)*$$

where:

D_{665} = absorbance (optical density) reading at 665 mμ

v = volume of (acetone) extract in ml

l = length of spectrophotometer cell in cm.

If chlorophyll *a* and *b* are required more accurately, equations derived from a simplification of Parsons & Strickland's trichromatic equations for chlorophyll *a*, *b* and *c* (1963) may be used. The absorbances at the red absorbance peaks for these pigments at 665 and 645 mμ are determined (D_{665} and D_{645}); then, for unit cell length (1 cm):

$$D_{665} = 0 \cdot 089 \text{ Chl. } a + 0 \cdot 0063 \text{ Chl. } b \qquad \text{Eq. (1)}$$
$$D_{645} = 0 \cdot 0218 \text{ Chl. } a + 0 \cdot 054 \text{ Chl. } b \qquad \text{Eq. (2)}$$

where Chl. *a* and Chl. *b* are the concentrations of chlorophylls *a* and *b* in μg/ml of 90% acetone, respectively.† Rearranging, the following equations are derived:

$$\mu\text{g Chl. } a \text{ per sample} = (11 \cdot 6 \, D_{665} - 1 \cdot 3 \, D_{645}) \cdot (v/l) \qquad \text{Eq. (3)}$$
$$\mu\text{g Chl. } b \text{ per sample} = (19 \cdot 1 \, D_{645} - 4 \cdot 7 \, D_{665}) \cdot (v/l) \qquad \text{Eq. (4)}$$

2.23 Biomass without removal

The percentage cover may be determined using a glass bottomed view-box (Walker 1947; Bernatowicz 1960) or from aerial photographs taken from a

---

* The factor 11·9 is the reciprocal ($\times 10^3$) of an empirical specific absorption coefficient, taken as 84 when defined in units of g/l (acetone) and 1 cm. This makes allowance for the presence of chlorophylls *a* and *b*.

† Multiplied by 1000, the numerical factors are the specific absorption coefficients for the pigments (in g/l acetone and 1 cm) at the specified wavelengths.

mast, a balloon, a cable, a helicopter or an aeroplane (Walker 1950; Edwards & Brown 1960; Lang 1967). If cover and mean density (kg/m^2) can be related, which may involve a depth term, rough estimates of biomass can be made (Walker 1950).

Sometimes an optical method (Westlake 1964; Owens *et al.* 1967) may be appliable and for this purpose it can be simplified. It is based on the observation that the optical density of a suspension of water weed is directly proportional to the concentration. Optical density is $\log_{10} \dfrac{100}{T}$, where T is the percentage transmission of light to a given depth. The mantissa is easily found on a suitable slide rule by reading from T on the reciprocal scale to the logarithm scale. First take horizontal light readings at a series of depths in open water (*cf.* 5.2), expressing the results as percentages of the readings on the surface cell. For this purpose it may be assumed that the cell matching, surface loss and position matching factors (Westlake 1964) are constant or negligible, but the appropriate corrections for the neutral density filters and meter scales in use must be made. Plot the percentages on semilogarithmic paper and fit the best straight line. Then take at least 10 readings in each of at least three typical weed-beds, holding the photocell under the base of the weed mass, or on the bottom, expressing the results in the same way. Convert these percentages to optical densities and average them to give the mean total optical density of each weed bed (D_T). Measure the depth (M) of readings so that the transmission through the water alone may be read off the graph and converted to an optical density (D_H). The optical density of the weed, D_W, equals $D_T - D_H$. Cut and weigh the weed within a square metre around the site of each set of readings to find the concentration of weed in the water column (C kg fresh wt/m^3). Calculate the optical density per unit depth per unit concentration from D_W/CM (= E_W the vertical extinction coefficient of weed in units of 1 m and 1 kg/m^3). Then take readings of depth and transmission to the base of the weed at random, or on a regular grid, and calculate the optical densities of the weed as before. Find the standing crop of shoots (W) in kg/m^2 from $W = D_W/E_W$.

Necessary precautions are:

(1) Between 3 and 10 readings should be taken at each station, depending on the variability.

(2) If the surface light is constant (within $\pm 5\%$) initial and final surface readings will suffice, otherwise pairs of readings will be needed.

(3) After inserting photocell ensure that weeds have returned to normal position.

(4) Try to avoid disturbing silt. Some cannot be avoided, but will also be present in the calibration.

(5) If weed movements cause readings to fluctuate rapidly, take ten readings at random intervals.

(6) In very dense weed beds remove the opal disc for greater sensitivity.

(7) If the weed is floating free of the bottom take depth and readings immediately underneath to avoid errors from lateral scatter.

(8) There is great variability (C.V. c. 50%), so at least 100 stations should be used.

(9) In exceptional weed beds there may be no detectable light at the bottom. Determine the light at frequent depth intervals higher in the weed bed, and extrapolate semi-logarithmic plots to the bottom.

(10) Always convert to optical densities before calculating averages because T is not proportional to C.

(11) A correction factor will be needed to include the roots.

2.24   Leaf index

This is the area of the photosynthetic organs per square metre of water surface. For broad-leaved plants techniques used for land plants may be applied. The simplest is plants/unit area × leaves/plant × mean area/leaf, the latter being found by planimetry or weighing cut-outs of tracings or contact prints of a sample of leaves. The punch method (Watson & Watson 1953) which is based on the weight, number and known area of discs punched from a random heap of the weighed leaves from each quadrat may be more convenient.   Fine leaved aquatic plants with photosynthetic stems are more difficult technically, and if the whole surface area is determined it is debatable if this would be comparable with terrestrial measurements which are based on the area of the upper surface of the leaf only. Planimetry of contact prints will give the projected area of the photosynthetic organs, which is often about 1 m² per 10 g dry weight (Edwards & Owens 1965). Point quadrat techniques (Warren Wilson 1959) are applicable in theory but might not be easy under water. Harrod & Hall (1962) have described a method for total surface area using surface active agents. Instrumental methods for leaf area are reviewed in the PT Grasslands Manual (Milner & Hughes 1968), and the air-flow method seems likely to be the most useful (Jenkins 1959).

2.3 PERIPHYTON
R G WETZEL and D F WESTLAKE

The organisms on sub-aquatic surfaces form an extremely heterogeneous and complex association. The photosynthetic components include a similarly diverse assemblage of algal forms, and some lichens, that colonize nearly every conceivable type of substrate available in the littoral regions. The terminology applied to the various algae in individual habitats is almost as varied as the number of investigations (cf. reviews of Sladečkova 1962; Wetzel 1964). A uniform system of terminology is recommended whereby the term periphyton includes all of the plant organisms, excluding rooted macrophytes, growing on submerged materials in water. Submerged materials include all substrata: sediments, rocks, debris, and living organisms. In restricted studies of organisms on specific type of material, e.g. mud, rocks, sand, macrophytes, usage of the general term periphyton should be modified by an appropriate adjective, such as epipelic, epilithic, epipsammic or epiphytic periphyton.

The variability of natural substrata and the many changing physical and biotic factors influencing distribution on the substrata means that the distribution of periphyton is often extremely heterogeneous. Methods must be devised to take account of this (cf. 2.21). The simplest is to take numerous samples (cf. Pieczynska 1965) but more sophisticated methods can reduce the number needed. Demarcation between large attached algal periphyton and macrophytes is not sharp and in certain instances a mixture of periphytic and macrophytic techniques are necessary. Diurnal phototactic migration is common among many epipelic forms and introduces further variations into distributional patterns. The biomass must finally be expressed per unit area of water surface, not per unit area of substrate (Pieczynska 1968).

No attempt will be made here to review the great number of devices and methods that have been used in qualitative and quantitative studies. Rather the general methods of approaching quantitative estimates of biomass and production rates are critically discussed. Much of the choice of methodology must be made by the investigator in view of the individual habitats and questions under investigation. Current investigations are likely to produce improved methods, particularly at Bristol University (England, Dr F.E. Round), the Kellogg Biological Station, Michigan State University (Michigan, U.S.A., Dr R.G.Wetzel), the University of Warsaw (Poland, Dr E.Pieczynska), the Department of Water Technology, Prague (Czechoslovakia,

Dr A. Sladečkova) and the River Laboratory (Wareham, England, Dr A. Marker).

2.31   Qualitative and biomass sampling

The most thorough recent discussion, including detailed descriptions of many variations in apparatus, is the review of Sladečkova (1962). Supplementary critical reviews are given by Cooke (1956), Castenholz (1960, 1961), Round (1965), Sladeček & Sladečkova (1964), and Wetzel (1964).

(a) Qualitative methods

Studies concerned only with systematics of periphyton require no elaborate or complicated apparatus for the collection of samples. Knives, scrapers, and similar implements have been variously modified for specific habitats, e.g. a curved knife for scraping epiphytic periphyton from bulrushes. Some taxonomic, cytological and behavioural observations are facilitated by working with living material on transparent artificial substrata (see below). Published papers should cite the taxonomic keys and other sources of nomenclature used. In most cases qualitative analyses are combined with more precise quantitative sampling.

(b) Biomass methods

A few situations permit direct microscopic enumeration on the natural substrata. The epiphytic periphyton on leaves of certain macrophytes and epiphytes of phytoplankton are sufficiently visible for direct analyses. Generally, however, the periphytic forms must be removed quantitatively from a given area of substratum for the measurement of biomass. Young's (1945) 1 or 2 cm² hollow square instrument, or a similar small coring device, aids in the delineation of a known area on many substrata such as logs, rocks, larger plants, etc. An open ended polythene bottle held tightly against hard materials while brushing the periphyton free from a known area is useful where the substrata can be removed from the water (Douglas 1958). A similar device, closed by an internal brush and with a siphoning system for transfer of detached periphyton, is applicable to hard substrata underwater (Douglas 1958). In certain cases a collodion, or similar synthetic film may be applied directly to epilithic periphyton (Margalef 1949). After the periphyton is embedded in the surface film, the community can be peeled off for direct analyses. There are some situations where it is still impossible by present methods to remove encrusting algae or lichens. Phototactic responses of algae can aid in separation of certain epipelic periphyton from sediments (cf. Lund 1942; Round 1953, *et seq.*). The phototactic techniques are particularly effective for quantitative analyses of epipelic algae where much interfering flocculent detritus is present (Round & Eaton 1966) and have been critically evaluated by Eaton & Moss (1966). Acid treatment is practical in assisting the removal of certain diatoms from sand grains for taxonomic observations and dry weight determinations. In deeper situations coring devices, grabs, and diving may be necessary to obtain satisfactory samples.

The provision of uniform artificial substrata for periphytic colonization has a long history and it is the most widespread of the techniques applied to studies of algal periphyton. Glass (smooth and etched), wood, concrete, slate, tiles, tocks (sterilized and polished), bricks, asbestos, porcelain, metals, celluloid, styrofoam, Plexiglas (smooth and roughened) and other plastics are some of the materials that have been exposed in various habitats for differing periods of time for colonization. While some conflicting evidence exists in the literature, results generally indicate that, although the species composition of the periphyton on artificial substrata is usually similar (but not necessarily identical) to that on the natural substrata, there are often large differences in quantity (e.g. Sladečkova 1962; Pieczyńska and Spodniewska 1963).

The position at which artificial substrata are held makes considerable differences to the values obtained. Substrata supported horizontally often develop a periphytic biomass similar to natural substrata conditions but also collect large amounts of detritus and sediment (Castenholz 1961). Vertically held substrata support more uniform growths but retain less than those in a horizontal position. In a majority of the studies on algal periphyton artificial substrata have been suspended in the pelagic regions of standing bodies of water or in the main flow areas of lotic situations. Natural periphytic substrata, however, are primarily benthic and macrophytic in nature. Any substrata that occur for any length of time in the open water are strictly fortuitous and completely insignificant to the ecosystem as a whole. Therefore, many of the reported estimates of periphytic production represent only colonization rates of certain of the phytoplankton and may be entirely unrelated to true periphyton productivity, particularly where turbidity severely limits macrophytic and benthic areas suitable for colonization to relatively small regions of the uppermost littoral zone. The duration of submergence is critical in estimates of maximal colonization and productivity (see also 3.53). Periods of exposure necessary for climax conditions are variable with the trophic conditions of the waters and the season. Lengthy exposure can lead to losses through peeling and sloughing-off. Detailed suggestions for the collection, preservation, and transport of periphyton on artificial substrata are given in Sladečkova (1962).

(c) Treatment of samples
After taking samples further separations may be needed to obtain the algae relatively free from detritus and mineral matter. Firmly attached algae may be washed before they are removed. Sedimentation, centrifuging and use of photo-tactic responses are other possibilities. Many of the usual preservatives can be used, but Lugol's iodine (see 2.11 & 12) and 5% mercuric chloride are particularly suitable.

2.32　Quantitative evaluations

(a) Counting
After removal from known areas the periphyton is usually mixed thoroughly and counted in standard cells and chambers with the procedures and statistics normally applied to phytoplankton (cf 2.12 & 13). Transparent slides used as substrata permit direct microscopic enumeration and identification if populations are not excessively dense. Removal from glass and similar plates is quantitatively accurate.

(b) Volumes and mass
Volumes of periphyton, determined in graduated tubes by displacement, have relatively limited applicability. Wet (fresh) weights should be avoided because of the variability in water content. Organic weight ($550°C$; ash-free dry weight) is practical and more acceptable than dry weight ($105°C$) since inorganic sedimentation can be a major portion of the observed weight (see 2.22 if carbonates present). Organic sedimentation, or heterotrophic bacteria and fungi, can constitute a major portion of the observed organic weight in certain polluted waters and, if the algae are not separated, will invalidate gravimetric determinations. The use of algal organic weight, if possible, is recommended for comparative investigations in combination with other measures of biomass (cf. Kevern *et al.* 1966). If direct determinations are not possible indirect estimations from chlorophyll *a* concentrations should be attempted.

(c) Chlorophyll

Determinations of the photosynthetic pigment concentrations of periphytic organisms as an indirect measure of biomass have been meagre (reviewed in Wetzel 1964). Such measurements are often made on the phytoplankton (see 2.16), where there are relatively few dead algae and pigment extraction can be facilitated by grinding or sonification, but several problems often arise when attempting to determine the pigment content of periphyton. First there are usually many dead or moribund algae among the living which will contribute interfering chlorophyll degradation products, so that the total pigment per unit area or per cent biomass will increase with time as successive algae colonize and die (cf. also Waters 1961). Unless the living algae can be separated from the dead (e.g. the phototactic techniques described by Eaton & Moss 1966), corrections must be made for the degradation products. Secondly, if the algae cannot be removed from a mineral substrate, grinding is difficult, which may result in incomplete extraction. If the substrate is a larger plant the pigments of the periphyton and the substrate will be indistinguishable. Finally many firmly attached algae and lichens are very resistant to extraction with acetone and it may be necessary to use methanol.

Whenever possible 90% aqueous acetone, shaken up with magnesium carbonate, is recommended for pigment extractions because the spectral properties of the solutions of most of the pigments and their degradation products are well known. With appropriate volume-area conversions the formulae of Parsons & Strickland (1963; corrected equations based on those of Richards with Thompson 1952) can be applied to populations or isolates of healthy periphyton (cf. section 2.16). If dead and moribund cells and degradation products are present, especially phaeophytin, corrections will be needed. Sometimes these can be obtained by fluorescence techniques (Yentsch & Menzel 1963; Holm-Hansen *et al.* 1965) which are highly sensitive, but expensive (cf. 2.16). Lorenzen (1967) has described a method which is suitable for equipment more generally available and which will be adequate for most ecological purposes. The absorbance (optical density) of an algal extract is read before and after acidification. Provided that negligible errors arise from small absorbancies of other pigments at the chosen wavelength (including chlorophylls *b* & *c* and their degradation products) and that the absorbancies of the degradation products are unaffected by the pH change, the concentration of chlorophyll *a* in the presence of its degradation products can be calculated. The general equation is:

$$\text{Chl. } a = (D_b - D_a)\,[R/R - 1] \cdot (v/l) \cdot (10^3/\alpha_c)$$

where: Chl. a = concentration of chlorophyll a in μg/sample

  D_a = optical density of extract after acidification

  D_b = optical density of extract before acidification

  α_c = specific absorption coefficient for chlorophyll a
           (units of g/1 cm)

  v = volume of solvent used to extract the sample in ml

  l = path length of spectrophotometer cell in cm

  $R = D_b/D_a$ for pure chlorophyll a (neglecting the small change in molecular weight when chlorophyll is changed to phaeophytin, it also equals the ratio of the specific absorption coefficients of chlorophyll and phaeophytin).

The general principles behind this method may lead to other procedures suitable for special problems, but it has only been used for aqueous acetone solutions so far. Vernon (1960) used a similar approach to calculate chlorophyll and phaeophytin a and b, and it could theoretically be extended to include the c pigments. These procedures are not recommended for routine investigations.

A known quantity of attached algae, i.e. from a known area of substratum or of sediment, is extracted in an appropriate volume of basic 90% v/v aqueous acetone (redistilled or best analytical grade; rendered basic with a small amount of $MgCO_3$ or a drop of concentrated NaOH per litre) such that the resulting optical densities are not above 0·6 in a 1-cm spectrophotometer path length. Grinding, sonification, or some other disruptive mechanism is strongly recommended for certain attached algae, e.g. epipsammic diatoms and many Chlorococcales. Usually 30—60 minutes is adequate for elution of the pigments but this should be tested by repeat extractions. The extracts or a portion thereof are then centrifuged and aliquots used for spectrophotometric analysis in a narrow beam spectrophotometer. All manipulations should be carried out at low temperatures in shade or darkness. Absorbance (optical density) is read at 750 and 665 mμ (red absorbance peak for chlorophyll a) in the spectrophotometer before and after acidification to convert chlorophylls to phaeopigments. Acidification can be accomplished directly in the spectrophotometer cell with 1–2 drops of 1 N HCl. The absorbance can be controlled by the amount of algal substrate extracted, the volume of acetone used to extract the sample, and the length of the cell. Accuracy is improved if the absorbance of the initial reading at 665 mμ is kept above 0·2.

The readings obtained at 665 mμ before and after acidification, corrected for turbidity by the appropriate 750 mμ reading (see 2.16) and cell differences, are substituted in the general equation. Lorenzen (1967) used a value of 1·7 for R, giving a constant of 2·43 for R/(R – 1), and took a value of 91 for α_c at 665 mμ. However, a value of 84 may be preferred, which gives:

$$\mu g\ \text{Chl. } a \text{ per sample} = 11·9\left\{2·43(D_b - D_a)\right\} . (v/l)*$$

The ratio may be checked experimentally for different communities either on samples free from dead or moribund algae or on pure chlorophyll separated by simple chromotography.

If required, the phaeopigment (P) may be calculated by subtracting the optical density of the chlorophyll from the total optical density before acidification, and converting the optical density of phaeopigment to μg by using a coefficient derived from R and the specific absorption coefficient for chlorophyll *a* (cf. definition of R). These equations simplify to:

$$\mu g\ \text{phaeopigment per sample} = 11·9(v/l) . (1·7\ D_a) - \text{Chl. } a$$

This can be shown to be equivalent to Lorenzen's equation for phaeopigments.

If acetone does not extract the pigments completely, methanol (methyl alcohol), rendered basic with magnesium carbonate, may be more successful. However, the absorption coefficients of chlorophylls and degradation products in this solvent are inadequately known at present. In these circumstances it is recommended that the absorbances (D_m) of 90% methanol extracts are read at 665 mμ. As the chlorophyll is rather less stable in methanol than in acetone the readings should be taken as quickly as possible at not more than 24 hr after adding the solvent. The absorbancies may be used as a relative measure of pigment concentration when expressed for a standard spectrophotometer cell length (1 cm) or, in the absence of degradation products, an equation derived from Talling & Driver (1963) will give a close approximation to the weight of chlorophyll *a*:

$$\mu g\ \text{Chl. } a \text{ per sample} = 13·9\ D_m . (v/l)†.$$

---

* The 'absorption coefficient' (A) used by Lorenzen in his equations is actually the reciprocal of the true specific absorption coefficient for chlorophyll *a* in 90% acetone solution, which was taken from Vernon (1960) as 91 at the wavelength of maximum absorption. In this procedure the conventional wavelength of 665 is adopted, which may not be exactly on the maximum absorption, also chlorophylls *b* and *c* may be present, with their degradation products. In these circumstances Talling & Driver's empirical coefficient of 11·9 (reciprocal $\times 10^3$ of 84) may be appropriate (cf. 2.16 and 2.22b).

† The factor 13·9 is the reciprocal ($\times 10^3$) of an empirical specific absorption coefficient taken as 72 (cf. 2.22b).

In the presence of degradation products it is suggested that readings be taken for neutral solutions before and after acidification. There is hope that the need for more information about methanol solutions will enable the chlorophyll *a* concentrations to be calculated subsequently. If a population (or culture) can be extracted by both acetone and methanol it may be possible to calibrate methanol readings from the acetone results.

In conclusion it should be reiterated that over long periods pigment quantities give only rough estimates of biomass because the pigment per unit weight is influenced by many environmental and internal variables (life cycle, age, irradiance, temperature, salinity, nitrogen, phosphorus, magnesium, iron, antimetabolites, etc.). Very approximate conversions of the chlorophyll *a* to organic weight can be made by multiplying by 60 for high-chlorophyll populations (not limited by nutrients) or 120 for low-chlorophyll populations (nutrient limited). These factors are derived from Strickland (1960) assuming that most chlorophyll is chlorophyll *a* and that carbon is 50% of the organic weight. Such estimates may be between one-third and three times the true value.

However, it is often impossible to determine the biomass of periphyton directly. Chlorophyll is then recommended as an indirect measure because it is closely linked to photosynthesis and is easier to determine than many other indirect measures, which are themselves subject to similar variations in relation to biomass.

(d) Other components

The methods recommended in 2.14 are generally applicable if the algae have been separated from the substrate and detritus.

3
Methods for Measuring Production Rates

Joint chapter edited by R.A. VOLLENWEIDER

General principles. The fundamental relationship governing primary production processes can be summarized with the well known equation:

$$6\,CO_2 + 6\,H_2O \xrightarrow{\;light\;} C_6H_{12}O_6 + 6\,O_2$$

As first discussed by van Niel (1941) this overall process can be understood as a redox reaction, wherefore the above equation may also be written more generally as

$$CO_2 + 2\,AH_2 \xrightarrow{\;h \cdot v\;} (HCOH) + 2\,A + H_2O$$

AH_2 stands for a H_2 donator, and represents H_2O as well as H_2S, or a reduced organic carbon compound. In this form the equation is not restricted to aerobic photo-autotrophs, but includes photo-autotrophic bacteria, and also some other bacterial reactions. With regard to the goal of measuring primary production rates, this means that several methodological approaches are equally justifiable. One can measure the carbon uptake as well as the oxygen production, or the formation of organic compounds, or the gain of chemical energy of the system, or changes of the cell internal redox system.

These last possibilities, however, have not yet developed sufficiently already to be used in practical primary production studies. However, one may note here that the present stage of primary production methodology is in an evolutionary phase, and that further developments, even revolutionary, are still possible.

The practical performance of primary production measurements on natural waters is based on two conceptually different approaches:

(a) Measurements are performed on *isolated samples of natural communities*. Either such isolated samples are re-suspended, or fixed in some way, near the locality from which they have been collected, i.e. in their natural environment (so-called '*in situ*' measurements), or the collected samples are exposed on shipboard, or in the laboratory under artificial conditions. In the first case, certain environmental factors, as light and temperature, during the time of exposure, will be almost the same in both the isolated and non-isolated communities; whereas, of course, other factors, such as turbulence, nutrient replenishment, grazing, etc., may more or less differ in the isolated samples from natural conditions. In the second case, light and temperature may be similar to that of the natural environment (depending on the experimental device), or they may be simulated, or, in most instances, kept constant. Turbulence, on the contrary, is normally simulated using a moving system of suspension, or some stirrer.

(b) Measurements are performed directly in the *natural environment*, i.e. on *non-isolated communities*, taking advantage of the overall community metabolism. This metabolism can be detected by measuring changes of certain factors, such as O_2, pH, conductivity, etc., during short periods. In some respects, this kind of approach may give more 'natural' information about the biological activity of a community, but this advantage is likely to be offset by other complications.

A third approach to productivity estimations is indirect. In this case, production rates are estimated from changes taking place during longer periods. These changes may refer to biomass increase, nutrient depletion, hypolimnetic oxygen consumption or carbon dioxide accumulation, etc. It is obvious that estimates based on such indirect methods are likely to be less accurate than those based on direct methods, and in many cases—depending on the environment to be studied—it is even impossible to apply indirect methods at all.

The following discussion refers in part to procedures (chemical, physico-chemical and physical methods), described independently of the way of approach. The outline of such procedures is only approximate, and for more details, readers are invited to consult other handbooks (e.g. the IBP Manual on chemical methods, text books of analytical chemistry, tracer techniques, etc.). Only the ^{14}C methodology is treated more accurately because, up to now, no text book does give a sufficient introduction to the subject with regard to needs for primary production measurements. In contrast, more attention is paid to the general methodology of primary production measurements, for which particular procedures can be adequately adapted. The selection of a particular method, as well as any modifications needed, depend primarily on the type and kind of water to be studied. It must be emphasized here that no particular method should be used unless the general chemical properties of a water are known. Simple oxygen determinations may be disturbed by trace metals and organic substances, and alkalinity determinations altered by a high ammonia content, etc. Therefore, ignorance of such properties may lead to wrong results in primary production estimates, and entire investigations may become useless.

3.1 CHEMICAL AND PHYSICO-CHEMICAL PROCEDURES DIRECTLY INVOLVED IN PRIMARY PRODUCTION MEASUREMENTS
R A VOLLENWEIDER

Some of the procedures used to study the chemical and physico-chemical properties of waters are also of particular importance in primary production studies. These are especially the procedures to determine dissolved oxygen, pH and CO_2 in its various forms.

3.11   Oxygen determinations

(a) The classic procedure for determining the oxygen content of a natural water is the well known 'Winkler method', and its various modifications. The same method is normally used in the 'light-dark bottle techniques' (see below) for studying production rates. Students using this method should carefully investigate, prior to initiating any routine work, which particular analytical procedure is most suitable for their kind of waters.

Due to the fact that, in primary production studies, the arithmetical difference of two oxygen contents (e.g. in the light and dark bottle, respectively), are needed for further calculations, precision of the oxygen analyses is more important than accuracy of the analytical method. Well trained analysts will easily reach a precision for a single oxygen determination of about ± 0.05 mg O_2/l. In accordance with statistical considerations, the arithmetic difference between two oxygen contents, therefore, must be then at least 0·15 mg O_2/l to be significant. The precision can be improved by taking the arithmetical mean from several parallel determinations of the same water.

(b) For certain studies, i.e. if the oxygen variations during short periods are high (1 mg/l and more), electrometric procedures, e.g. with so-called oxy-testers, can also be applied. The accuracy of such determinations is far below that of direct Winkler analyses, but it may be sufficient in highly productive standing and running waters.

For studies on natural, non-isolated communities, electrometric oxygen recording may be particularly useful. Some instruments for this purpose are highly developed (e.g. gas phase analysers) and may become of increasing interest in primary production studies.

3.12 CO_2-system analyses

Beside oxygen variations, variations of the various forms of CO_2 (free CO_2, bicarbonate and carbonate) are of paramount interest for production studies. Basically, analyses of this system can be a method of choice, replacing the oxygen methodology; in this case, pH is a most sensitive property for detecting variations of the system. Further to this, *a precise knowledge of the inorganic carbon content of a water is indispensable for using ^{14}C procedures.*

(a) Brief theoretical introduction
As is well known, the components of interest in the CO_2-system of a natural water are:

$$Ca^{..}, CO_2, H_2CO_3, HCO_3', CO_3'', OH' \text{ and } H^.$$

Except CO_2 and H_2CO_3, these components are present in ionic form; a small amount of $CaCO_3$ may also be present in non-ionic form. Other ions, normally, do not participate directly on the system but, in higher concentrations, they do influence the equilibrium constants by virtue of the ionic strength. These constants are given by:

$$(1) \quad K_{Ca} = (Ca^{..}) . (CO_3'')$$

$$(2) \quad K_1' = \frac{(H^.) . (HCO_3'')}{(CO_2) + (H_2CO_3)} .$$

$$(3) \quad K_2 = \frac{(H^.) . (CO_3'')}{(HCO_3')}$$

$$(4) \quad K_{H_2O} = (H^.) . (OH')$$

Besides ionic strength, the numerical values of the above constants depend on temperature.

The above system can be solved for any one of the components, considering further that

$$(5) \quad 2 (Ca^{..}) + (H^.) = 2 (CO_3'') + (HCO_3') + (OH')*$$

* All concentrations in mmol/l!

Titration of the water, made with standard acid against methyl-orange (or a pH of approximately 4·5) gives the right hand side of equation (5), and is called 'total carbonate (or methyl orange) alkalinity'. If titration is made against phenolphthalein (or to a pH of approximately 8·3), only CO_3'' and OH' ions are removed; the respective titration value is called 'phenolphthalein alkalinity'. Titration of the water with a standard sodium carbonate solution against phenolphthalein, on the other hand, gives the sum of $CO_2 + H_2CO_3$.

It must be noted that the alkalinity titration of a natural water may be influenced by the presence of H_4SiO_4, H_3BO_3, NH_3, and colloidal $CaCO_3$. Accordingly, 'total alkalinity' must be corrected with appropriate factors to get 'carbonate alkalinity'. Difficulties may arise in waters having high contents of humic acids.

It is obvious from the above that 'carbonate alkalinity' is not a sufficient information from which to calculate the total CO_2 content of a water; at the least, an additional measurement of pH is needed.

In order to simplify calculations, the above equations (neglecting Ca) can be re-elaborated to give free CO_2, HCO_3', CO_3'' or total CO_2 from carbonate alkalinity and pH. For ^{14}C work, the total CO_2 is most important, and gives the following equation:

$$\text{Total } CO_{2\ (mmol)} = \text{Carb.-Alk.}_{\ (mval)} \times \frac{1 + a_H/K_1' + K_2/a_H}{1 + 2\,K_2/a_H}$$

a_H is the hydrogen ion activity as found from pH measurements. Using numerical values for K_1' and K_2, as given by Buch (1945) for various salinities, or considering the ionic strength of dilute solutions, the right hand quotient can be tabulated as function of the pH and temperature, $f_{pH,\ T}$ and the above calculation reduces to

$$\text{Total } CO_{2\ (mmol)} = \text{Carb.-Alk.}_{\ (mval)} \times f_{pH,\ T}$$

To get carbon (mg/l), this value is multiplied by 12.

Figure 3.1 is a graphical representation of the factors $f_{pH,\ T}$, calculated for ionic strength $= 0$. In most fresh waters, this is a sufficient approximation, and the graph can be directly used for ^{14}C work. The graph is not appropriate for brackish and sea water.

(b) Practical performance

Technical details of oxygen determinations, alkalinity determinations, pH measurements and the recording of these factors are outlined in the I B P

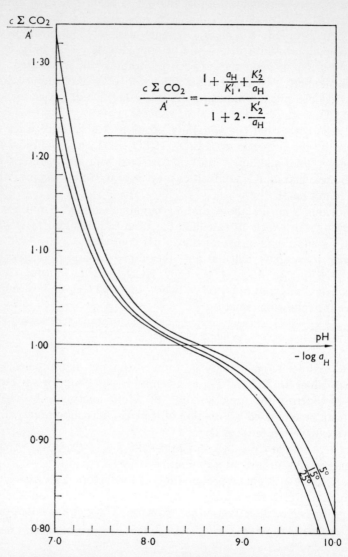

Figure 3.1. Correction factors $f_{pH,T}$ to obtain total CO_2 from titration alkalinity, pH and temperature, at ionic strength 0. Calculated according to formulae given by Buch 1945. To be used in fresh waters of low salinity only!

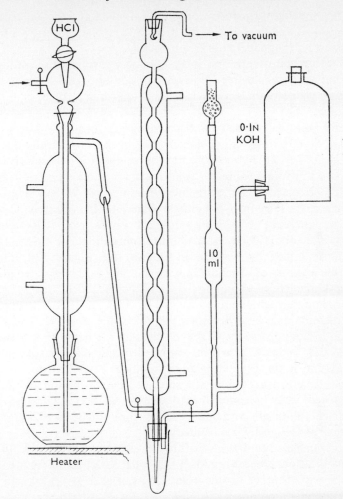

Figure 3.2. Apparatus for determining total CO_2 by distillation procedure. After Sorokin.

Manual on Chemical Methods. Readers are invited to consult this textbook. Here, only some brief hints will be given.

Total alkalinity is usually titrated with standard acid (0·1, 0·05, 0·02 or 0·01 N according to concentration and amounts of water used for titration; usually 100 or 50 ml but also less are used). Suitable indicators are: methyl orange, or a mixed indicator of brom-cresol green and methyl red. Methyl red alone is unsuitable unless the free CO_2 evolving during titration is removed by a strong air stream free from CO_2.

Another method of titration is by a known surplus acidification of the sample and removing the free CO_2 evolved by boiling; then a back titration is made using phenolphthalein, phenol red, brom-thymol blue, or methyl red as indicator.

The end point can further be detected by pH recording during titration (end point at 4·5), or by conductometry. With this latter technique the end point does not depend on free CO_2, and the technique is particularly indicated in waters of low total alkalinity (titrations are possible down to 0·05 mval/l) and in the presence of NH_3 at higher pH values (cf. Vollenweider 1962).

In some cases (e.g. in hypolimnetic waters in the absence of dissolved oxygen and presence of H_2S, in very acid waters, etc.) it is advisable to determine the total CO_2 by a distillation procedure. For this purpose, an apparatus described by Sorokin is suitable (see Figure 3.2). The water sample (the quantity of which is chosen according to the expected alkalinity) is poured in the left hand boiling flask and then acidified with 5% sulphuric acid containing an admixture of $CuSO_4$ to consume H_2S. The absorber in the centre contains a known volume of 0·05 or 0·1 N KOH. The sample is heated up to boiling and the CO_2 evolved is driven out with a stream of air free from CO_2. Thus CO_2 will be absorbed in the alkaline solution. When the distillation is finished the alkaline solution is washed out with boiled distilled water into a flask, 3 ml of a saturated $BaCl_2$ solution are added, and the stoppered flask is heated for 10 minutes at 80°C. Titration is made against phenolphthalein with 0·05 N HCl; 1 ml of 0·05 N HCl corresponds to 0·3 mg C of CO_2 or hydrocarbonates.

It is recommended to use this distillation technique (as a check for normal alkalinity titration procedures to obtain total CO_2) more frequently than during the past. Further to this, total CO_2 can also be determined by gas-chromatographic procedures.

3.2   [14]C TRACER TECHNIQUES

Introduction

R A VOLLENWEIDER

The tracer techniques commonly used for measuring ^{14}C activity are relatively simple; nevertheless, it is advisable for everyone using ^{14}C to acquire a basic knowledge of tracer techniques in general, handling of radioisotopes, statistics, safety and hazard problems, etc. Many excellent introductory books on this subject are available on the market in almost all important scientific languages.

In comparison with many other radioisotopes ^{14}C offers at least two advantages: (1) Because of its weak β-radiation (emission maximum at 0·15 MeV) hazard and safety problems are minimized, but should not be entirely neglected. (2) ^{14}C labelled samples can be stored for months without noticeable reduction of their specific activity*, because their half-life is very long (c. 4700 years). For the same reason, however, care must be taken to avoid any contamination of the counting equipment.

Sample preparation as well as selection of the counting equipment must be done in accordance with the basic characteristics of weak β-emitters. Absolute values of disintegration rates for ^{14}C samples may be obtained using appropriate techniques, but relative values are usually sufficiently adequate for the purpose of primary production measurements. For absolute β-counting organic samples labelled with ^{14}C are burned, or chemically oxidized by van Slyke procedures to carbon dioxide and measurements are made with a gas-phase or ionization counter (e.g. a Dynacon). This procedure is the most accurate, and is the only completely reliable method of determining the efficiency of Geiger-Müller counting (see below). However, this somewhat tedious and costly technique is not particularly suitable for routine measurements.

3.21   Apparatus

(a) Instrumentation for β counting

C R GOLDMAN

Any one of a great variety of Geiger-Müller detectors may be used for counting the rather weak beta radiation of ^{14}C labelled algae. Three types of GM counters are in general use: these are windowless, thin window, and thick window in order of their relative efficiency of detection. The higher efficiency of windowless GM counters is off-set to some degree by complications. The most important is probably the development of a static charge on filters under certain conditions which decrease the counting rate (Thomas 1964). The thin

---

* However, substantial losses of ^{14}C labelled material within the first 24 hr of storage, from marine and freshwater phytoplankton, have been reported recently by Wallen & Geen (1968).

window gas flow detectors are probably the best compromise with an efficiency of from about 20 to 35% and high reproduceability. Thick window counters with counting efficiencies below 10% often require excessively long counting time to achieve a statistically reliable total count and are not recommended if the thin window counting equipment is available.

The scaling equipment which records the total number of counts per unit time may be of the 'preset count' or 'preset time' variety. Preset counting has the advantage of counting all samples to the same total count and hence the same statistical accuracy. Many units are now available which automatically change the samples and usually record for each sample the time to reach a preset count.

(b) Accessory equipment for preparation of ^{14}C sources
R A VOLLENWEIDER

(i) The ^{14}C samples to be counted may be prepared using suitable metallic cuvettes (cylinders), metallic discs, or planchets. The choice depends on the nature of the original ^{14}C sample and on the particular scope of the experiment. Although filters fixed on planchets are most commonly used, ^{14}C labelled liquids can also be dried on discs (cf. e.g. 3.34 'Extracellular products'), or be absorbed on active carbon which then is transferred to metallic cuvettes. In this latter case, counting is done at the so-called saturation height (cf. Joyet 1949).

(ii) In most productivity work, however, the labelled material (phytoplankton, or other biological material; also $Ba^{14}CO_3$ for standardisation procedures) must be separated from the liquid phase. For this purpose various kinds of filter apparatus are used, some of which are ordinary laboratory devices, others are specifically adapted to primary productivity studies, and may also be used in the field (cf. e.g. Doty & Oguri 1958, 1959; Steemann Nielsen 1958). The most commonly used filters are Millipore or Membrane filters having a pore size of 0·5 μ.

A specific filter device, constructed and used by Yu. I. Sorokin, is described below. Other systems may be devised but it should be borne in mind that, once a system is adopted for work, no essential change at the filter level should be made; otherwise all previous standardisations will have to be repeated.

(iii) *Filtration device* (Yu.I.Sorokin). Figure 3.3 shows the device, with 3 funnels for the filtration of samples through millipore filters (Sorokin 1963).

The device has been used on shipboard for productivity work in reservoirs and at sea.

Before the filtration, the stopper of the bottle is changed to the rubber stopper with the tube in it (B). The end of the tube is cut at a slant and held with the clamp. The bottle is placed into the support of the device upside down. The end of the tube passes into the upper part of the funnel (A). Then, by simply opening the clamps, the whole volume of the bottle is automatically filtered through the filter. During the filtration in one of the funnels, the other can be prepared for the next filtration. After filling of the container (E), its content is poured into a special disposal container.

A compact filtration unit was also described by Doty & Oguri (1959), and is principally similar to that of Sorokin. For field study purposes a small one-chamber filtration unit, constructed by E.Steemann Nielsen (1957), has proved to be very useful.

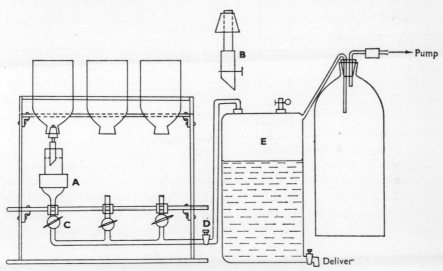

Figure 3.3. Filtration device by Yu.I.Sorokin (see text).

3.22   Preparation of 'working solutions'
R A VOLLENWEIDER

The 'working solution' is that which is ultimately used in ^{14}C productivity assays. Labelled carbon compounds are now available in a large variety of forms, either directly from radioisotope production centres (Amersham, Oak Ridge, etc.), or through national agencies and representatives. In some countries special licences are needed to get radioisotopes.

The normal form in which radiocarbon is used in productivity studies is a dilute $Na_2{}^{14}CO_3$ solution. Such a solution can be prepared either by dilution of a commercial solution of high specific concentration (1 to 5 mCuries/0·5–2 ml), or from solid $Ba^{14}CO_3$.

In this latter case, the radioactive barium carbonate must be transformed to sodium carbonate in a closed evacuated system by acidification of the barium carbonate and absorption of the evolved $^{14}CO_2$ in a sodium hydroxide solution. A simple one-chamber apparatus for this purpose has first been described by Steemann Nielsen (1952), and is shown in Figure 3.4.

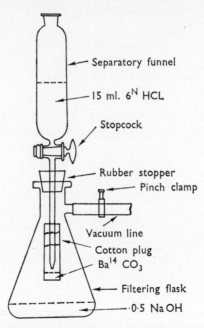

Separatory funnel

15 ml. 6^N HCL

Stopcock

Rubber stopper

Pinch clamp

Vacuum line

Cotton plug

$Ba^{14}CO_3$

Filtering flask

·0·5 NaOH

Figure 3.4. One-vessel device to be used for preparing ^{14}C 'working solutions' from solid $Ba^{14}CO_2$. After Doty & Oguri 1959.

For the preparation of 400 ml of working solution proceed as follows:

(1) Preparation of a 0·5 N NaOH solution. Weigh a slightly larger amount than is needed for 100 ml solution of NaOH (about 2·1 g; only high grade

chemicals!), wash the surface rapidly with double-distilled water and dissolve the rest in 100 double-distilled, boiled water. This solution has to be freshly prepared every time a 'working solution' is made up.

(2) 10 ml of this solution are poured into the vacuum flask.

(3) Bring the radioactive barium carbonate + carrier (see below) into the vial, and fix this vial in some way at the rubber stopper (simple systems can be found by everyone) so that the mouth of the separating funnel is about 1 cm above the barium carbonate. Close the upper part of the vial with cotton as indicated in the figure. Close the vacuum flask and fill the separating funnel with 15 ml of 6 N HCl.

(4) Evacuate and check for leaks; then close pinch clamp or stopcock.

(5) Add acid in small (! !) portions to the vial until no further CO_2 evolves. Close the stopcock of the separating funnel and wait at least one hour. To ensure a complete absorption of the evolved CO_2 in the bottom solution, place the vacuum flask on a magnetic stirrer at a low speed.

(6) Open slowly the pinch clamp or stopcock, and remove the separating funnel + vial, being careful not to spill any of the contents.

(7) Dilute the contents of the vacuum flask with double-distilled boiled water to about 350 ml, and adjust the pH, by adding portions of 0·1 N HCl, checking frequently, to about 9·5 (but not lower!). Fill up to 400 ml with distilled water.

Carrier. The total weight of high activity $Ba^{14}CO_3$ may be too low to be measured with a normal analytical balance, and furthermore the amount of CO_2 evolved may be insufficient for complete transfer to the alkaline solution. For this, a certain amount of carrier, i.e. non-labelled barium carbonate, is added to the labelled portion. The amount added depends on the alkalinity of the water to be assayed; in other words, the 'working solution' should finally have a carbonate concentration similar to that of the natural water.

Two-chamber system. The simple system described above has the disadvantage that careless handling of the apparatus may spoil the working solution. Therefore, a two-chamber system, in which the gaseous $^{14}CO_2$ is carried from the acid chamber to the alkaline chamber by means of a slow N_2 gas stream, is more suitable. Like the one-chamber system, such a two-chamber system can easily be built with standard laboratory glassware.

In general, however, direct dilution of a high activity $Na^{14}CO_3$ solution is now a more common procedure. Also in this case, a certain amount of carrier (Na_2CO_3) is added to the labelled solution, and dilution is made with a freshly prepared 0·01 or 0·005 N NaOH solution, and pH is finally adjusted as above.

If the 'working solution' serves for experiments in brackish or sea water, then a certain amount of NaCl (according to the salinity of the water to be assayed) must be added (Doty & Oguri 1959).

In either case, it is recommended that all manipulations be practised first without labelled carbonate to get perfectly acquainted with the technique and to avoid the unhappy experience of losing costly ^{14}C. Further, it should be born in mind that only high grade chemicals and distilled water (best on quartz) must be used for preparations. Utmost cleanness in all manipulations is imperative!

Activity of the working solution. The activity needed per millilitre of the 'working solution' in individual experiments, and hence the total activity to be dissolved, depends on several conditions, e.g. production rates expected, duration of the exposure, bottle size, etc. Some authors prefer adding standard amounts of 1 ml of 'working solution' per bottle, other workers use only fractions of millilitres (e.g. 0·2 ml) per bottle. In this latter case, the specific activity of the 'working solution' should be correspondingly higher, and the injection of the solution to the water assayed is done by means of a calibrated syringe. As a general rule, however, 1 μCurie* per 100 ml of a moderately productive water gives a sufficient number of counts after an exposure time of 4 to 6 hours at light optimum, provided that the counting efficiency of the GM equipment used is not too low (i.e. not lower than 10%).

Preparation of ampoules. The 'working solution' can be stored in a clean stoppered Pyrex glass bottle, but it is more advisable to distribute it into ampoules in portions of 1, 2, 5, 10 or 20 ml according to needs in later experiments. In either case the working solution, or the sealed ampoules should be autoclaved to prevent growth of bacteria.

3.23   Standardisation of working solutions
R A VOLLENWEIDER

Introduction

The specific activity of working solutions is known only approximately. Although the original activity of the labelled compound is determined by the manufacturer, and hence the final activity of the working solution could be found by calculation, a certain amount of activity may be lost during

* 1 μCurie $= 3·7.10^4$ decays/sec (absolute decays!)

subsequent manipulations. It is therefore necessary to determine the final activity individually for any newly prepared working solution.

As most procedures using ^{14}C give 'relative counts' (see above), besides the 'absolute activity', the 'relative activity' of the working solution has also to be determined.

Absolute activity determination

The surest way of determining the specific activity is by gas phase counting which gives directly 'total decays/ml second'. In order to manipulate this value correctly in further calculations, the counter efficiency of the GM counter used for routine analyses must be known. This can be achieved by comparing the absolute activity—determined by gas phase counting—with the relative activity—determined by means of the routine equipment—of test samples; these test samples can be precipitated $Ba^{14}CO_3$ filtered off, or—better—they are filtered subsamples of labelled natural phytoplankton prepared for this purpose. Checks of the GM counter efficiency should be made from time to time; if no gas phase counter is directly available this may be done in some specialized physics institute.

Relative activity determination

If no gas counters are available at all, some approximate relative standardization of the working solution can be achieved by other, relatively simple procedures. Yet, as experience during recent years has suggested, the results of such methods are not particularly reliable; errors as high as 30% have been reported.

(a) Chemical precipitation of ^{14}C as $Ba^{14}CO_3$

Precipitation, according to the equation:

$$Na_2{}^{14}CO_3 + BaCl_2 = \frac{Ba^{14}CO_3}{\downarrow} + 2\,NaCl,$$

is done in an alkaline medium having a pH of at least 10. The precipitated $Ba^{14}CO_3$ is filtered off from the solution by means of membrane filters, and the activity is measured after desiccation.

A serious problem in this procedure arises from self-absorption of the weak β-radiation with increasing amounts (or 'thickness') of barium carbonate per unit filter area. To overcome this difficulty, two modifications of the procedure outlined are commonly used in radioisotope laboratories. In the first, *constant amounts of activity* are precipitated, increasing, in a series of test tubes, the amount of Na_2CO_3 added per tube, so that the total amount of barium carbonate precipitated progressively increases in the series. From each tube, the whole amount of precipitate is filtered off.

Accordingly, each filter (theoretically) should have the same number of decays/second, but the measured specific activity (^{14}C/mg $BaCO_3$) decreases with increasing sample thickness. The (crude) relationship which governs the measured (relative) activities (a, in counts/second) in relation to sample thickness (t, in mg $BaCO_3/cm^2$) and self-absorption (μ=self-absorption coefficient), is given by

$$a = a_o \cdot \frac{1}{\mu \cdot t} (1 - e^{-\mu \cdot t})$$

a_0, i.e. the activity at zero thickness (which is of interest in this connection) cannot be determined directly but must be estimated by extrapolation from a linear or semi-log plot, or by calculation.

This procedure, proposed by Steemann Nielsen (1952), was used by many workers in the field of primary productivity. However, serious criticism can be raised against its further application. Primarily, $BaCO_3$ is insufficiently precipitated at very low concentrations as a simple consequence of the solubility product; hence, zero thickness activity will be underestimated. Secondly, as was demonstrated by Hendler (1959), the above formulation—although theoretically founded—does not hold in practice. A hyperbolic function was found in better agreement with experimental data. Thirdly, under certain conditions of counting (thick window counter, large source-counter distance) selective and scattering effects were observed, whereby the maximum counting does not occur at the (theoretical) zero thickness but at a thickness of 1 to 2 mg $BaCO_3/cm^2$. In this case, zero activity would be over-estimated by extrapolation from a data plot.

A sound approach to overcome some of the difficulties was proposed by Sorokin (1962), and will be presented below.

In the second modification of the precipitation technique, the ^{14}C activity is precipitated at a constant level of $BaCO_3$; the amount selected was determined experimentally in order to balance completeness of precipitation with minimal self-absorption. After precipitation and remixing of the precipitate, increasing portions of the same solution (1, 2, 3 ml) i.e. increasing amounts of activity, are filtered off, and the best straight line through a linear plot of activity counted versus mg filtered is extrapolated to the activity of the total precipitate.

This technique has been widely used by Vollenweider (see below), and (allowing for counter efficiency), gives only slight underestimates in comparison to gas-phase checks.

(b) 'Biological' standardisation of zero activity

In this procedure the ^{14}C activity of an adequate subsample of the working solution is entirely absorbed, by processes of photosynthesis, and assimilated by an algal culture. Zero thickness activity is determined from an aliquot of the labelled algal material filtered off. The principal advantage of this procedure lies in the fact that the zero activity is measured almost under the same conditions as, later on, the activity of the experimental natural phytoplankton.

The details of the technique are outlined below by the author (E.Steemann Nielsen). The whole procedure appears to be relatively simple. However, as there is still little experience with it, the results should be checked against other independent methods.

(c) Scintillation counting

Few authors have used scintillation techniques for ^{14}C studies in primary productivity (this is true at least in fresh water environments), although the choice of scintillation procedures may have incontestable advantages. The shortcoming is—at least in part—due to the fact that, for a long time, weak β-radiation scintillation equipment was not easily available commercially.

A short outline of the standardisation technique is given below by Dr Jitts.

(d) Some specific procedures
Standardisation procedure used by Yu. I. Sorokin

Self-absorption correction factors for $Ba^{14}CO_3$ precipitates can be calculated by constructing an empirical curve which is based upon the known zero thickness activity of a ^{14}C sample of labelled algae or bacteria.

In practice, the self-absorption curve is obtained as follows: an aliquot of the labelled algal material is filtered off through a Millipore molecular filter as a thin layer and its activity is measured under the same conditions as subsequent measurements are done; then the filter is combusted by van Slyke procedure in a closed system in which the evolved $^{14}CO_2$ is transferred quantitatively into a dilute NaOH solution. Brought up to a mark (e.g. 100 ml), this solution of known activity at zero thickness is distributed, in portions of 5 ml, to test tubes. To each portion is added a certain amount (the value of which is increased from tube to tube) of non-active carbonate, and $BaCO_3$

is precipitated by standard procedure. After filtration the activity of each sample is measured, and the corresponding values are plotted against their weights per 1 cm²; cf. Fig. 3.5. The activity of a 5 ml portion of the original solution is taken as 1, and relative correction factors are calculated for each individual subsample. In this manner, a set of factors are obtained as a function of the weight of $BaCO_3$ thickness (cf. Table 3) which later on are used for the correct standardisation of the working solutions.

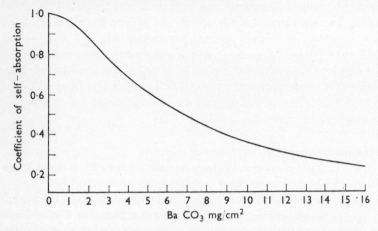

Figure 3.5. Curve of self-absorption of ¹⁴C radiation in $BaCO_2$ precipitates.

For the standardisation of the working solution proceed as follows: To a test tube, 2 ml of 0·4 N KOH, 3–4 ml tap water, and 1–2 ml of the solution to be tested (the activity should be in the range of $1–5 \times 10^3$ c.p.m.; if stronger, the solution must be diluted with 0·001 N KOH + 100 mg/l Na_2CO_3) are added and mixed. Then 1 ml 10% $BaCl_2$ solution is added, and the stoppered test-tube is heated at 80°C for 10 minutes. After cooling, the $BaCO_3$ precipitate formed is filtered on a previously weighed membrane filter; the filter is dried, counted under the counter, and again weighed. Using the table, the self-absorption correction coefficient can be found from the weight of precipitate per 1 cm² filter surface, and the zero thickness activity is calculated from the actual activity of the precipitate multiplied by the corresponding correction coefficient.

It must be emphasized that only in this way can the actual activity of the $BaCO_3$ precipitate be correctly extrapolated for the standard conditions of ¹⁴C measurement, as used in counting the activity of phytoplankton and bacteria in primary production studies. By other methods, the ^{14}C radio activity in organisms would be measured in one physical state, and the radioactivity of the hydrocarbonate in quite another, and hence the values obtained would not be comparable; cf. Jitts & Scott 1961; Sorokin 1962.

TABLE 3. Correction coefficients (K) for self-absorption

BaCO^3 mg/cm^2	K	BaCO$_3$ mg/cm^2	K
0·0	1·0	3·6	1·415
0·4	1·012	4·0	1·495
0·8	1·032	4·4	1·581
1·2	1·065	4·8	1·664
1·6	1·111	5·2	1·733
2·0	1·161	5·6	1·810
2·4	1·213	6·0	1·902
2·8	1·272	6·4	2·086
3·2	1·342	6·8	2·170

Standardisation procedure used by R.A.Vollenweider

Reagents: 1. Sodium carbonate solution 0·1 M (1·06 g Na$_2$CO$_3$/100 ml aq. dest.).
2. Buffer solution: 25 ml 1 M NH$_4$NO$_3$ and 25 ml 1 M NaOH mixed with CO$_2$-free distilled water to 500 ml (0·05 M NaOH + NH$_4$NO$_3$).
3. BaCl$_2$, solid.

Procedure: To a 100 ml measuring flask, containing about 50 ml of CO$_2$-free distilled water, 10 ml of solution (2) and 3 ml of solution (1) are added. The mixture should have a pH of 10–11.

1 ml, or an aliquot containing about 0·5 to 1 μCurie, of the ^{14}C solution to be tested is carefully measured with a calibrated syringe, and mixed with the above solution. Then a surplus of BaCl$_2$ is added, and the measuring flask brought up to mark with distilled water. It is allowed to precipitate for several hours.

After thorough mixing, 1, 2 and 3 ml are filtered through millipore filters, distributing the BaCO$_3$ precipitate homogeneously on the filter area. To avoid creeping of the BaCO$_3$, the filters are pressed on the filter plug by means of a ring-like holder having practically no walls (see Fig. 3.6). Prepare at least two replicates.

After drying, the ^{14}C activity of the filters is counted on the GM equipment. The values obtained, appropriately corrected for background counts

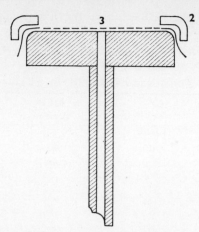

Figure 3.6. Filtration apparatus used by Vollenweider for ^{14}C standardisation. (1) Metallic filter plate, (2) Ring-like filter holder, (3) Membrane filter.

and coincidence losses, are then plotted on millimetre paper, and the total activity of the solution to be calibrated is determined by extrapolating the straight line which fits best the 1 and 2 ml counts starting from zero. The 3 ml counts are used as a check, and should be somewhat below the corresponding value on the interpolation line as predicted by self-absorption.

Precision: With repeated duplicates, the statistical error was found to be about $\pm 2\%$.

Accuracy: Compared with gas phase countings (appropriately correcting the GM countings for counter efficiency), the above procedure was found to give estimates about 4–5% below the theoretical values.

Standardisation by means of algae

E STEEMANN NIELSEN

It has always been assumed that the determination of ^{14}C in an ampoule by means of a $BaCO_3$-self-absorption correction curve is only an approximation. Recent observations have shown that the errors are worse than expected, particularly if Geiger-Müller tubes with thick mica windows are used. Other techniques have been suggested, therefore. One technique is to transfer all $^{14}CO_2$ from an ampoule into the organic matter of small plankton algae and determine the radioactivity of these algae in exactly the same way as when measuring the activity of the algae from ordinary experiments. Steemann

Nielsen (1965) has outlined such a technique which will be the basis for all work done by the International ^{14}C Agency, Denmark, from 1 January 1966.

As first shown by Egle & Schenk (1952), the carbon dioxide compensation point in *Chlorella* is found below 0.001% (volume) CO_2. By working at a pH of about 4·0, where all CO_2 is in the form of free CO_2, and by starting at a CO_2-concentration of about 0.5%, it is thus possible to let *Chlorella* assimilate practically the total amount of CO_2.

In practice, the work has been done in the following way: In a separating funnel containing 1339 ml of a culture *solution* (0.5% per volume CO_2, reduced tension of O_2 and N_2), an amount of centrifuged *Chlorella pyrenoidosa* and the content of a ^{14}C-ampoule were introduced. The final pH was 4·2. Twelve clear-stoppered 15 ml bottles were filled and placed on a rotating wheel in a water-thermostat illuminated at 10 klux. Every 30 minutes a bottle was removed, and two samples of 5 ml each were filtered by membrane filters. One of the filters was quickly dried and counted by means of an end-window tube.

When three consecutive filters have given the same counts, it is assumed that all CO_2 has been assimilated. As a control, 30 ml from two other bottles are mixed in a separating funnel (130 ml) with fresh culture medium, the concentration of free CO_2 being 0.25%. Six 15 ml bottles are filled and placed on a rotating wheel. When, according to the first part of the experiment, all free CO_2 should have been assimilated, the first bottle is removed and 15 ml is filtered.   After a subsequent 30 minutes the same is done with the next bottle, and so on. As is to be expected, all $^{14}CO_2$ is already assimilated during the first part of the experiment. The weight of algae per cm² on the filter is kept far below 0·1 mg, preventing almost any influence of self-absorption.

In special experiments, the fraction of extra-cellular assimilates has to be measured. It is about one per cent of the total assimilates.

When using the equipment at the International Agency (mica-window = 1·3 mg/cm², efficiency about 7%), the biological technique gives results which are about 31% lower than the values obtained by the original $BaCO_3$ technique. The new determinations agree with measurements by means of scintillation counting (personal communication by Dr P.V.Ramachandran Nair).

When using windowless Geiger-Müller tubes, the errors due to standardisation by means of $BaCO_3$-self-absorption correction curves are less. In some preliminary experiments we have found that the biological technique gives results about 10% lower.

Scintillation technique for calibrating ^{14}C stocks

H R JITTS

Outline: The efficiency of the Geiger counter is determined by first counting thin films of labelled perspex with the same geometry as phytoplankton samples, then measuring the absolute activity of the films by liquid scintillation counting. The absolute activity of ^{14}C stocks is also measured by liquid scintillation. The zero thickness activity of the ^{14}C stocks is calculated from their absolute activity and the counter efficiency (Jitts & Scott 1961).

Method: A millipore filter is immersed in distilled water. ^{14}C labelled Perspex (Amersham CFP3) dissolved in acetone (26 mg/ml) is dropped onto the surface of the water, where it forms a very thin film. The film is deposited on the millipore filter by lifting the filter under the film. The filter is then dried, cut to size, and its activity measured in the Geiger counter.

The films are then dissolved in 10 ml toluene phosphor containing 4 g P.P.O. and 100 mg P.O.P.O.P. per litre and their scintillation activity counted. Their absolute activities are then determined by adding a known amount of ^{14}C hexadecane standard (Amersham CFR5) and recounting.

The ^{14}C stock solutions are diluted with water containing 1 g/l $(NH_4)_2CO_3$ to obtain suitable count rates. 50 µl of this is added to 15 ml of a liquid scintillator with the following composition:

400 ml	toluene
400 ml	para-dioxane
240 ml	ethanol
50 g	naphthalene
45 g	P.P.O.
100 mg	P.O.P.O.P.

The absolute activity of the ^{14}C stocks is determined by counting its scintillation activity before and after adding a known amount of ^{14}C hexadecane standard.

3.3 MEASUREMENTS (IN SITU) ON ISOLATED SAMPLES OF NATURAL COMMUNITIES

3.31 The enclosure of phytoplankton communities

C J SOEDER and J F TALLING

Introduction

In order to determine the total production in a given water column, it is necessary to run a vertical series of measurements with samples from various depths.

The collection and exposure of samples is primarily intended to show the variation of photosynthetic activity per unit volume with depth. From this relationship (depth-profile), the activity below a unit area of surface can be calculated as the integral represented by the area enclosed by the profile—making due allowance for the horizontal and vertical scales used. In most instances a number of water samples (at least 5 is desirable) are collected from various depths spaced over the euphotic zone, and each used to fill one or more experimental bottles which are then suspended at the depth from which the original sample was taken. The vertical spacing of the samples to be collected and exposed depends mainly on the transparency of the water. As a general rule, active production will extend to the depth at which the incident light intensity (measured at the surface of the water) is attenuated to about 1 % (e.g. Talling 1960). In greater depths catabolic processes prevail.

When the euphotic zone is well mixed by turbulence, the distribution of photosynthetic activity with depth may be equally well shown by using homogeneous samples from a single level (e.g. the sub-surface), redistributed in bottles over the euphotic zone. Even when stratification and differentiation exist, the depth profile of activity obtained from such homogeneous samples can provide an instructive comparison with the more truly *in situ* exposures (e.g. Talling 1965). With homogeneous material, dark bottles need not be exposed at each depth, as the only environmental factor likely to affect dark processes is temperature. In very stratified situations with large vertical variations of population density and composition, more numerous depths of sampling and exposure may be necessary (e.g. Findenegg 1964).

For the calculation of integral production (Talling 1957a; Strickland 1960; Rodhe 1965; Vollenweider 1965b) the determination of the depth of maximal photosynthesis is essential. The position of the most productive layer in the depth profile often shows diurnal changes (Vollenweider & Nauwerck 1961). Diurnal curves for total production per unit time are not necessarily parallel to the concomitant changes of light intensity, and asymmetrical day-curves have been reported (Doty & Oguri 1957; Ohle 1958; Vollenweider & Nauwerck 1961). For routine measurement one has to select a representative exposure time. It is also possible to restrict the measurements to one representative depth (Rodhe, Vollenweider & Nauwerck 1958; Nauwerck 1963).

The normal *in situ* exposure of samples fully meets the requirements of determining primary production in a given body of water. For the solution of special problems some other procedures are recommended. The study of horizontal inhomogeneities of photosynthetic capacity in the open sea, in large lakes, or in reservoirs makes it necessary to compare, more or less synchronously, the performance of samples from various stations under identical conditions. This is accomplished by placing the samples in thermo-constant incubators either on board ship or in the laboratory. The phyto-plankton is then exposed to natural daylight or to artificial light (fluorescent lamps) for several hours (Steemann Nielsen 1952, 1957; Sorokin 1958; Bachmann, Saunders & Trama 1961). *In situ* light conditions can be simulated for various depths by appropriate combinations of neutral and coloured filters in daylight incubators (Cushing 1957a, b; Steemann Nielsen 1957). The results of *in situ* experiments have been compared with parallel measure-ments under standardized conditions by several authors (e.g. Rodhe, Vollen-weider & Nauwerck 1958; cf. also Strickland 1960).

A further method for studying integral photosynthesis has been described by Sorokin (1956). The following tests are run in parallel: (a) surface samples exposed at the surface, (b) samples from various depths, including surface, exposed in a light incubator under identical conditions, (c) a sub-divided sample from the surface (or from one other depth) exposed at various depths *in situ*. This method has been successfully adapted by Saunders *et al.* (1962).

Particular problems of primary productivity, such as phytoplankton dynamics in relation to nutritional factors, may require enclosure of larger water masses in large carboys, plastic bags, tubes or cylinders which can be suspended in the natural environment.

(a) Remarks on sampling
For sampling equipment and techniques see chapter 2.11. Only a few recommendations need be added.

(i) The volume of the sampler should be sufficient to fill all of the light and dark bottles of one batch, and to determine alkalinity and pH (or additional chemical factors). If plankton counts are desired, preserving agents should be added as soon as possible.

(ii) The risk of light injuries (Steemann Nielsen & Hansen 1959; Goldman, Mason & Wood 1963) is reduced by using samplers of black material. Exposures of unadapted algae to full sunlight should be avoided. One can fill the bottles and add radiocarbon in the shelter of a wide bag of black cloth, or using a special working box for light protection.

(iii) Any contact of the water sample with bare metal surfaces may be either detrimental to the algae (Doty & Oguri 1958) or stimulating (Goldman 1963). Metal parts of the sampler can be coated with epoxy, or another reliable plastic.

(b) Enclosures
(i) *Bottles*
The classical method of measuring phytoplanktonic photosynthesis *in situ* proceeds from the enclosure of water samples in glass bottles with ground glass stoppers. Pyrex or glassware of similar quality is sufficient for most purposes. The absorption of light by glass is, however, considerably greater than by most lake or sea waters, especially in the short wavelength range. The 'light climate' inside the bottles will hence differ from natural conditions, and the experimental results depend on glass quality (Ohle 1958). Findenegg (1966) demonstrated striking differences between carbon assimilation rates in glass and in quartz bottles. In full sunlight, glass protects phytoplankton to a certain degree from surface inhibition. The production in glass bottles can exceed the parallel values in quartz bottles by 50% or more. If, on the other hand, light is the limiting factor of production (greater depth, cloudy weather, dawn, etc.), the values obtained with quartz bottles can be considerably higher than with glass. There can be little doubt that the use of quartz flasks will provide more natural light conditions. The high costs of quartzware seem to be an obstacle to its general use in field work. For financial reasons it may be of interest that the optical properties of plexiglass and comparable plastic materials are rather similar to quartz.

The volume of the bottles should not be less than 100 ml. Most authors work with exposure flasks of 100–200 ml. Dark bottles are usually prepared by covering the glass surface with a double layer of black scotch tape. Black paint seems to be less reliable. Elster & Motsch (1966) enclose normal bottles in metal boxes which are also filled with the sample water.

(ii) *Plastic bags, cylinders*
Exposure times of phytoplankton in bottles are rather limited (cf. subsequent paragraph on exposure times). For this reason, several devices have been developed which permit long-term experiments with native phytoplankton under almost natural conditions in lakes and in the sea. However, it should be borne in mind that studies of this kind require great skill and a well-equipped team of experts.

Thomas (1959, 1962) used the 'Plankton-Test-Lot', a vertical Plexiglas tube of 5 cm inner width and 6–8 m length. Two anchored buoys were connected with metal rods from which several of the bottomless tubes could be hung into the lake, thus separating a defined volume as an artificial 'micro-lake' from the environment. By means of this setup Thomas was able to study diffusion kinetics in the epilimnion, and the population dynamics of phytoplankton with and without additional mineral nutrients. For determining dark processes and decomposition rates, Thomas employed black plastic tubes of the same size. Stepanek & Zelinka (1961) studied the development of phytoplankton populations in large containers (2 m wide, 10 m long), made from transparent plastic film. These cylinders were exposed in the epilimnion of a reservoir. They were either closed at the bottom or open, and metal hoops stabilized the shape from the outside. A special float carried 8 containers with their upper rims being 20 cm above lake surface in order to avoid overspilling of waves. A similar plastic cylinder for *in situ* studies has been described by Goldman (1962). The same author also used an elongate plastic tube (72·5 cm dia., 25 m long) to demonstrate the influence of diluted sewage on the phytoplankton of an oligotrophic mountain lake.

The elaborate system of Strickland & Terhune (1961) consists essentially of a large sphere made from opalescent polyethylene film (diameter 6 m). A wide-meshed nylon net provides additional support to the balloon. A pair of metal rings at the lower pole bears some ballast. Corresponding rings at the upper pole support a cylindrical neck (45 cm wide) which rises above sea surface. Three anchored lines are attached to a third ring surrounding the equator of the sphere. The contents of the balloon (125 m^3) are continuously stirred. The paper by McAllister, Parsons, Stephens & Strickland (1961) proves the outstanding experimental value of this device.

Vertical glass cylinders may be applied occasionally, either to estimate, by a direct integration, average rates of photosynthesis or growth in a water-column of known depth, or to contain experimental populations under semi-natural conditions for tests of the effects of environmental factors upon growth. These applications have been rarely used. The first is most readily applied in very turbid waters, where the photosynthetic zone is shallow and can be covered by a cylinder less than 1 m long. In work on an extremely productive Ethiopian lake, Talling (unpublished) used an inverted measuring cylinder, with the bottom end closed by a rubber bung, and held vertically by a retort stand and clamp in shallow water. The contents are well mixed at the beginning and end of the exposure, and changes due to photosynthesis and respiration determined from 'light' and 'dark' cylinders. Any redistribution of the phytoplankton population during the exposure, by sinking or buoyancy, will obviously modify the average photosynthetic activity, and short exposures (<1 hour) are thus desirable. The method is unsuitable for populations initially stratified within the water-column sampled.

(c) Suspension

The most widely used method of suspending the paired light and dark bottles *in situ* is by attachment to a line or wire which is held in position by an anchored buoy or float. Tying the line to a boat includes the danger of shadowing the exposed samples. A metal snap is tied to the neck of each bottle, which can be fastened to rings along the line. The bottles will then hang in an almost perpendicular position. Goldman (1960) keeps the bottles from bumping or shading each other by a pair of crossed metal rods.

Ohle (1958) compared the production in light bottles being exposed in vertical and horizontal positions. The values of the latter were about 10% higher. Elster & Motsch (1966) confirmed this experience, and found differences up to 35%. They also report a marked influence of the flask position on the apparent depth profile of photosynthetic activity. For these reasons, they routinely suspend the bottles in horizontal position, using for support a light metal frame to which the flasks are fastened by rubber rings. Horizontal suspension of the bottles was also preferred by Saunders, Trama, & Bachmann (1962). Vollenweider (personal communication) prolongs a metal clamp, holding the bottle neck, into an arm of 15–20 cm length. This is a very easy means of keeping the flasks in an almost horizontal position.

A very elegant method for *in situ* experiments with light and dark bottles has been described by Watt (1965). The empty bottles are lowered to the desired depths on a weighted line. The cocks closing the bottles are opened by a sliding weight (messenger) and at the same time radiocarbon is released into the flask.

(d) Duration of exposure

Many of the undesirable features described in this section will tend to become more pronounced during long exposures, and so can be reduced by using short exposures, not longer than a few hours duration. Several authors (e.g. Ichimura & Saijo 1958; Vollenweider & Nauwerck 1961) have found evidence of a decline in photosynthetic rates during exposures longer than 4–6 hours, such as the 24 hour periods often used. In very productive waters, an exposure of even 1 hour may lead to an undesirably large supersaturation of oxygen and raised pH in samples near the surface. In very short exposures, of $\frac{1}{2}$ hour or less, the time occupied in manipulations becomes a more significant source of error. The onset of qualitative and quantitative changes in the enclosed populations has rarely been examined, but losses due to damage during manipulations could well be rapid (e.g. to sensitive flagellates), whereas at the optimum depth for growth a doubling of population density could equally well occur during a 12 or 24 hours exposure.

Notwithstanding the physiological advantages of short exposures for estimating photosynthetic production, in their interpretation allowance must be made for the influence of temporary weather conditions, and diurnal changes in illumination and possibly photosynthetic capacity of the populations. Estimates of production over longer periods are usually required, with the 24-hour day as the most convenient unit, although allowance should still be made for day-to-day and seasonal differences in illumination and day-length. Estimates of production per day have been calculated from long exposures (24 hours, or dawn to sunset), from the summation of a sequence of short (e.g. 3–4 hour) exposures (e.g. Vollenweider & Nauwerck 1961); from a half-day exposure (dawn to midday, or midday to sunset) multiplied by 2; and from the relationship, established empirically (e.g. Hepher 1962) or by calculation (e.g. Talling 1965; Vollenweider 1965b) between production during a short period and production during a full day. Here a choice must depend upon the local situation, objective, and time available. Where pronounced diurnal changes occur in phytoplankton density and/or its specific activity, the most laborious method—summation of short exposures—has an obvious advantage. For the estimation of net photosynthesis and respiratory consumption, the distinction between the daylight period and the full 24 hours has an added significance. See also 3.72.

When other growth responses of the algae to environment are being studied (e.g. to seasonal illumination and temperature, added nutrients), much longer exposures (e.g. 1 week) can be required and cultures may then be preferable to samples of natural populations. Responses of the latter to added nutrients (bioassay) may be followed by the estimation of population density or of photosynthetic activity (= population density × specific activity) in sub-samples removed at intervals (e.g. successive days).

(e) The oxygen light and dark bottle technique

When an exposure is made with sub-samples of a phytoplankton population in clear ('light') and darkened bottles, the initial concentration of dissolved oxygen (c_1) can be expected to fall to a lower value (c_2) in the darkened bottles by respiration, and to be changed to another value (c_3) in the clear bottles according to the difference between photosynthetic production and respiratory consumption. If other processes involving oxygen (e.g. photoxidative consumption) are absent or can be neglected, and if it is assumed that respiratory consumption is not altered by illumination, then the difference ($c_1 - c_2$) represents the respiratory activity per unit volume over the time interval involved, the difference ($c_3 - c_1$) the net photosynthetic activity, and their sum ($c_3 - c_1$) + ($c_1 - c_2$) = ($c_3 - c_2$), the gross photosynthetic activity. On this basis it is possible to estimate gross photosynthesis directly from the difference in concentrations between the clear and darkened bottles, but further knowledge of the initial concentration is needed for estimates of respiration and net photosynthesis. Recent general discussions of the method and its application are given by Lund & Talling (1957), Steemann Nielsen (1958, 1963), Gessner (1959, 1960), Strickland (1960), Strickland & Parsons (1968), and Winberg (1960, 1963).

The measurement of dissolved oxygen can be made by either chemical (Winkler method) or electrochemical determinations. The Winkler method has been generally used, often without significant modification. One considerable advantage is the high precision obtainable (about $\pm 0 \cdot 02$ mg/l in single determinations). Another is that biological activity in the samples is arrested by the addition of the reagents, which is easily and quickly performed in the field, and the determination proper left for more favourable laboratory conditions. If some delay is unavoidable after the end of an exposure, the 'unfixed' samples should be kept in darkness at low temperature, and the additional time allowed for in any calculations of respiratory rate. Storage of 'fixed' samples can take place either after iodine is liberated or—probably better— at the precipitate stage. Periods longer than two or three days are not advisable, and the best storage conditions involve submerging the bottles under water in darkness.

Using the Winkler iodometric estimation, a known volume of solution is transferred from the original bottle to a flask in which it is titrated with thiosulphate solution. Details of the procedure vary according to individual preferences, the size of bottle and sample, and the precision required, which in very productive waters need not be high. Titrations with N/320 thiosulphate, against a sample size of 100 ml with starch as indicator, have shown a precision (about $\pm$ 0·02 mg/l) with simple apparatus similar to the best claimed with other modifications (e.g. with starch substitutes as indicators, or using an amperometric end-point). The reproducibility and precision of estimations is much more important than their absolute accuracy, as activity is usually being measured from relatively small differences between determinations. Conditions affecting the titration, such as quantity of indicator used and the time taken, should therefore be standardized as far as possible. If the time is long, the loss of iodine by volatilization may introduce error (cf. Montgomery, Thom & Cockburn 1964). Some workers recommend the titration of two aliquots from each sample bottle, but this involves much extra time and often reduces the volume usable per titration. The use of more replicate bottles is a potentially better way of obtaining higher overall precision.

After analyses are completed, all traces of iodine should be removed from the bottles and stoppers by a rinse with dilute (say N/100) thiosulphate, followed by further thorough rinsing with water.

(f) The ^{14}C light and dark bottle technique
C R GOLDMAN, E STEEMANN NIELSEN,
R A VOLLENWEIDER, R G WETZEL

In the ^{14}C technique, the incorporation of tracer in the organic matter of phytoplankton during photosynthesis is used as a measure of the rate of primary production. If the content of total CO_2 of the experimental water is known (cf. 3.12), and if a definite amount of $^{14}CO_2$ is added to the water, then by determining the content of ^{14}C in the plankton after the experiment the total amount of carbon assimilated can be calculated. It is only necessary to multiply the amount of ^{14}C found by a factor corresponding to the ratio between the total CO_2 of the water and the total $^{14}CO_2$ added at the beginning of the experiment (Steemann Nielsen 1951, 1952). The excellent sensitivity of the method can be increased further by applying several correction factors.

(i) *Performance of experiments*
The ^{14}C working solution, prepared according to 3.22, can best be transferred to experimental flasks (filled previously with the experimental water) by means of a graduated hypodermic syringe having a needle not shorter than 5 cm. From any kind of water (depth) at least one light and one dark bottle is prepared.

By experience one becomes familiar with the amount of ^{14}C activity to be added to the bottles in order to produce a moderately radioactive plankton sample for assay. The resultant activity at the end of the experiment is dependent on numerous variables, such as growth rates, plankton density, length of incubation, amount filtered, etc. For many lakes of moderate productivity, an addition of 1–3 μCuries per 125 ml sample with a 4 hour incubation and filtration of 50 ml subsample yields a moderately 'hot' sample without excessive layering of plankton on the filter.

It is recommended to collect first all water samples from the various depths, to fill the experimental bottles immediately after collection and keep them in a dark box; then injection of ^{14}C to the various bottles is done rapidly, and, after thorough shaking, the bottles are lowered at once to the preselected depths of exposure.

(ii) *Alkalinity and pH determinations*

Determinations for each water sample collected should be performed as soon as possible either on board ship or in the laboratory. For higher precision it is advisable to take advantage of the possibilities of a chemical laboratory, on condition that this does not delay the determinations too much. Should this not be feasible, and determinations are made on board ship, then, in any case, the values should be checked later in the laboratory. In general, alkalinity does not change much within a few hours, but pH may suffer variations.

(iii) *Preparation of filters for counting*

After withdrawal of the experimental bottles from the various depths (an operation which should be performed as rapidly as possible to avoid light injury or further photosynthesis, particularly of those samples which were exposed at low light intensities), they are stored in a black box until the beginning of the filtration operation. Filtration may be done on board ship, or better in the laboratory.

For this, aliquots of the samples are transferred as rapidly as possible into a suitable filtration apparatus (cf. 3.21b) onto membrane filters of about 0·5 μ porosity (e.g., Millipore HA, or Membrane No. 2). If the funnels are kept clean and coated with a silicone film, the necessity of rinsing the walls of the funnel is eliminated. Vacuum applied to the filtration system should not exceed 0·5 atm, to reduce the possibility of rupturing more fragile cells. Vacuum should be released immediately after liquid has passed to avoid rapid air desiccation. The filtration operation should be done in a semi-darkened area.

After removal of the filters from the filtration unit, they are placed onto counting planchetts, avoiding any contact with the plankton on the filter surface, and then placed in a desiccator (containing e.g. silica gel). If carbonate precipitates are to be expected (e.g. in samples from waters of high alkalinity), it is advisable to expose the dried filters to fumes of HCl for 10 minutes to remove possible ^{14}C precipitates extracellularly; these filters are again desiccated before counting.

Counting of the 'hot' samples is done to about 5000 counts at a 'count preset' unit. Samples from dark bottles are relatively inactive, and sometimes require separation from the light bottle samples for counting which is then done to about 500 or 1000 counts only.

(iv) *Calculation*

The resultant activities are expressed as counts/second (cps), or counts per minute (cpm), in accordance with the expression used for the working solution.

The total carbon uptake is then calculated by the following equation:

$$^{12}C \text{ assimilated} = \frac{^{14}C \text{ assimilated (c)}}{^{14}C \text{ available (b)}} \times {}^{12}C \text{ available (a)} \times k_{1,\,2,\,3}$$

where

(a) = ^{12}C available = total carbonate alkalinity × pH$_t$ factor
    = (total carbonate alkalinity – phenolphthalein alkalinity) × 12 = mg ^{12}C/l available
    (n.b. alkalinity in mval/l)

(b) = ^{14}C available = ^{14}C activity added
    (e.g. expressed as 'zero thickness' activity, if only relative measurements are made, or as μCurie × counter efficiency at the given counter geometry)

(c) = ^{14}C assimilated = (total counts – background) × 1·06

The correction factors $k_{1,\,2,\,3}$, etc., have the following meanings:

k_1 = a correction for the aliquot factor. If, e.g., 50 ml were filtered from a bottle 133 ml, and 1 ml of working solution was added, then this factor is approximately 132/50 = 2·64.

$k_2 =$ a time factor either to reduce the measured activity to 'activity/hour', or to adjust variations of the effective exposure time to a preselected standard exposure.

$k_3 =$ a dimension factor, e.g. to convert mg/l to mg/m^3, etc.

(g) Possible limitations and artificial modifications

J F TALLING and G E FOGG

These may be grouped as (i) general limitations of enclosed samples, (ii) problems specific for the oxygen method, (iii) problems specific for the ^{14}C method.

(i) *General limitations*

J F TALLING

Conditions experienced by phytoplankton cells within the experimental vessel or enclosure may deviate from those without in various ways, and may affect the activity being measured. Where possible, tests with the specific working conditions and plant material are desirable, but the following possibilities can be borne in mind:—

Reduction of water circulation and turbulence may lead to cell sedimentation or (with many blue-green algae) buoyant rise, and alter the vertical disposition of population density in relation to environmental factors (e.g. light intensity) in large enclosures. The same reduction may retard uptake of nutrients, although there is little published evidence for this with phytoplankton (see also 3.61).

The activity may be modified through a persistent effect of some earlier condition or treatment. Examples include the exposure of cells to excessive turbulence or strong light during manipulations (cf. Goldman, Mason & Wood 1963), or their maintenance at a fixed point rather than a circulating path in the water column (cf. Findenegg 1964).

The population samples may diverge—by growth, decay, or animal grazing —in total density and in qualitative composition from the original population (e.g. Pratt & Berkson 1959). This is especially likely in exposures lasting longer than one day. Production rates then measured may diverge appreciably from the 'instantaneous' or differential rate (see Strickland & Parsons 1968). Growth of green 'weed' algae (e.g. species of *Chlorella* and *Ankistrodesmus*) is possible and such species are usually not typical of natural phytoplankton. Bacteria are also likely to increase in numbers, particularly in small bottles or on plastic surfaces, with effects upon overall respiration rates and possibly dissolved substances.

The chemical composition of the enclosed water may be altered and modify rates of plant growth and photosynthesis. Intense photosynthetic activity in dense populations may greatly alter concentrations of oxygen, total and free carbon dioxide, and pH (cf. Gessner & Pannier 1958). Other plant nutrients may be depleted by algal growth, or removed by adsorption on the walls of containers (e.g. Fe, PO_4), or otherwise altered by the activities of zooplankton (e.g. PO_4 excretion) and bacteria.

Some loss of light, by absorption and reflection, will occur at or in the transparent walls of the bottles or enclosures. Such loss is only likely to be considerable in the far ultra-violet region of the spectrum, where normal glass absorbs strongly, and if the walls become discoloured after prolonged exposure. The UV modification may possibly be important in relation to the depression of photosynthetic activity often found immediately below the water-surface (e.g. Findenegg 1966; see also 3.31b).

(ii) *Oxygen method*

Various limitations and possible or reputed sources of error with the oxygen method are discussed by Steemann Nielsen (1958), Gessner (1959), Pratt & Berkson (1959), Strickland (1960), Winberg (1960), and Patten, Norcross, Young & Rutherford (1964). They are listed below together with some precautions. It will be seen that long exposures (> 6 hours) are more susceptible to a variety of possible errors.

For reasons of analytical precision plus sources of experimental error, it is generally impracticable—even with 2 or 3 replicate bottles—to record a photosynthetic change of less than about 0·02 mg or 20 µg O_2/l. In terms of average photosynthetic rates this limit would correspond to roughly 7 µg O_2/l hour (= 7 mg O_2/m³. hour) for a 3-hour exposure, and about 2 µg O_2/l hour (= 2 mg O_2/m³. hour) for a 12-hour exposure. As a general and even more approximate indication, the method is not likely to be usefully applicable to phytoplankton densities expressed by concentrations of chlorophyll *a* lower than 1 mg/m³.

The presence of air or oxygen bubbles within the experimental bottles is a very common source of experimental error. The bubble may be introduced accidentally when a bottle is initially filled, may develop from temperature changes causing changes of volume or saturation concentration, or result from a supersaturation of oxygen produced by photosynthesis itself. Obvious precautions here include care in complete filling, stoppering, and handling the bottles; avoidance of strong changes of temperature, as may result from warming in air (a water bath can be useful); and by reducing the duration of exposures with very productive waters. An initial undersaturation is also advantageous when oxygen production is large, and has been introduced artificially (e.g. Jenkin 1937), although with some risk of modifying other rate-limiting factors. In practice, a considerable supersaturation (e.g. 200%) is often tolerable as regards bubble-formation, as large changes are less sensitive to errors introduced by single bubbles. Bubbles of carbon dioxide may develop after the acidification involved in the Winkler method, but even a considerable degree of effervescence is then tolerable before losses of solution are excessive. Such trouble is likely when the initial concentrations of bicarbonate plus carbonate (i.e. 'alkalinity') exceed 20–60 m.eq./l.

Errors can be introduced if the rate of respiratory uptake of oxygen varies with light intensity (Gessner & Pannier 1958) or with oxygen concentration and so differs between clear and dark bottles or between clear bottles at various levels of illumination. However, the respiration rate of the phytoplankton itself is usually only a small fraction (often $1/_{20}$ to $1/_{10}$) of the light-saturated photosynthetic rate; consequently short-period measurements of gross or net photosynthesis—though not their difference—need not be very critically affected by the debatable assumption of a light-insensitive respiration rate. Oxygen tension as a factor is only likely to be significant in extremely productive waters. A proportionately larger respiratory uptake can be found (e.g. by photokinetic effects) if active zooplankton organisms or bacteria are numerous, and this may vary with illumination, although agreement appears to be lacking in the tests at present described (cf. Vaccaro & Ryther 1954; Winberg 1960; Steemann Nielsen 1955, 1963). A heavy bacterial growth in the experimental bottles is certainly very undesirable (cf. Pratt & Berkson 1959), and is a danger most likely to develop in exposures lasting more than one day, or when the bottles used carry an initial inoculum on their walls (Verduin 1960).

From the above considerations it follows that the consumption of oxygen in dark bottles can only be interpreted as respiration by phytoplankton if uptake by bacteria and animals is known to be negligible. Even when this condition is satisfied (which is rarely known), the dark consumption may or may not equal the difference between gross and net photosynthesis. In general, more reliance can be placed upon estimates of gross photosynthesis than those of net photosynthesis.

A part of the iodine liberated in the Winkler analytical procedure may be absorbed by the phytoplankton, associated animals, or by dispersed reducing substances. Some workers have therefore used a modification of the procedure designed to eliminate such interference (see Golterman & Clymo, Manual on Chemical Methods). However, absorption of iodine by algal cells is usually reversed during the final stages of the thiosulphate titration, and error from this source is likely to be small compared to the photosynthetic changes in dense populations. Further, a constant underestimation of the true oxygen concentration will not affect the changes due to photosynthesis and respiration which are calculated by difference.

Occasional records have been made (Dugdale & Wallace 1960; Winberg 1960; Ohle; Vollenweider, both unpublished) of an anomalous and significantly higher oxygen content measured in dark bottles after exposure compared to clear bottles. No conclusive explanation of this anomaly, which is rare or absent in most experience, can be given on the evidence available. Photo-oxidation in strong light (cf. McAllister 1961) is one possibility.

(iii) *Oxygen-versus ^{14}C-methodology*

G E FOGG

Photosynthesis consists of a complex of reactions which do not necessarily have fixed relationships with each other. The oxygen and ^{14}C methods measure the rate of different reactions and thus may not always yield concordant results.

The change in oxygen concentration occurring in a water sample is the resultant of oxygen production by photolysis of water in chlorophyll-containing organisms and the consumption of oxygen in respiration by both photosynthetic and non-photosynthetic organisms. The actual amount of oxygen produced in the light is a measure of the *net photosynthesis*. In short term experiments, in which no great changes occur in the numbers and kinds of organisms in the samples, the amount of oxygen consumed in a parallel dark bottle may be added to the amount produced in the light bottle to give an estimate of *gross photosynthesis* (see 3.31d). In doing this the assumption is made that respiration rates remain the same in light and dark. There is now evidence that this is not correct for certain algae (Bunt 1965). Gross photosynthesis as determined by the oxygen method is a measure of the rate of conversion of radiant energy to potential chemical energy in the ecosystem. There may be circumstances in which plants carry out this conversion by cyclic photophosphorylation without evolution of oxygen (Arnon, Whatley & Allen 1958), and bacterial photosynthesis does not involve the photolysis of water, but it is not likely that these processes occur to any important extent in oxygenated waters.

Incorporation of ^{14}C, supplied as bicarbonate, into organisms may result from various different reactions not all connected with photosynthesis. If calcium carbonate is accumulated, e.g. as coccoliths, this may be eliminated by exposure of the sample to hydrochloric acid fumes, the residual radio-activity then representing fixation in organic matter (Paasche 1963). Fixation in organic matter may be the result of 'dark' carboxylation reactions involving scarcely any gain in potential chemical energy, or may be associated with substantial accumulation of potential chemical energy in organic compounds as a result of chemosynthesis or photosynthesis. Dark carboxylation reactions are likely to be especially active in moribund material. In photosynthetic organisms they may be suppressed by light (Fogg 1963), and cannot then be corrected for by subtracting ^{14}C fixation in dark bottles from that fixed in light bottles. The same amount of photosynthetic fixation of ^{14}C will represent different gains in potential chemical energy according to whether the product is carbohydrate, protein, or fat, and this will depend on the physiological condition of the algae and availability of nutrients. Interaction between respiration and photosynthesis is complex. Products of photosynthesis may be used preferentially in respiration, and in experiments lasting more than 24 hours the loss of photosynthetically fixed ^{14}C by respiration may be appreciable (Vollenweider & Nauwerck 1961).

There is uncertainty as to whether the radiocarbon method measures net or gross photosynthesis or something between the two (Steemann Nielsen 1963; Yentsch 1963), but methods of estimating respiration from ^{14}C data have been suggested (Steemann, Nielsen & Hansen 1959). Fixation of ^{14}C from bicarbonate does not give a true measure of total carbon fixation if organic compounds are assimilated at the same time. There is increasing evidence that photoassimilation of organic compounds by algae may sometimes be appreciable (Wright 1964; Wiessner & Gaffron 1964; Sen & Fogg 1966). Photosynthetic phosphorylation and photosynthetic nitrogen fixation result in increases in potential chemical energy without necessarily any concomitant fixation of carbon, but the effects of these are not usually likely to be large. Finally, in the conventional radiocarbon technique only fixation in particulate matter is measured, so that total photosynthesis is underestimated to the extent that soluble products of photosynthesis are released from the cells (see 3.34).

Comparisons of the oxygen and ^{14}C methods using laboratory cultures or concentrated samples of natural phytoplankton usually show close agreement with a photosynthetic quotient (P.Q. $= \Delta O_2 / - \Delta CO_2$) of a little more than unity (for references see Fogg 1963). P.Q. may vary from unity, when carbohydrates are the principal products, to as high as 3·0 when fats are being synthesized (the respiratory quotient (R.Q. $= \Delta CO_2 / - \Delta O_2$) is unity when carbohydrates are respired and less than this, about 0·70, when fats are respired). However, there may be great discrepancies between the results of the oxygen and ^{14}C methods when cells are exposed to high light intensity (McAllister 1961) and in unconcentrated natural populations (Antia, McAllister, Parsons, Stephens & Strickland 1963). It may be surmised that these discrepancies arise mainly from fixation of ^{14}C by carboxylation reactions and from release of extracellular products of photosynthesis (Fogg 1963).

Provided that primary production is enough for accurate measurements to be made after 24 hours, the oxygen method seems the more reliable. The ^{14}C method is, however, of far greater sensitivity, and is the only one that can be satisfactorily used in oligotrophic waters.

It should be emphasized that, in presenting primary production data, it should always be stated clearly how the results were obtained and what corrections, e.g. for respiration, have been applied. Where possible, the method used should be checked against an other, independent, method.

3.32   Some special phytoplankton problems and techniques

(a) Extracellular products of phytoplankton

G E FOGG

Escape of soluble organic products from healthy cells of phytoplankton is a normal occurrence and is a possible source of error when total primary production is estimated by the ^{14}C method (Fogg, Nalewajko & Watt 1965). The relative amount released appears to increase with increasing oligotrophy of the water, being only a fraction of 1 % of the total carbon fixed in highly eutrophic fresh water but rising to 35 % or more in oligotrophic waters. The percentage release also increases, sometimes to over 90 %, when photosynthesis is inhibited by high light intensity (Watt 1965a).

Fixation in extracellular products may be determined as follows (method of Watt 1965a): Phytoplankton samples are incubated with ^{14}C-bicarbonate of high activity (10^7 cpm/100 ml). About 50 ml of each sample is passed through a membrane filter and the filtrates collected. A few drops of universal indicator are added to each filtrate and sufficient 0·5 N HCl to give a pH of 4. The filtrates are bubbled with 100 ml (or more) of air per minute for half-an-hour to remove inorganic ^{14}C. 0·5 N NaOH is then added to bring the pH up to 10, and aliquots of about 0·2 ml are pipetted on to the centre of metal discs of the same diameter as the membrane filters used. In this way particulate and extracellular ^{14}C are estimated with similar geometry. The drop is dried on the disc and more solution is added and dried 0·2 ml at a time. With most fresh waters and with artificial culture medium up to six applications may be made without measurable self-absorption. In practice three applications have given sufficient activity for accurate ^{14}C estimation.

When it is not desired to estimate extracellular fixation separately from particulate, the total primary production can be estimated without membrane filtration. Instead, formaldehyde is added to each bottle immediately on bringing it to the surface. A pH indicator is added and inorganic ^{14}C is removed by acidification and bubbling as described above. The resulting sample contains particulate ^{14}C in suspension and extracellular ^{14}C in solution. 0·2 ml aliquots of this preparation are pipetted on to metal discs for estimation of total organic ^{14}C.

Release of extracellular products occurs in the dark but is a different process from that in the light and is suppressed in the light. It is not therefore necessary to correct 'light' extracellular values by subtracting 'dark' values (Fogg, Nalewajko & Watt 1965; Watt 1965a).

(b) Bioassay technique for nutrient limiting factors

C R GOLDMAN

The basic fertility of any given aquatic ecosystem is apt to be limited by light, temperature, or any one of a variety of essential plant nutrients. In shallow standing waters the upper level of productivity is likely to be set by such essential macronutrients as nitrogen or phosphorus, but micronutrients may in some situations assume particular importance. Bioassays are frequently a more sensitive estimate of the biological availability of nutrients for plant growth than chemical analyses. The purpose of the following commentary is to tailor the actual nutrient addition to the individual needs of the aquatic environment in question. This can best be achieved by first determining which nutrients are most limiting. A properly conducted bioassay experiment can tell the experimenter which nutrients are most limiting and at what level they might be applied to stimulate the primary production of the environment.

(i) *Preparation of glassware and nutrients*
1. All flasks and screw caps, large mixing vessels, volumetric pipettes, graduated cylinders and any other equipment to be used for the experiments should be thoroughly washed with a stiff glassware brush in a hot lab soap (Labtone, etc.) bath. The lab sink should have previously been cleaned well to remove any residual chemicals or other contaminants. (It is a good idea to prepare 1 or 2 extra flasks or other vital equipment pieces in the event of breakage).

Rinse all glassware well in hot tap water and then give at least one full flask rinse in a 20% concentrated HCl solution. Rinse all equipment thoroughly at least five times in distilled and deionized water. If possible, steam cleaning and autoclaving should be utilized. Flasks may also be capped and left in bright sunlight to kill bacteria just prior to use. Quartz glass flasks which would allow more complete light transmission are unfortunately extremely expensive.

2. Make nutrient solutions in sufficiently large volumes from the highest obtainable grade of reagents. Dilutions should be made with distilled-deionized glass distilled H_2O. The solutions should be autoclaved in ampoules in concentrations and volumes suitable for easy field additions (i.e. from 1 to 10 ml per experimental flask). Small additions are difficult to make accurately and larger ones may dilute the culture significantly. All dilutions of nutrients from stock solutions should be made just prior to the experiments.

(ii) *Procedure for establishing bioassays*
1. All flasks and the large mixing vessel or carboy included screw caps, are rinsed several times with water taken from the depth at which the samples will be obtained. Wrap the large container or carboy with black cloth or other opaque material to prevent light injury to plankton during handling.

2. Collect enough water for experimental use, and to rinse any transfer glassware with a non-metallic water bottle, and bring the water in a carboy for mixing.

3. Have all nutrient solutions, pipettes, cylinders and other necessary items ready for use. Carry on all phases of the work in a dim corner out of direct sunlight to prevent any plankton light shock or inhibition. From this point, and until incubation begins, speed and care are essential. Make sure all flasks and caps are numbered or marked clearly.

4. Add enough ^{14}C activity to a subsample of the large carboy (previously poured into a separate vessel; the amount should suffice for the subsequent

experiments), and shake vigorously; then distribute the labelled water to the experimental flasks remembering to keep them in a light shaded box or container. Further reserve a subsample of each experimental water to establish the initial activity level.

5. Add the nutrients in increasing portions (according to the scheme previously established), going from least to most, and shake. Always include at least one control at the beginning and one at the end of each series; this permits one to determine later if any sub-sampling or filtration errors are present. If enough glassware and incubation space are available, duplicate or triplicate experiments of each type are advisable.

6. For the exposition in the lake connect flasks quickly to the support, and return them to the depth from which the original sample was taken. As an alternative, exposition may also be done in the laboratory, or on board ship under controlled light and temperature conditions.

7. After exposition (or on all subsequent samplings), remove flasks from the incubation site as expeditiously as possible, and shake flasks before sub-sampling. Have filters pre-labelled and the filtration apparatus ready to use, so that the time out of water is kept short. Of course, filtration may also be done later in the laboratory at the earliest convenience.

In general, incubation time should be kept to short periods (2 to 6 hours) to limit the influence of bacterial growth on the results.

8. If the oxygen method is to be utilized under eutrophic conditions, sub-samples must be carefully taken from the experimental flask without allowing loss or increase of the gas through agitation. Addition of the necessary reagents must be done immediately, and titration carried out within a few hours.

3.33 The enclosure of macrophyte communities

R G WETZEL

The annual production of most aquatic macrophytes can generally be estimated satisfactorily by maximal seasonal biomass measurements as discussed in section 3.52. However biomass is not directly indicative of the gross production, or the current net production (Wetzel 1964; Westlake 1965b), and for certain studies direct measurements of metabolism may be desired.

The metabolism of the aerial shoots of emergent macrophytes requires different techniques, similar to those used for land plants (see PT Grasslands

Manual, Milner & Hughes 1968). Changes in gaseous carbon dioxide and oxygen may be followed in enclosures (Barber 1961; Baker & Musgrave 1964) or, if at least 100 m² of community and finance for the equipment are available, the consumption of carbon dioxide from the free air and the soil can be determined by gas gradient methods (Monteith 1962). Nasyrov, Giller, Loginov & Lebedev (1962) have described the use of ^{14}C to study photosynthesis by grasslands and their methods may be adaptable to reedswamp.

(a) The use of isolated shoots

The most frequently used method of investigating the photosynthesis and respiration of macrophytes has been to simply incubate apical portions of the shoots in flasks. Usually changes in oxygen concentration have been determined, but other techniques such as the pCO_2 or ^{14}C can be applied. However manipulation of benthic plants from the surface is difficult. Generally they have been sheared or torn free by some collecting device and may have been damaged. Separation of shoots and roots may affect nutrient uptake and metabolism and even if the roots remain attached they may behave differently when removed from the substratum. Removing the macrophytes, placing them into flasks, and returning them to their original depth imposes abnormal conditions that may seriously alter resulting experimental values. Many of the plants are adapted to low light intensities and even brief exposures to intense surface light could seriously alter subsequent metabolic rates. Use of only the apical, vigorous, portions of the plants weights the results towards greater production when photosynthesis measurements per unit weight are converted to production per unit area of community by determining the total biomass per unit area. The water used for incubation needs to be taken from the same location as the plants because of the stratification of nutrients, temperature, etc., in many habitats. For these, and further reasons, *in situ* incubation of submerged macrophytes growing undisturbed is strongly recommended for ecological investigations (cf. Wetzel 1964), although the isolated shoot method may be suitable for some physiological experiments.

(b) Oxygen exchanges in light and dark enclosures in situ

Changes in dissolved oxygen in transparent and opaque enclosures have been extensively used to determine the photosynthesis of phytoplankton (cf. 3.31), but have rarely been used for submerged macrophytes under field conditions. Numerous mechanical and physiological difficulties seriously encroach on the validity of the application of the oxygen techniques to macrophytes.

Some specimens of macrophytes require long periods of incubation for significant changes in oxygen concentrations of the water to occur. During lengthy incubation, especially greater than six hours, bacterial populations increase greatly on the newly provided surfaces of the enclosure vessels (Zobell & Anderson 1936). Moreover, critical nutrients can be depleted and related effects of stagnation become more important during extended periods of incubation. When moderate to high rates of photosynthesis are encountered, oxygen saturation and supersaturation frequently occur and result in the emission of gas bubbles and loss from analyses of dissolved oxygen. Boiling (Pomeroy 1959), applying a vacuum (Hammann 1957), or in some other manner reducing the initial oxygen content of the water to alleviate highly saturated conditions not only hinders field techniques but can markedly alter the supply of carbon (Felföldy & Kalko 1958) and the nutrient equilibria of the environmental medium. Several workers have found that considerable periods of equilibration of the plants to the modified medium were necessary before results were reliable. When enclosure vessels are employed *in situ*, the contribution of other components of the enclosed community to changes in oxygen can be significant, even though the macrophytes may dominate a particular situation. Oxygen production by phytoplankton, epiphytic and epilithic periphyton, and losses through sedimental oxidative processes and faunal consumption may influence resulting values considerably. Many of these errors could be circumvented with controls on adjacent bottom areas without macrophytes or with the larger plants removed. Injection of some layer-forming material (e.g. kieselgur, heavy organic liquid) to prevent epipelic periphytic photosynthesis and restrict diffusion of oxygen to the mud may assist in alleviating some of these difficulties. In the latter case, it would be essential that the added substances do not reduce transparency or were not inhibitory to macrophytic growth.

An important limitation and source of error in the application of the oxygen techniques to macrophytes arises from the internal storage and utilization of oxygen produced in photosynthesis. Large discrepancies in productivity were found in simultaneous measurements by oxygen and ^{14}C techniques (Wetzel, 1964, 1965b). Large errors caused by lacunal storage of oxygen have been shown by the studies of Gorski (1935) and Hartman & Brown (1967). The latter demonstrated a rapid diurnal accumulation of oxygen in the internal atmosphere and a slow diffusion into the surrounding water. Dissolved oxygen concentrations of the surrounding water were not proportional to production of internal oxygen and this lag persisted for several hours. The greater the intensity of assimilation, proportionally lesser amounts of oxygen diffuse into the water and more is accumulated in the intercellular lacunae. Use of stored internal oxygen for respiration during periods of darkness can occur without effect on the concentrations of dissolved oxygen of the medium under natural and experimental conditions (Gorski 1929; Bourn 1932; Hartman & Brown 1967). Low velocity currents, such as occur in the littoral region in a highly irregular fashion, may considerably modify the diffusion gradients between the internal atmosphere and the environment (Westlake 1967). Intermittent stirring within the enclosures is suggested in check experiments for the effects of different degrees of stirring. During the incubation period stirring once, once per half-hour, and at 10 minute intervals in different replicates should demonstrate these effects (see also 3.33c). In some cases at least, in flowing or stirred conditions, a steady-state transfer of oxygen may be reached in less than an hour (Westlake 1967).

Many of these errors are difficult or impossible to circumvent in field investigations, but equipment for ^{14}C determinations may not be available. Also it is often desirable to determine the gross as well as the net production. In such circumstances the oxygen method may be used, but careful consideration must be given to possible sources of error and the results must be interpreted with extreme caution.

For general details of the enclosure of macrophytes *in situ* see below (3.33c). Determinations of changes in dissolved oxygen in the enclosures, without removing them from the water, may be accomplished by a diver, by withdrawing a small sample (*ca.* 4 ml) of water through a lateral port of the chamber which contains a serum-bottle stopper. A screw-controlled syringe permits the semi-micro oxygen analyses to be performed within the syringe (cf. Fox & Wingfield 1938; Laessle 1961). With the exception of sulphuric acid, reagents are of the Alsterberg (azide) modification of the Winkler method. Concentrated *o*-phosphoric acid is used in place of sulphuric to eliminate the liberation of free iodine. A glycerine stabilized starch solution (van Landingham 1960) is far superior to other solutions for an indicator in the thiosulphate titrations (see also the PF Chemical Methods Manual, Golterman & Clymo).

Gross photosynthesis is equal to the net oxygen produced in photosynthesis (increase in light chamber) plus the oxygen used by respiration (loss in the dark chamber). The value for gross photosynthesis is therefore the oxygen concentration of the light chamber minus that of the dark chamber. The initial concentration of the water at the beginning of incubation does not need to be determined unless the values for community net oxygen produced and respiration are desired. The amount of gross production is then calculated per unit organic weight of biomass per plant species. With adequate simultaneous determinations of the area distribution of biomass, gross photosynthesis can be estimated on a square metre basis. Net photosynthesis can only be estimated if the respiration of the plants can be separated from the respiration of other organisms. The best approximation is probably obtained from experiments on washed isolated shoots in dark bottles.

(c) ^{14}C techniques in situ

The ^{14}C technique for measuring the primary production rates of submerged macrophytes is essentially an extension of the ^{14}C methodology originally developed for the phytoplankton. However, the rapid self-absorption of the weak beta radiation by the plant tissues necessitates changes in radioassay which will increase the cost and sophistication of the experiments. The heterogeneous distribution of most stands of macrophytes requires thorough simultaneous determinations of biomass for complete evaluations of areal production rates. It may be assumed that the ^{14}C results are closer to the net production of the period of exposure than the gross under most environmental conditions, when exposures of several hours are used (Strickland 1960; Ryther & Menzel 1965; Wetzel 1965b).

It is recommended that the incubation chambers are cylinders made of clear Plexiglas (or equivalent cast, not extruded material) in various sizes to permit placement *in situ* around different species of plant. Transmittance of light is nearly identical to that of glass, absorption of ^{14}C is negligible and the material is easily worked (Wetzel 1964).

Approximately midway to one third the length of the cylinder a lateral port, containing a thin serum bottle stopper, is placed for insertion of syringes. A small propeller shaped piece of Plexiglas projecting into the cylinder, the shaft of which exits through a small rubber grommet, permits mixing of the contents of the chamber. A small stopcock at the top of the chamber permits venting of water when a chamber is placed over the plants and slowly worked into the sediments. The volume of the chamber must be calibrated.

Experimental chambers are placed at regular intervals along transects perpendicular to the shoreline in as many areas, and including as many different types of associations, as possible. Manipulation of the apparatus requires self-contained diving apparatus in deep areas (see 2.21b). Chambers are placed over the plants *in situ*, gently forced into the substratum, and the resulting volume noted. Several species can be included in the same chamber with separation later before weighing and combustion. Injection of an exact amount of ^{14}C is accomplished with an automatic syringe or may be facilitated by a simple syringe modification (Traylor & Crane 1961). The internal water is then mixed with the stirring apparatus and incubation is allowed to proceed for 3–5 hours. Check experiments in replicate enclosures with stirring at different intervals (cf. oxygen techniques) should be made to determine the importance of water movement for the exchange of metabolites. Once per half-hour may often ensure that the metabolism is not limited by stagnation effects but it is probable that more frequent stirring may be necessary in some experiments. It is not yet possible to recommend apparatus for continuous stirring but ways of achieving this may be developed in the near future.

After incubation the entire plants including roots, are removed by cutting the sediment under the cylinder with a steel plate.   The samples are quickly separated from the sediment, briefly blotted, placed into polyethylene bags, and quick-frozen between blocks of solid carbon dioxide. The incubation period is a convenient time to collect water samples for analyses of carbon availability, temperature, and other parameters required. Samples to determine the biomass should be taken at similar transect intervals to those of the productivity measurements, preferably using diving techniques. The inclusion of rooting organs is essential.

Self-absorption problems of ^{14}C radiation by the plant tissues are circumvented by van Slyke chemical combustion techniques for conversion of organic carbon to CO_2 and radioassay in gas-phase. Production rates are calculated in a proportional manner as in the techniques for phytoplankton (3.31f).

Prior to oxidation and conversion to CO_2 a known quantity of plant material should be exposed to fumes of concentrated HCl for removal of extracellular contamination of ^{14}C precipitated as carbonates. Brief exposure (10 minutes) to fumes of HCl is a superior technique to rinsing in dilute solutions of acid that may cause cellular loss, even though it is less convenient (Wetzel 1965a). Following combustion the CO_2 is collected in ionization chambers and assayed with an electrometer system directly in microcuries (Wetzel 1964). Efficiency is 100% ($\pm 1\%$) with an instrument accuracy of $\pm 2\%$. Alternatively the CO_2 may be precipitated as $BaCO_3$ (see 3.2).

Calculation of the production is done according to the outline given above (cf. 3.31f). Only a few notes are added here:

(i) Estimates of daily values. It is desirable to keep the incubation to a short mid-day period (e.g. 10.00–14.00) of four hours to avoid as much as possible the deleterious effects within containers that occur with prolonged incubation (Zobell & Anderson 1936). In order to calculate very rough daily values, the production rate of the mid-day four hour increment can be expanded by a factor determined from the integrated area of the incubation period on the light curve as a fraction of the total integrated area of the daily photoperiod. This method is a practical expedient when a large number of samples does not permit determination of diurnal four hour production measurements. While large variations in diurnal photosynthetic efficiencies do exist, evidence suggests that the production rates of the mid-day increment (c. 10.00–14.00) are good mean values under a majority of light and other environmental conditions (Wetzel 1965a).

(ii) The excretion of organic matter, especially carbohydrates, during photosynthesis by macrophytes presents a possible source of error in the employment of the ^{14}C techniques. The magnitude of this loss is largely unknown at the present time and highly variable with environmental conditions and among species (Wetzel 1965b); such loss is not included in the above calculations.

(iii) It is difficult to estimate the 24-hour net production and the gross production. If results can be obtained from a uniform stand exposed to a range of light intensities (e.g. under a set of shades or neutral filters) it may be possible to estimate respiration rates by extrapolation to zero light on a plot of net photosynthesis against irradiance. Or an approximate respiration rate may be calculated from the biomass and the results of experiments to determine the oxygen uptake of washed, isolated shoots in dark bottles.

(d) Other in situ techniques and their applicability
The pH-CO_2 method has been applied in only a few cases (Verduin 1952; Whitwer 1955) to production measurements of freshwater macrophytes. Ruttner (1948, 1960, *et seq.*) used changes in specific conductance as a measure of photosynthetic rates in physiological studies on carbon assimilation by aquatic macrophytes. As discussed above concerning the oxygen

method, changes in such parameters reflect alterations in community metabolism within the enclosing vessel rather than that of the macrophytes alone and therefore generally are subject to considerable error under *in situ* conditions. The uptake of phosphorus-32 and zinc-65 by marine macroalgae has been correlated with several environmental factors in addition to gross productivity (Odum, Kuenzler & Blunt 1958; Bachmann & Odum 1960). Use of strongly emitting isotopes has the distinct advantage of penetration of dense tissues for radioassay, but associated problems of adsorption phenomena indicate that apparent correlations with production rates are not entirely valid (e.g. Gutknecht 1963). Nutrient stimulation from additions of the isotope and its carrier must also be considered.

3.34   The enclosure of periphyton communities
R G WETZEL

Few attempts have been made to assay the growth rates of natural populations of periphyton *in situ* (see reviews of Wetzel 1964, 1965b). Direct *in situ* measurements of production rates are more meaningful than indirect estimates, although technical problems are many and centre around the difficulties of the heterogeneous distribution of periphyton on natural substrata. A few examples of methodological variants are presented here to indicate possible approaches to this difficult area of study.

(a) Oxygen methods (see also 3.31 & 3.33b for procedural details and general discussions)
Assman (1951, 1953) placed transparent and opaque external casings of Liebig condensers directly around the stems of the horsetail (*Equisetum*), encrusted with epiphytic periphyton, in which changes in the oxygen concentration of the water were determined. Production rates of epilithic periphyton on tile plates in pools has been estimated by light and dark oxygen techniques (Kurasawa 1959). Attempts at estimating the production rates of periphyton from flowing situations (e.g. Odum 1957; McConnell & Sigler 1959; Kobayasi 1961) by oxygen methods in closed containers must be viewed with reservation. Metabolism of rheophilic periphyton is greatly affected by restriction of water movements (Whitford 1960; Whitford & Schumacher 1961). Several recent experimental studies applicable to natural populations have shown the importance of flow (Kevern & Ball 1965; McIntyre & Phinney 1965; Thomas & O'Connell 1966).

(b) ^{14}C methods (see also 3.2, 3.31, 3.33)

^{14}C techniques have been applied to periphyton in only a few cases. Vollen-weider & Samaan (1958) suspended glass rods of known surface area at various depths, vertically among emergent macrophytes for simulated colonization (3–4 weeks) of periphyton epiphytic on the larger plants. The rods colonized with algae were carefully placed into bottles of pre-filtered lake water, inoculated with ^{14}C and incubated at the depth from which they were taken. After a brief incubation period, the periphyton was removed from the rods, homogenized in a small aliquot of water, and a portion filtered onto a membrane filters for radioassay and analysis similar to that of phytoplankton. Glass slides have been similarly employed in studies of periphyton in the Ohio River (Eichelberger 1963). An extension of these techniques could include chemical combustion of the algal matter and analysis of the $^{14}CO_2$ in gas phase (Wetzel 1963, 1964), eliminating self-absorption problems, or as $BaCO_3$.

In studies of the productivity of the epipelic periphyton of a Danish fjord, Grøntved (1960, 1962) devised a sampling technique whereby a suspended subsample of the benthic algae and some of the littoral phytoplankton were incubated in bottles with ^{14}C. By a complicated series of manipulations the fraction of the total assayed carbon fixation was estimated for benthic producers. Self-absorption of radiation by the sediment particles was estimated by several techniques of radioassay of filters before and after removal of the larger inorganic particles. The resultant values were expressed as the potential rate of production because the experiments were not per-formed *in situ*. The actual rate of production was tentatively suggested as one-half of the potential rate at optimal light intensity.

In investigations on light inhibition and injury effects on photosynthesis of phytoplankton in Antarctic ponds (Goldman, Mason & Wood 1963), a few assays of carbon fixation were made of the epilithic algal mat by suspension of small discs of the algal material in bottles. Following brief incubation the discs were dried, combusted to CO_2, and counted in gasphase.

Excellent, nearly complete replication of natural stream populations of epilithic periphyton was found on polyethylene film substrates exposed for 30 days positioned among natural substrates (Backhaus 1967). Selective species colonization occurred on both sides of the 0·2 mm sheets in relation to light distribution. Discs were removed and exposed to ^{14}C in test tubes, con-taining a bubble of air, that were suspended freely to be agitated by the current. After a four-hour period of incubation the samples were removed, dried, and assayed.

The only assays of ^{14}C measured production rates of benthic periphyton *in situ* are the studies of Wetzel (1963, 1964) on the homogeneous littoral covering of small, angular pebbles of a shallow lake in the coastal mountains of northern California. Plexiglas chambers were worked by short rotational movements into the sediments along transects perpendicular to the shoreline (cf. 3.33). A ^{14}C inoculum of known assay was injected underwater and the chambers sealed. After a four hour incubation the chambers were removed by working a plate under the open end which permitted removal of the entire sample, effectively an undisturbed core of the superficial sedimentary material and the overlying water. The water was then removed by a large syringe and the upper centimetre of sediments was frozen under desiccation. The organic material of the samples was oxidized to CO_2 by Van Slyke combustion for radioassay in gas phase. While these techniques are tedious, they circumvent the problems of self-absorption of the weak beta-radiation. If gas-phase assay is not possible the CO_2 may be precipitated as $BaCO_3$ (see 3.2).

Further developments of *in situ* techniques are likely to give the best and most realistic estimates of the contribution of the periphyton to the productivity of waters. Brock & Brock (1967) have developed micro-autoradiographic techniques to determine the detailed distribution of assimilated carbon and phosphorus among the cell materials. The techniques must always take account of the heterogeneous distribution of periphyton communities if the validity of the results is to be extended beyond small areas of a particular community to large areas supporting a variety of communities. Current researches are likely to lead to improved methods.

3.4 MEASUREMENTS ON NON-ISOLATED NATURAL COMMUNITIES
Introduction
D F WESTLAKE

In many aquatic habitats the metabolism of the plant and animal communities causes measurable changes in the chemical composition of the water. Often there are very large diurnal changes in the concentrations of oxygen and carbon dioxide, accompanied by large changes in pH. There may also be longer term changes in important nutritional elements such as nitrogen, phosphorus and silicon. In principle these changes in the natural environment may be used to estimate primary productivity just as the similar changes in enclosures are used.

The advantages of this approach are several. The changes in concentration resulting in an enclosure often differ from the natural changes. Since rates of metabolism may be influenced by the external concentrations, determinations based on the natural changes may be a better measure of the natural behaviour of the plants. It is very difficult in an enclosure to reproduce the natural conditions of water velocity and turbulence and the radiation reaching the plant may be affected by shading or selective extinction by parts of the apparatus. Observations on the natural changes can be continued over long periods, whereas experiments in enclosures are limited in duration by excessive changes in concentration of metabolites, the development of micro-organisms on the walls and 'fatigue' effects on the enclosed plants.

On the other hand use of natural changes has some considerable disadvantages. The rates of input and output of the substance measured to and from sources other than the plant, must be known or known to be negligible. Thus, when following changes in oxygen and carbon dioxide the exchanges of gas between the air and the water must be calculated or determined. The dark respiration must be determined, which usually requires night observations, and, as this is a community respiration of all the animals, micro-organisms and plants present, in the water and in the bottom deposits, only gross photosynthesis can be directly determined. Techniques are available for estimating the respiration in bottom deposits and by suspended organisms but these only allow rough estimates of the net production of communities dominated by macrophytes to be made by difference. When following changes in elements such as nitrogen, phosphorus and silicon it will be necessary to know the input and output to and from streams, the hypolimnion, or the bottom, and the rate of turnover of these elements in the community, or to know that these are negligible. Several of the factors needed in calculations are affected by changes in temperature and the absolute concentrations, so allowances must be made for these effects. If the rate of production is required in terms of organic matter or energy, conversion factors will be required which may be less readily estimated than for short-term oxygen or carbon dioxide changes in enclosures.

3.41   In running waters
M OWENS

Many efforts have been made to determine the metabolism of stream communities from analysis of diurnal curves of dissolved oxygen (Odum 1956, 1957; Hoskin 1959; McConnell & Sigler 1959; Edwards & Owens 1962; Gunnerson & Bailey 1963).

In a stretch of river receiving no tributaries or run-off water the change in the concentration of dissolved oxygen in the water per unit area of surface between an upstream and downstream station can be expressed as follows:

$$X = P \pm D - R, \tag{1}$$

where X is the rate of gain or loss of oxygen per unit area of surface between the stations, P is the rate of production (photosynthesis) per unit area, R is the rate of oxygen utilization (respiration) per unit area, and D is the rate of oxygen uptake or loss by diffusion (depending upon whether the water is under-saturated or super-saturated with oxygen with respect to air). These rates are all generally expressed as $g/m^2.h$.

$$X = (C_2 - C_1)\frac{F}{\Delta}, \tag{2}$$

where C_1 is the dissolved-oxygen concentration (mg/l) at the upstream station at time T_1, C_2 is the dissolved-oxygen concentration (mg/l) at the downstream station at time T_2, such that $(T_2 - T_1)$ is the average retention time between the upstream and downstream stations, F is flow (m^3/h), and Δ is the surface area (m^2) between stations. Determinations of dissolved-oxygen concentrations should be made at each station as frequently as possible; temperature measurements should be made at the same time. Rates of flow can be determined radiochemically using ^{82}Br (as ammonium bromide). The 'total count' or 'gulp' method can be employed as described by Eden (1959). The use of radioactive tracers is probably best avoided unless absolutely necessary. Lithium may also be used as a tracer for measuring rates of flow (Agg, Mitchell & Eden 1961). If it is not possible to determine the flow rate of the stream directly then it can be estimated from the time taken for marker dyes or floats to pass from the upstream to the downstream station and from the average cross-sectional area of the reach. When floats are used, correction factors should be applied for they tend to travel at velocities greater than the average.

During the hours of darkness, the rate of change of the dissolved-oxygen content of the water is determined only by the rates of community respiration and of diffusion through the water surface,

$$X = D - R. \tag{3}$$

The rate of reaeration (diffusion) depends upon the degree of saturation of the water

$$D = \frac{f}{100}(\bar{C}_s - \bar{C}), \tag{4}$$

where f is the exchange coefficient of the reach (cm/h), $\bar{C}_s$ is the average saturation concentration within the reach, and $\bar{C}$ its average dissolved-oxygen concentration. If the oxygen deficit is large, and the difference between the deficits at the two stations is relatively small, then the average driving force causing oxygen absorption is very nearly equal to the arithmetic mean of the deficits at the two stations. On strictly theoretical grounds it would be more accurate to use the geometric average (Edwards, Owens & Gibbs 1961).

Thus during the hours of darkness

$$X = \frac{f}{100}(\bar{C}_s - \bar{C}) - R. \tag{5}$$

By measuring the rate of change of oxygen (X) at different times during the hours of darkness at different saturation deficits $(\bar{C}_s - \bar{C})$, it is possible to calculate the exchange coefficient f and the respiration R from Equation 5.

It is necessary however to make assumptions concerning the effects on oxygen consumption of temperature and dissolved-oxygen concentration changes during this period. If one assumes that the community respiration during this time does not vary (Odum 1956) then

$$f = \frac{100\,(X_2 - X_1)}{(\bar{C}_{s2} - \bar{C}_2) - (\bar{C}_{s1} - \bar{C}_1)} \tag{6}$$

where f is the exchange coefficient, and X_1 and X_2 the rates of change of oxygen between stations at the average saturation deficits $(\bar{C}_{s1} - \bar{C}_1)$ and $(\bar{C}_{s2} - \bar{C}_2)$ respectively.

When pronounced changes occur in the temperature and oxygen concentration it is probably better to apply correction factors to the rate of community respiration (Edwards, Owens & Gibbs 1961; Edwards & Owens 1962; Odum & Wilson 1962; Beyers 1963), for although the oxygen consumption of aerobic bacteria generally appears to be independent of the oxygen concentration of the medium above 1 mg/l (ZoBell & Stadler 1940) this is not so for plants, animals, and aquatic muds. Measurements of oxygen consumption of aquatic macrophytes in relation to oxygen concentrations and temperatures have been made by Gessner & Pannier (1958) and Owens & Maris (1964). In both investigations the rate of oxygen consumption of the species studied varied with the oxygen concentration. In the latter study the relation between oxygen consumption and oxygen concentration (for a range of 1·5 to 16·0 mg/l dissolved oxygen) was of the form $R^1 = aC^b$ where R^1 is the rate of respiration per unit dry weight of weed, C is the oxygen concentration, and *a* and *b* are constants. A similar relation was found by Edwards & Rolley (1965) between the oxygen consumption of muds and oxygen concentration. Temperature coefficients (Q) of 2·7 (*Callitriche*), 2·3 (*Ranunculus*), 2·2 (*Berula*), 1·5 (*Hippuris*) and 2·0 (mud) were obtained between 10° and 20°C.

Only when (a) the relation between oxygen consumption, oxygen content, and temperature for each major component of the community (plants and mud), and (b) the relative amounts of oxygen consumed by each component at any oxygen content and temperature, are known can a correction of the form given below be applied for changes in the oxygen consumption of the aquatic community with oxygen concentration and temperature, i.e.

$$f = \frac{100\ (X_2 - rX_1)}{(\bar{C}_{s2} - \bar{C}_2) - r(\bar{C}_s - \bar{C}_1)} \tag{7}$$

where *r* is the ratio of the oxygen consumption of the aquatic community at the oxygen concentration $\bar{C}_1$ to that at $\bar{C}_2$. Each consumption is adjusted to correspond to the prevailing temperatures.

This method may be used for the calculation of *f* and R only when there is a large change in the saturation deficit during the hours of darkness. Where no such large change occurs naturally, the concentration of oxygen can be reduced by the controlled addition of sodium sulphite and a cobalt catalyst (Gameson, Truesdale & Downing 1955; Edwards, Owens & Gibbs 1961), and the rate of change of oxygen content between stations measured before and during the passage of the partially de-oxygenated water.

In small productive streams where there is a pronounced diurnal rhythm in the dissolved-oxygen concentration, an alternative method can be used to determine the exchange coefficient (Edwards 1962). An opaque plastic sheet was suspended on a nylon net above the river surface and fixed to the river banks, thus effectively darkening the reach and preventing photosynthesis. The change in oxygen concentration down the covered reach was measured throughout 24 hours. This method makes use of the naturally occurring changes in oxygen concentration brought about by photosynthesis upstream.

Odum, Siler, Beyers & Armstrong (1963) have also covered ponds with plastic sheets to determine diffusion, but in this instance a translucent plastic was used to prevent diffusion occurring, the plastic sheet being laid on the water surface. Estimates of the rate of diffusion were made by determining the differences between the diurnal oxygen curves obtained in the covered pond and in an uncovered pond.

Rates of diffusion may also be determined by enclosing part of the water surface either under a free-floating polythene tent, supported by metal frames and floats (Department of Scientific & Industrial Research 1964), or under a clear plastic dome (Copeland & Duffer 1964) and measuring the amount of oxygen taken up by the water from air or oxygen enclosed by the tent. Although such tents or domes affect turbulence within their confines, comparative experiments using this and other methods have given similar results.

Attempts have been made to develop a method for predicting the rate at which de-oxygenated stream water will absorb oxygen from the air from hydraulic and water quality parameters (Streeter & Phelps 1925; O'Connor & Dobbins 1956; Churchill, Elmore & Buckingham 1962; Dobbins 1964). Data collected by the Water Pollution Research Laboratory, Great Britain, and Churchill, Elmore & Buckingham (1962) on reaeration rates in streams have been combined and analysed using multiple regression procedures (Owens, Edwards & Gibbs 1964) and constants derived from the equation relating the exchange coefficient to the average velocity and depth of the stream

$$f(20°C) = 50·8 \; U^{0·67} \; H^{-0·85}, \tag{8}$$

where f is the exchange coefficient (cm/h) at 20°C, U is the average velocity (cm/sec), and H is the mean depth (cm). This equation makes it possible to predict, with a reasonable degree of accuracy, the reaeration rate which would be expected in rivers from their mean velocities and depths provided these are within the experimentally observed ranges (velocity 3·0–150 cm/sec, depth 12·0 – 335·0 cm). The observed values of exchange coefficient used in obtaining the above relation were determined under a variety of wind conditions, and no attempt was made to correct for wind-effects which can be quite pronounced (Department of Scientific & Industrial Research 1964). These computed values are for clean water only and have to be corrected when applied to polluted water, for pollutants reduce reaeration rates (Downing, Melbourne & Bruce 1957). The effect of temperature on the exchange coefficient has been described by the Committee on Sanitary Engineering Research of the American Society of Civil Engineers (1961);

the rate of reaeration was shown to increase by 2·4% per 1°C throughout a temperature range of 5° to 30°C. Hart (1967) has published a nomogram for the determination of the exchange coefficient.

Having determined the exchange coefficient (f) the average night-time rate of community respiration can be calculated from Equation 5.

Before rates of oxygen production by photosynthesis (P) can be determined for daylight hours from Equation 1, the oxygen consumption (R) must be calculated over this period. Odum (1956 and 1957), Odum & Hoskin (1958), and Hoskin (1959) assumed that respiration was constant throughout 24-hour periods of observation. Varying respiration rates have been applied by Odum & Wilson (1962) and Odum, Siler, Beyers & Armstrong (1963). When pre-sunrise and post-sunset values of respiration rate differed in their experiments, a constant rate of change in respiration during the intervening period was assumed in estimating photosynthesis. When pronounced changes occur in the temperature and oxygen concentration it is probably better to apply correction factors to the average of the night-time respiration values calculated from Equation 5. A rough estimate of net production may be obtained by calculating the plant respiration from the biomass, respiration per unit biomass, the oxygen concentration and the temperature (see above, and Owens & Maris 1964).

Odum (1956) has proposed a simplification of the upstream-downstream oxygen method in which diurnal rhythms at a single station are utilized to calculate diffusion, and respiratory and photosynthetic rates. This method may be employed only where the whole of a reach of river is 'experiencing a simultaneous rise and fall of oxygen' and under these conditions 'a second station would reveal a curve identical with that of the first station'. Although the analysis of a single curve is less satisfactory than the analysis of twin-curves (Edwards & Owens 1962), nevertheless in regions of comparative homogeneity the analysis of single curves of diurnal oxygen fluctuation could be useful for assessing the general magnitude of processes causing changes in the dissolved-oxygen content and for detecting reactions between these processes and environmental factors such as light, temperature, and wind.

One possible source of error in the estimation of gross primary production from changes in dissolved-oxygen concentrations is the loss of oxygen to the atmosphere in the form of bubbles (Odum 1957; Edwards & Owens 1965). Estimates should be made of the amount of oxygen produced during photosynthesis which is lost in this way.

Although the omission of corrections to the respiration rate for changes in oxygen concentration and temperature is probably one of the most important sources of error in the analysis of twin curves, the effects of longitudinal mixing may also lead to anomalies. While it does seem possible to embody mixing corrections based on the distribution of flow tracers, this refinement is at present probably outweighed by complications in processing the field data, particularly as the mathematical models at present proposed for mixing in rivers do not agree closely with experimental data derived from tracer distributions (Owens, Edwards & Gibbs 1964).

3.42   In standing waters
J F TALLING

Use has been made of three types of reactions of organisms upon their water environments. These are (i) depletion of a plant nutrient, such as phosphorus or silicon, during plant growth, (ii) diurnal changes in the content of oxygen or carbon dioxide, due primarily to photosynthesis, (iii) depletion of oxygen, or accumulation of carbon dioxide, accompanying decomposition in the hypolimnion. The last approach cannot differentiate between the contributions from primary and secondary production, and will not be considered here.

(i) The depletion of plant nutrients over long periods is usually difficult to interpret quantitatively, especially because of the problems of assessing regeneration *in situ* or supplies from inflows. Phosphate is particularly troublesome, since the connexion between its removal and organic synthesis may be obscured by adsorption and by accumulation in plant cells. More reliable estimates can be obtained from the relation between diatom production and silicon depletion. The latter is often considerable during periods of diatom growth, can be estimated accurately by present-day methods of chemical analysis, and is normally not affected by rapid recycling within a lake basin. An example of its use in freshwaters for estimating diatom production is described by Lund, Mackereth & Mortimer (1963).

(ii) In productive waters the contents of dissolved oxygen and carbon dioxide show appreciable diurnal variation as a result of photosynthesis and respiration. As in flowing waters, the analysis of such diurnal curves can be used to obtain estimates of primary (photosynthetic) production per unit area; indeed this general approach was first applied to standing waters (for historical aspects see Winberg 1960, 1963). Since a regular water flow is absent, methods involving upstream–downstream stations (see 3.41) are inapplicable, and the analysis is normally based on a 'single curve' record. However, periodic checks at several stations within the chosen area are desirable, both to guard against fluctuations caused by irregular lateral transfer (advection) and to confirm the representative nature (for the area) of the diurnal changes measured. If the plants involved are chiefly macrophytes with an uneven distribution, deviations from the condition of horizontal uniformity are particularly likely. Should vertical uniformity exist, the calculations of gaseous content per unit area (e.g. in g O_2 or CO_2/m^2) are greatly simplified; otherwise they must be made by planimetry of the areas of concentration—depth profiles measured on successive sampling occasions. The depth range concerned is often taken as the average depth of the water-body, although in stratified waters the diurnal variations are usually confined to a much shallower stratum, and in small basins the reduction of water volume in successively deeper strata (hypsographic curve) may require attention when calculating quantities per unit area. Where possible, sampling occasions should not be separated by more than four hours, should include examples at or near sunrise and sunset, and extend over more than one diurnal cycle (24 hours).

Oxygen rather than carbon dioxide has been the gas measured in most work, due to the simple analytical methods (Winkler, electrochemical) available and the ease with which its percentage saturation relative to air can be estimated. Examples and further references can be found in Talling (1957), Winberg (1955, 1960, 1963), Odum & Hoskin (1958), and Odum & Wilson (1962). For the sake of simplicity, the examples used here refer to oxygen changes, although the principles are also applicable to changes in total carbon dioxide, provided that allowance is made for the special characteristics affecting CO_2 exchange at the air/water interface (see, e.g., Kanwisher 1963; Teal & Kanwisher 1966; Teal 1967). Where attempted, estimations of carbon dioxide changes have usually been made indirectly using measurements of pH and titration alkalinity, from which the varying content of total CO_2 was deduced. Examples of these include Verduin (1956) and Park, Hood & Odum (1958). Such indirect calculations of carbon dioxide content should be checked, whenever possible, by direct determinations of total CO_2 (e.g. Wood 1964) or by artificially induced CO_2 changes of known magnitude (e.g. Beyers & Odum 1959; Beyers, Larimer, Odum, Parker & Armstrong 1963).

Assuming that the daily changes due to photosynthesis are appreciable, the variation of oxygen content per unit area is likely to show a minimum shortly after dawn and a maximum some time before sunset. Thus one can distinguish two measures of the daily increment of oxygen per unit area— the difference between the maximum and minimum content (ΔO_2^{max}), and the (smaller) difference between the contents at the end and beginning of the period of illumination (ΔO_2^{illum}). Each of these quantities has been used as a basis for calculating the gross daily photosynthetic production, by introducing factors or terms to take account of gaseous exchange with the atmosphere and respiratory uptake. It may be convenient to apply these corrections (as rates of change in oxygen) to the diurnal observations expressed graphically as rates of change in oxygen content per unit area over successive (e.g. hourly) periods (e.g. Talling 1957c; Odum & Hoskin 1958).

The rate of exchange with the atmosphere depends partly upon the degree of super- or under-saturation of the surface water, and partly upon the physical conditions (turbulence, etc.) at tha air-water interface. Effects of the latter on gaseous exchange across the interface can be expressed by an exchange coefficient (f in section 3·41: equivalent expressions in other units, such as $gO_2/m^2.h$ at 0% saturation, are possible). If the value of this coefficient is known, it can be used to calculate the gain or loss of oxygen to the water-column during a given period. Unfortunately, the coefficient can vary considerably with surface conditions and is not easy to measure reliably. Its magnitude can be very roughly guessed from an estimate of surface turbulence and previously published data (e.g. Odum 1956); or assumed constant over the diurnal period and estimated from the observed rates of oxygen change at night under different levels of saturation (e.g. Winberg 1955, 1960, 1963; Odum & Hoskin 1958); or estimated using diurnal measurements of wind velocity and an empirical relationship with this variable established previously (e.g. Odum & Wilson 1962).

The rate of respiratory uptake of oxygen, taking place in the free water or at the mud-water interface, can be estimated from the nocturnal rate of decline of oxygen corrected for atmospheric exchange. The possibilities, and difficulties, in assessing the latter have been noted above. Under favourable conditions, it may be avoided (cf. Winberg 1960, 1963) by considering periods during which the saturation level of oxygen in the surface water is close to 100%. This point is often passed at some time during the night period, and during the latter as a whole the effects of conditions promoting oxygen loss to and gain from the atmosphere may be roughly equal. Under such favourable circumstances, the average rate of oxygen decline at night should approximate the average rate of oxygen consumption in the water column

Chapter 3

(e.g. Talling 1957c). This formulation implies a constancy of the consumption rate over the 24-hour period, a much-used assumption which can be quite unjustified in some situations of periodic stratification or low oxygen tensions. Some examples of these are given by Winberg (1955, 1960, 1963); see also section 3.41 above.

Calculations (reviewed by Winberg 1960, 1963) have also been based upon ΔO_2^{max}, the observed daily increase in oxygen between minimum and maximum values. In general this quantity is a less suitable starting point than ΔO_2^{illum}, but if the surface oxygen concentration does not fall below saturation ΔO_2^{max} will not be less than the gross oxygen production.

In general, the chief advantages of methods based upon diurnal changes lie in the avoidance of artificial enclosures and the inclusion of both planktonic and attached forms of vegetation. The disadvantages are, however, often severe: the chief are limited sensitivity (precluding their use in unproductive waters), susceptibility to unwanted effects from horizontal exchange (advection), and the possibility of errors from short-term fluctuations in rates of oxygen consumption and atmospheric exchange coefficients that are difficult to assess.

3.5 PRIMARY PRODUCTION RATES FROM CHANGES IN BIOMASS

General
R A VOLLENWEIDER

To a limited extent primary production can be estimated from changes in biomass, a procedure which is widely used in studies on terrestrial communities. In aquatic environments the best results are to be expected from littoral and sublittoral higher aquatics, or in shallow lakes grown over with macrophytes, and from periphytic communities. Changes in phytoplankton communities, in general, are more difficult to analyse. It is obvious that rates calculated from a temporal set of biomass measurements are minimum estimates referring to net production. Since, during prolonged periods, there is always a certain loss due to grazing, current transport, etc., even net production tends to be underestimated.

In order to get comparable results, biomass measurements must be referred to 'ash free dry weight' (cf. 2.14), and if 'net carbon exchange per unit of surface area and unit of time' is to be calculated, then appropriate conversion factors have to be applied. It is obvious how problematic such results can be, but often the procedure in question may be the only one available to get an insight into the quantitative aspect of production. Further, it should be remembered that the numerical results can either be positive or negative according to the production phase considered, and that the arithmetic sum over prolonged periods of time is normally zero.

3.51   Phytoplankton
R A VOLLENWEIDER

It has already been mentioned that rate estimates from changes in phytoplankton biomass are subject to many uncertainties. In fact, although there is considerable knowledge about the seasonal variations of phytoplankton communities, little attempt has been made to analyse these data from the point of view of primary production. One of the main reasons for this is undoubtedly that many observations made in the past were from monthly collections of phytoplankton, and most authors felt that—given the relatively short life duration of phytoplankters, and the many possibilities of losses by grazing, sedimentation and by outflow—a too close analysis of numerical data would but falsify our insight. Restricted to some species, this question and problems have been thoroughly discussed by Grim in some classic papers (Grim 1939, 1950a, 1950b, 1952). This author combined observations on standing crop changes, sedimentation rates (measured *in loco* and with the aid of sedimentation vessels (Sinktöpfe)), and growth rates from enclosed cultures suspended *in situ*. With this methodology it could be shown that the total production of certain diatom species (*Cyclotella, Synedra, a.o.*), before reaching their standing crop maxima as observed *in loco*, is likely to be 10 times, or more, the production which would be inferred from the highest density observed. In other species this quotient may be much lower (e.g. less than 2 for *Dinobryon*). Growth rates of other diatoms (*Asterionella, Fragilaria, Tabellaria, Melosira*) have also been calculated from changes in standing crop under natural conditions by Lund (1949, 1950, 1954) and Talling (1955). It should be mentioned that all these attempts are not identical with rate estimates of primary production; nevertheless, the problems touched are close to the question.

If primary production rates are to be calculated from biomass changes (including all constituents of the phytoplankton communities), and these evaluations shall have some reliability, then a number of basic requirements must be fulfilled: First, the spacing in time of sampling and biomass determinations should be as close as possible, possibly not exceeding one week; secondly, the horizontal pattern of the phytoplankton distribution must be fairly homogeneous and not influenced by wind and current actions; in any case it must be established that increases are from growth at the locality under observation, and not imported from other areas or by back-transport from the hypolimnion due to mixing. Third, no strong losses through grazing, sedimentation and the outlet should occur during two consecutive observations; fourth, 'biomass' should be expressed as 'total phytoplankton volume', 'ash free dry weight', or 'carbon content', and these values should be referred to the single groups of phytoplankton present. This last recommendation is made for the sake of comparability with other results.

In order to avoid some of the difficulties, it is best to work from averages resulting from a horizontal net of sampling station and samples taken from various depths at each station. Biomass changes per unit of surface area or per unit of volume (the first expression is probably less subject to large errors) between two consecutive observations can then be calculated, and reported as average daily increase or decrease. The pertinent results, however, refer to 'total changes', which, even in an increasing phase, are not identical with production. In fact, if B_1 signifies the biomass determined at time t_1, and B_2 that at time t_2, the change of biomass, $B_2 - B_1$, is not a function of B_1 but is rather an expression like

$$B_2 - B_1 = B_1 - B_1' + B_1' \cdot e^{k(t_2-t_1)} - B_1 - R(t_2 - t_1)$$
$$= B_1' \cdot e^{k(t_2-t_1)} - B_1' - R(t_2 - t_1)$$

B_1' refers to the biomass of the trophogenic layer at time t_1, k to the exponential growth rate and R to all possible losses (respiration, grazing, losses to the sediments and through the outlet) along the time interval $t_2 - t_1$. It is obvious that the entity R is the critical one for an exact determination. In a more general form, the equation of change can be written as,

$$\frac{d\,B}{dt} = B\,(p - r - g - s),$$

where p, r, g, s are the coefficients of production, respiration, grazing, and losses by sedimentation and through the outlet. Such an equation can be solved only for short periods with sufficient accuracy; the inherent problems have been thoroughly discussed by Riley, Stommel & Bumpus (1949) for the sea, but for lake environments little has been done, as yet, to apply this theoretical framework. Grazing problems in relation to phytoplankton production have been studied e.g. by Nauwerck (1963).

For practical purposes, and in order to get more realistic information, it is advisable to supplement calculations on biomass changes with information obtained from sedimentation vessels suspended, e.g. below the trophogenic layer and above the lake bottom (cf. also Thomas 1955; Bachofen 1960, *a.o.*). Though it will not be possible to account for all losses, it may be possible to account for some of the more resistant forms (diatoms, and many Chlorophyceae). In addition, dead floating individuals, e.g. shells of diatoms, should be counted separately during species enumeration to complete the description of biomass production. However, specific recommendations as to how these figures should be treated for production estimates cannot be given, because this depends upon local conditions, sedimentation time (e.g. algae slowly settling may be counted twice if the interval between two observations is short) and other factors. The problem becomes particularly evident in a stationary state situation during which apparently no, or almost no numerical changes are to be observed, but in most instances it is justifiable to consider increases with time of dead forms as due to previous production. If flushing time of a lake is very short, or epilimnic layers are washed out strongly during a seasonal cycle, then these losses must be accounted for separately, but in such circumstances estimates of biomass changes are normally but of little value for production estimates.

As a whole, however, the technique should be further developed, and, in particular, it should be combined with other production estimates in order to deliver a basis for a true analysis of the dynamics of phytoplankton production.

3.52 Macrophytes
D F WESTLAKE

If, apart from respiration, there are no losses of plant material between two sampling times the net production, by definition, is equal to the observed change in biomass (Westlake 1963, 1965b). In many aquatic macrophyte communities there are few losses of the current year's production before the maximum biomass is reached, or determinations of the losses are possible, and the annual maximum cumulative net production is the most generally useful parameter of production (Westlake 1965b). Over short periods of up to several weeks losses may usually be neglected, but variability in the results may obscure the increase in biomass unless large numbers of samples are taken.

The seasonal maximum biomass should be found by frequent sampling if it is to be used for estimation of the annual production. If the approximate time of the maximum is known then samples at two week intervals during the month before and after will usually be desirable but if the time is unknown, or variable, this frequency of sampling may need to be continued for longer periods. For the rest of the year sampling at monthly or even two monthly intervals will often suffice; and in general, numerous samples taken at intervals of one or two months are a better use of labour than a few samples taken at shorter intervals.   In tropical communities, with an almost constant biomass, it will not be profitable to search for an annual maximum.

Boxes planted with shoots may be used for some experimental purposes, but the shoots must be planted at the natural density and placed within a natural community if the results are to be relevant to the community production.   Also the growth of many perennials is atypical for a year or two after transplanting. It is usually better to determine biomass changes by adequate sampling of the natural community.

Concomitant observations of the growth cycle and phenology of the plants and plant parts must be made so that the biomass determinations can be corrected for persistence of material from previous years, losses of material by death, disease or damage, and grazing. Many temperate freshwater macrophytes, or at least their green shoots, show annual regrowth. In this case practically none of the previous year's growth remains by the time of the maximum biomass and therefore it is not essential to determine the spring biomass. If all the spring biomass persists until after the maximum then the annual production is the observed difference, but if only a proportion of the old growth survives, an appropriate correction must be made, often a deduction of 20–40% of the maximum. When underground organs are well developed, material may persist there for several years and green shoots and underground organs must be treated separately. If the annual increments underground cannot be distinguished readily the total weight underground is divided by the average age (Westlake 1968). In many healthy communities losses from the current year's production may be only 2–15% before the maximum biomass is sampled but in some communities there may be large losses. In many tropical and subtropical communities there is no pronounced seasonal periodicity of the biomass and productivity can be estimated from biomass determinations only if the rate of turnover can be found. As a rough check such communities as have been studied show turn-over rates for the shoots of 2–3 times per year. Even in some temperate communities initiation and growth of shoots may occur at the same time as maturation and death. In some such communities it is suggested that an approach based on 'Allen' graphs as used in fishery research be tried (see the PF Manual on Fish Production, Ricker 1968; and Mathews & Westlake 1969). These are plots of the number of survivors of the shoots initiated in one month, against their mean weight, in successive months. Suitable data can be obtained from labelling the shoots in permanent quadrats and plots of log. weight against log. length of random samples of shoots.

Apart from the determination of seasonal changes in biomass the other observations required to determine losses, persistence, age or turnover need to be chosen to suit the particular species being studied, so it is difficult to generalise. For example Petersen (1913) was able to determine the turnover rate for *Zostera marina* because the summer and winter nodes differed in length and lost leaves left distinct scars, but such observations could not be made on a plant like *Ranunculus pseudofluitans*. Borutskii (1950, 1959), recorded numbers and lengths of stems, numbers of dead and live leaves, numbers of young branches and buds and weights of young and old branches and roots. Assuming that the total loss during a year was equal to the annual production, he tried to determine the *losses* of biomass. This approach may be particularly useful in communities with high losses and indistinct seasonal maxima.

Any differences between old and new parts such as colour, size and epiphytes should be exploited and it may be possible to sort and weigh them separately. It may be necessary to create artificial differences or label in some way. Underground parts or green shoots may be measured and labelled *in situ*, or before planting out, and subsequently recovered after varying periods (Westlake 1968). Labelling may be done with pencil on anodized aluminium tags, embossed plastic labels, or by injections of gentian violet. Dead material from the current year may be collected with the biomass samples and subsequently sorted out. If the amount is large it may be necessary to correct for losses from the dead material, for example by determining the proportions and average weights of complete and incomplete leaves. Sometimes the time taken for the original biomass to regenerate on denuded areas may be used as a rough measure of the average age of shoots (e.g. MacFarlane 1952, working on *Ascophyllum*).

At this point it is convenient to emphasise that the first sample of a new sampling occasion or site should be sorted by the senior scientist personally. Not only will he be able to observe morphological changes and make phenological observations, but he may be able to adapt the sorting procedure to provide more information. For example, May samples of *Glyceria maxima* might need sorting only into dead leaves and live shoots, but the September samples might profitably be sorted into new shoots, old shoots, dead leaves on live shoots, dead shoots and loose dead material (Westlake 1966a).

In many water bodies grazing losses from macrophytes are insignificant and most of their primary production enters the consumer part of the ecosystem after death. The first step is to observe the animal population to see if grazers are present. Fish, reptiles, birds and mammals are likely to be the most important grazers, and most grazing, including invertebrate grazing, occurs on plants with emergent or floating leaves.

If the leaves are grazed, and the leaf shape and size suitable, the grazing losses may be determined from the average number of grazed leaves per quadrat and the difference in weight between grazed and ungrazed leaves. In large quadrats the average number of grazed leaves is best found from the number of shoots per quadrat and the average number of grazed leaves per random shoot. The difference in weight often cannot be determined from the simple difference in mean weight between a random sample of grazed and ungrazed leaves because there may be some other bias in size.   For example grazing by snails and leaf miners on *Glyceria maxima* is most intense in the spring and is concentrated on earlier, and hence smaller, leaves. Therefore a large number of grazed/ungrazed pairs must be selected, alike in size and age. If most grazing produces holes in the leaf, after maturation, determinations of the total area and the area of holes by tracing onto graph paper may be used (e.g. Bray 1961). In collaboration with zoologists the consumption of plant material may be estimated from the daily food requirements of the grazing population (Smirnov 1961; see also PF Manual of Methods for Secondary Productivity, Edmondson in prep.).

Where larger animals are grazing it may be possible to exclude them from experimental areas, some of which should then be artificially 'grazed' by removing material until the enclosed areas visually match the exposed areas. The material removed then gives an estimate of the consumption and the effects of grazing on the production of the residual population can be studied. Details of methods for use in heavily grazed communities may be found in the PT Grasslands Manual (Milner & Hughes 1968).

There are no differences in principle between the applications of these techniques to macrophytes in freshwater and wetlands, although the practical problems may be very different. One special problem arises when determinations of the production of floating macrophytes are to be made from biomass observations. In such communities the biomass per unit area may remain constant, only the total area increasing. The production per unit area should be conventionally expressed as the total production divided by the mean of the initial and final areas.

3.53 Periphyton

R G WETZEL

Estimates of periphytic production rates may have been made employing the accumulation of biomass per time on colonized artificial substrata (cf. 2.3). The biomass accumulating on a known area of substratum within a given period (e.g. $mg/dm^2.day$; $g/m^2.year$) is a measure of approximate overall net production rates, i.e. the rate of gross production minus losses from respiration, decomposition, consumption, etc. It is also influenced by the rate of inoculation or colonization by new propagules, which is generally faster when conditions for growth are better, so the observed accumulation of biomass is a compound of colonization and production (Westlake 1966b).

In some circumstances it may be possible to determine biomass changes on natural substrata (cf. Kevern, Wilkin & Dyne 1966) but the observed changes will often bear little relation to the production because there is a rapid turnover of individuals, reproduction and growth roughly balancing death and losses. The rate of population turnover represents an average of several variable species rates and is difficult to determine. Moreover, subjective errors occur in determinations of rates of population turnover that are dependent on the frequency of sampling and estimation of what degree of colonization represents a climax stage of the community (Sládeček & Sládečková 1964). Higher turnover rates result from increased frequency of sampling especially when the intervals are less than a month, as is frequently the case.

Although methods based on colonization on artificial substrata present numerous sources of error in estimating production of periphyton, this approach to the problem is often useful in view of periphytic heterogeneity on natural materials. In many instances the production values so obtained are only relative but yet useful in ecological and comparative studies, e.g. to compare the fertility of polluted and unpolluted waters.

3.6 MEASUREMENTS OF PHOTOSYNTHESIS USING ILLUMINATED CONSTANT-TEMPERATURE BATHS

J F TALLING

Illuminated constant-temperature baths enable measurements of activity to be made other than by exposure in the natural water-body. Potential advantages include the saving of ship time, greater ease of manipulating samples under laboratory conditions, and the standardization and control of conditions of illumination and temperature. Disadvantages include the impossibility of fully reproducing the conditions of illumination in a natural water-column, particularly with respect to spectral modification and angular distribution with depth, and the high intensities (irradiance) present near the water surface in bright weather.

3.61 Techniques

Two major alternatives exist regarding the type of bath used, depending on whether the illumination is by sunlight or some artificial source. With sunlight, a series of light filters can be used over the samples to *simulate* illumination at various depths in a water-body, but uncontrollable fluctuations in intensity are likely. With an artificial source, simulation is more difficult, but intensity can be controlled and the basic characteristics of photosynthesis (e.g. the relationship to light intensity) more easily determined. In either case, temperature control usually requires a water bath, with the water either continually renewed from some large source with a sufficiently constant temperature (e.g. surface water from outside a ship, or tap water), or with temperature controlled by thermostat, heater, and cooling coil. In the choice of operating temperature, possible variation in the photosynthetic zone with depth or time of day should be considered. Vessels containing samples have also been exposed by trailing them at the water surface in a ship's wake (e.g. Owen 1963); such exposure conditions are obviously limited, and the activity measured is liable to include a pronounced 'surface depression'.

Examples of baths for which sunlight is used as the light source are described by Saunders, Trama & Bachmann (1962) and Jitts (1963). Shading of samples by the side-walls should obviously be avoided. The most convenient and adaptable form of light filter can be made from sheets of fine metal or plastic gauze (e.g. McAllister & Strickland 1961). Transmission is spectrally unselective, and can be varied either through the density of mesh or by using several layers of the material. A major danger with such unselective trans-mission is that ultra-violet radiation of considerable physiological activity will be over-represented by comparison with its usual rapid absorption in a natural water-column (e.g. Steemann Nielsen 1964b). It may therefore be necessary (Jitts 1963) to substitute or at least superimpose an additional selective filter, to remove ultra-violet radiation and possibly attempt some further simulation of the spectral modification of underwater light.

Examples of baths which involve use of an artificial light source are described by Steemann Nielsen & Jensen (1957), Doty & Oguri (1958, 1959), Talling (1960), and McAllister, Shah & Strickland (1964). Illumination of the samples may be unilateral or multi-lateral, and its measurement is less difficult in the former case. A range of intensities can be obtained by light filters between source and sample, for which the fine gauze mentioned above is suitable. It can either be wrapped around the individual sample vessels, or used in compartments which are isolated optically (e.g. by partitions of black plastic) from their neighbours. A bank of closely spaced white fluorescent tubes can provide an extended light source with minimal heating effect, but a battery of incandescent filament lamps is preferred by some workers. Tung-sten-iodine vapour lamps (McAllister *et al.* 1964) can be useful in obtaining high levels of irradiance. Some standardization of the spectral quality of illumination, with possibly greater resemblance to the quality found in a natural water column, may be achieved by an additional overall filter of coloured glass, plastic, or liquid (e.g. Jitts, McAllister, Stephens & Strickland 1964).

Sample bottles are usually attached by clips to some supporting framework, which, if movable, may also enable their contents to be shaken. The vertical rotating wheel used by Steemann Nielsen (e.g. 1958), with bottles attached around its periphery and illuminated from a side window of the bath, is an example. However, it is difficult to introduce much turbulence into samples which completely fill their vessels (glass beads have been used; also magnetic stirring). The general value of shaking during short exposures has perhaps not been established, and in at least some tests (e.g. Talling 1960) appeared to make little difference in comparison with unshaken controls. In other cases large differences have been observed (Vollenweider pers. comm.).

In measuring the light to which the samples are exposed, determinations of irradiance (energy flux: e.g. in cal/cm^2. min, langleys/min, or $kerg/cm^2$. sec) are greatly preferable to determinations of illuminance (e.g. lux, foot-candles) with a photometer, as the latter will possess a selective spectral response unrelated to the action-spectrum of photosynthesis. Some specification of the spectral distribution of energy is also most desirable. High levels of irradiance can be easily measured with some form of radiometer (thermopile, bolometer). Low levels may require a photometer of selective spectral response (e.g. the selenium barrier layer cell, commercially available in many forms), readings from which can be converted into units of irradiance by comparison with the response of an instrument measuring energy flux of the same spectral distribution (e.g. Talling 1960; McAllister *et al.* 1964).

3.62 Calculations and conversion to activity in situ

Varied approaches and formulae have been used to estimate activity *in situ* (per unit area of water surface) from measurements in incubator-baths; none can be universally or unreservedly recommended. Examples, with some comments, are given below.

The greatest difficulty arises when the vertical gradient of light intensity *in situ* is accompanied by a strong stratification of temperature and/or population density. It may be noted that the characteristic which can be most reliably measured from an incubator exposure is the light-saturated rate of photosynthesis per unit volume of water at a given temperature, as this is insensitive to the exact intensity or spectral composition of the light used. However, the light-saturated rate does usually increase markedly with temperature within the usual ecological range (often 5–10% per °C), although rates at low intensities—and so the initial gradient of the rate versus intensity curve—are more or less temperature-independent. Deviations between the incubator temperature and the *in situ* temperature therefore produce differing effects upon photosynthetic activity, according to whether the upper or lower part of the photosynthetic zone is involved; for the lower part the effects will be minimal.

Estimates of photosynthetic production per unit area usually require (i) some reconstruction of the vertical profile of photosynthetic rates per unit volume, and (ii) summation or integration of the contributions from various depth strata, which integral is expressed by the area enclosed by a depth profile. If, as usual, depth is measured in metres, rates per unit volume should be expressed per cubic metre.

(a) a simple approach consists in obtaining samples from various depths of known percentage or fractional light levels (e.g. 100%, 50%, 10%, 5%, 2%)

relative to the surface-incident, photosynthetically-available irradiance, and then measuring their activity when exposed to daylight below filters giving the same relative light levels (e.g. Jitts 1963). A depth-profile of activity is then reconstructed by inserting the rates measured at the appropriate optical depths. The chief difficulties here are in the correct measurement of relative levels of irradiance in the water body, complicated by spectral modification, and the water-bath; in the possible over-representation of damaging ultra-violet light in the bath (see above); and in possible effects of temperature differences between water-body and bath. Preliminary tests involving direct comparisons with exposures *in situ* are always essential.

(b) in another approach the photosynthesis / depth profile is treated as the product of two components—a less variable depth curve, showing activity relative to that measured at the surface or at the optimum depth, and a more variable distribution of absolute photosynthetic rates in samples from various depths, measured under conditions of light-saturation or under surface illumination. Two variants, outlined below, have been much used in surveys of the spatial distribution of photosynthetic productivity in oceans and lakes.

Sorokin (1959, 1960, 1963) has devised and used a calculation based on measurements of three quantities. These are (i) the photosynthetic rate of near-surface water exposed immediately below the water surface, e.g. in a water bath (C_s function), and expressed in absolute units (mg C/m^3. h), (ii) the vertical distribution of photosynthetic rate shown by samples of surface water exposed at various depths, expressed *relative* to the rate from (i) above (K_t function); and (iii) the distribution over samples from various depths of the potential photosynthetic rate achieved under surface illumina-tion (K_r function). The quantities C_s and K_r are measured in a water bath, e.g. on ship-deck, and the K_t/depth distribution from bottles suspended at appropriate depths. The product $[K_t \times K_r]$ is then calculated for each depth ($=K_s$) and integrated *with depth* ($=K_f$). Rates per unit area of water surface are then obtained from the product of the absolute rate C_s and the relative factor K_f. The treatment is applicable to very stratified populations, provided that the K_r measurements are a reasonably faithful 'weighting factor' for the consequences of varying population density and specific activity. This condi-tion may not be met if a 'surface depression' of activity is well marked, and if samples from various depths differ considerably in the relationship between photosynthetic rate and irradiance. These difficulties could probably be reduced by substituting measurements of photosynthetic rates under light-saturation (which can be measured with artificial illumination) for the rates measured immediately below the water surface in direct or shaded sunlight (cf. Talling 1966).

Steemann Nielsen (e.g. 1954, and Steeman Nielsen & Jensen 1957) has used such measurements of rates, at or near light-saturation, in conjunction with measurements *in situ* of light penetration which defined roughly the expected vertical thickness of the photosynthetic zone. By comparison with more direct measurements of photosynthesis from bottles suspended *in situ*, he found that, for tropical oceanic areas, the daily photosynthesis below unit area of water surface could be approximated by the expression

$$\left[\frac{2a + 2b + c}{5} \right] \frac{d}{2} \cdot e$$

where e is the period in hours between sunrise and sunset, d is the depth (approximating the euphotic layer) at which 1 % of the surface intensity of light (measured in the blue and green spectral regions) persists, and a, b, and c are rates of photosynthesis per hour measured at 18,000 lux and sea-surface temperature for samples respectively from the water surface and the depths at which 10 % and 1 % of light were found. Such manipulation of the rates expressed by a, b and c provides a rough 'weighting' for the contributions from three depth strata in relation to an average depth-profile of photosynthesis. Though some changes of detail may be needed (e.g. use of another fraction of d), the principle could be adapted to conditions in other areas, provided that preliminary tests with measurements *in situ* are made. The conversion from hourly to daily rates by the factor e will be invalidated if strong diurnal changes occur in photosynthetic capacity.

(c) A number of more analytical attempts have been made to express the integral photosynthesis below unit area in terms of component variables, which can be measured separately. A revision, and development of the theoretical background, was recently given by Vollenweider (1965b).

The chief are the surface-incident light intensity (I_0), the intensity (I_k) which measures the onset of saturation in the photosynthesis/intensity relationship, a measure of vertical light absorption in terms of some extinction (attenuation) coefficient (ε), the population density (n), and specific photosynthetic capacity per unit of population (P_{max}). A simple formulation is impossible when population density (and so photosynthetic capacity per unit volume of water, $n P_{max}$) is strongly stratified within the euphotic zone, but a graphical calculation may be used (e.g. Manning & Juday 1941; Ichimura, Saijo &

Aruga 1962; Steemann Nielsen 1964). Otherwise reference can be made to the formulations of Riley, Stommel & Bumpus (1949), Talling (1955, 1957b, 1957c, 1961, 1965), Ryther (1956), Ryther & Yentsch (1957), Vollenweider (1956, 1958, 1960, 1965), Rodhe, Vollenweider & Nauwerck (1958), Berge (1958), Wright (1959), and Steele (1962). Any use of the equations proposed should be preceded by an examination of the limiting conditions and assumptions, with empirical checks if possible with determinations *in situ*. Though apparently diverse, many treatments involve a similar formulation of the integral photosynthesis per unit area in terms of a product of the quotient

$\dfrac{n\ P_{max}}{\varepsilon}$ and a factor which has been estimated graphically (e.g. Ryther 1956;

Ryther & Yentsch 1957) or otherwise (Talling 1957b, c, 1961, 1965; Vollenweider 1960, 1965) from radiation data or from empirical comparisons with determinations *in situ* (e.g. Rodhe, Vollenweider & Nauwerck 1958).

3.7 INTERPRETATION OF RESULTS

The aim of the International Biological Programme is, '. . . to obtain internationally comparable observations of the basic biological parameters' (IBP News, No. 2). All IBP investigators should bear this in mind, whenever possible, and look beyond their own peculiar problems in order to serve the common purpose. It is desirable to know precisely what is being measured, to describe the results in mutually comprehensible terms, to express the results on some comparable basis and to use convenient and standard units.

It is expected that research will be published in the normal journals. It is hoped that reprints will be sent to the IBP Central Office and that detailed original data which cannot be published will be preserved and made available on request.

3.71 Units and comparability
D F WESTLAKE

(a) Units
Data should be given in metric units, though local equivalents may be given as well. Biomass and daily rates of production may be given in units close to those in which they are measured, e.g. grams or kilograms per square metre (g or kg/m²). The former gives more convenient numbers for daily

production rates and phytoplankton biomass. Comparisons are often facilitated if annual production rates are estimated for relatively large areas and this may be reflected in the use of metric tons per hectare per year (m.t/ha.yr, i.e. $10^3 kg/10^4 m^2$. yr) which gives numbers between 0·1 and 60 for the annual net primary production of fertile ecosystems. Units for energy budgets are subject to controversy but, following the precedent of the International Geophysical Year and at least some of the other IBP Manuals, gram calories (g cal) are recommended, despite the preference of physicists for the joule. The g cal is convenient for comparisons with meteorological and nutritional data. The standard nutritional units (SNU, i.e. 10^6 kg cal) gives convenient numbers for annual energy fluxes per hectare and is close to the annual food requirements of a human being. Radiation should then be measured in g cal/cm². min, not in lux (metre-candles) which are only valid for white light as detected by the human eye. Standard conversion factors for lux to energy are valid only for the specified light source in the absence of selective attenuation between source and photometer (cf. 5.2). This factor (the reciprocal of the luminous efficiency) for daylight varies from about 10–15 mg cals/cm². min. per kilolux, according to weather, time of day, season and location.

(b) Terminology
It is hoped that the terminology used in this Manual is in general agreement with the recommendations being considered for IBP programmes, and in other manuals. Any departures from this terminology should be stated and the terms then used be fully defined. It is often necessary to qualify 'biomass', e.g. the biomass of the net phytoplankton at the spring maximum, the green shoots of submerged macrophytes (with associated periphyton), the green shoots of emergent macrophytes (without their periphyton and the under-storey submerged macrophytes), etc.

(c) Problems arising from differing methods
Primarily the investigator should try to select methods which, within the limits of the available resources, will give the most meaningful results when applied to the particular community to be studied. If possible, however, he should also try to apply some other methods to facilitate comparisons. Different investigators will have to select different methods and their results will be readily comparable only if the need for comparability is continually kept in mind. For example one will select the fixation of ^{14}C per unit

volume to determine the daytime net production of phytoplankton, another the oxygen exchanges per unit area to determine the daytime gross production of periphyton, another the biomass changes as organic weight per unit area to determine the monthly net production of reedswamp or grassland and another the total biomass and losses as dry weight per unit area to determine the mean annual production of woodland. It will be impossible to compare the initial data from such disparate studies and, as far as possible, information must be provided to convert the original data as directly as possible into other likely criteria. As an ideal, rarely attainable in practice, especially with algal material, biomass determinations should be accompanied by data on the dry weight per unit fresh weight and volume and the ash, carbon, chlorophyll *a* and energy contents. It is also desirable that production rates should be accompanied by data on the photosynthetic quotient, the relations between gross and net photosynthesis over the period studied and over the growing season and the year, as well as factors for conversions into dry weight, organic weight, carbon and energy. (See also 2.13, 14 & 15). For conversions throughout IBP it is probable that the annual net organic production and the annual net fixation of energy are likely to be central criteria of production rates. The need to study both organic production and energy flow, arising from changes in the calorific content of plant material, has been discussed (e.g. Davis 1967).

Such information is valuable for interpreting the growth and physiology of the organisms (cf. 2.13) in addition to its use for comparisons. Accurate results are essential for the former purpose, and also for comparisons when a series of conversions is required (e.g. dry weight to organic weight, to carbon, to net carbon fixation, to gross carbon fixation) because errors are likely to multiply. When a single, direct conversion can be applied even a rough estimate may provide a useful comparative value.

Biomass is generally defined as weight per unit area of habitat, and most IBP investigations will determine this directly. However, most phytoplankton determinations are made per unit volume of water, and the conversion to surface area units requires a depth factor which may be difficult to define. In a productivity study the role of biomass is, as a possible measure of production, a measure of food available and to permit comparisons of the productivity per unit biomass. Lake and ocean ecosystems are best considered as containing at least two sub-divisions; an upper, euphotic, or trophogenic, region where primary production is possible, and a lower region where biological activity is confined to the consumption of imported energy. The division between these two is usually made at the compensation depth, where gross photosynthesis balances the respiration over 24 hours. During the most productive periods this is often approximately the same as the depth to which the surface waters (epilimnion) are mixed. If the compensation depth is below the limits of the epilimnion the effective biomass of primary producers should include the populations above and below the thermocline. If the compensation depth is above the thermocline the average phytoplankton organism may sometimes be near the surface and capable of positive net photosynthesis, and at other times at greater depths where it can only respire, while it is available as a food source in both regions. The effective biomass then includes the organisms which at any instant are below the compensation depth but will subsequently be transported above it. The production per unit biomass will be reduced in such a situation. The gross productivity per unit area will not be affected, but the net production will be reduced because of the respiring population below the compensation depth. This must be remembered when designing experiments to determine net production, and when making gross to net conversions, which are therefore extremely difficult to make accurately for phytoplankton communities.

Nevertheless, comparisons between results obtained as gross photosynthesis and those obtained as net photosynthesis are frequently necessary. Even within the techniques used for hydrobiological investigations some methods (e.g. oxygen changes) give gross production directly and others (e.g. biomass changes) give net production. The ^{14}C methods give values, depending on the length of exposure and environmental conditions, somewhere between gross and net production (see 3.31). Using oxygen methods the true net production can only be measured if the respiration of bacteria and zooplankton can be assessed. When using ^{14}C methods, exposures of different duration or at different intensities could supply some information on the relations between gross and net photosynthesis. Theoretically the two methods could be used in parallel. The effect of the period of determination on the net: gross relation should be remembered. If a ^{14}C experiment is carried out during the hours of daylight the night respiration must be allowed for when determining the 24 hour net production. If the biomass of a macrophyte community is measured at its seasonal maximum a deduction may be needed to obtain the true annual net production, to allow for subsequent respiration by the senescent community, in excess of any further production.

The meagre evidence available suggests that annual net productions are very roughly 50% of the gross. The ratio net/gross production tends to rise in cool well-illuminated communities with rapid turnover and to fall in warm, shaded communities with much old material. Under the most favourable conditions, for short periods, the ratio may rise to 90—95%. It is hoped that IBP work will supply more information on this subject.

Problems of converting daily rates to annual rates are discussed in 3.73.

Another difficult problem is the comparison of oxygen output with carbon dioxide uptake. Assuming that the gas exchanges are the result of the photosynthetic production of the conventional hexose, the photosynthetic quotient (P.Q = O_2 output/CO_2 uptake, by volume) should be unity and hence g oxygen × 0·375 gives g carbon. However it is not likely that the observed gas exchanges of a plant composed of many substances other than hexose will have an average photosynthetic quotient of 1·0 over a long period. The elaboration of substances such as protein and fat leads to higher values, potentially rising to 1·6 when nitrate is the nitrogen source for pure protein synthesis. Experimental data on the ratio are difficult to obtain, especially in the field, because experimental errors and inherent biases in the methods can easily obscure the relatively small differences due to the ratio. Again, the meagre evidence available suggests that over a year P.Q values of about 1·2 are likely (g oxygen × 0·312 gives g carbon). Higher values (e.g. 1·35, g oxygen × 0·278 gives g carbon) may be expected when growth is rapid in the presence of nitrate or under conditions favouring the accumulation of fat (such as a community dominated by diatoms). Lower values may be expected in short term experiments in high light intensities, especially when carbon dioxide is abundant and nitrogen is deficient or supplied as ammonium.

Westlake (1963, 1965b) has given a more detailed discussion of the problems of making comparisons, but the arithmetical errors in the section on the photosynthetic quotient in the first paper should be noted.

3.72   Calculation of day rates per unit of lake surface

R A VOLLENWEIDER

Experimentally determined production rates refer to measurements performed over a time interval that is normally a fraction of a whole day. Consequently, in order to get production rates per day, the experimental data have to be elaborated on the basis of some conversion procedure. Although the question of how best to do this is a fundamental one for the whole field treated in this Manual, surprisingly little attention has been paid to it up to the present;

the pertinent literature shows that almost every author has followed his own criteria and procedure.

Generally speaking, the problem cannot be solved for all communities—phytoplankton, higher aquatics, periphyton, and bacteria—on the same basis but needs separate treatment for each type. Analytical solutions have been attempted only for phytoplankton and higher aquatics.

(a) Phytoplankton

Ideally, the simplest way to measure daily production would be to expose complete *in situ* series over the whole day (i.e. from dawn to dusk), and to integrate the rates obtained, plotted as a linear rate-depth diagram, either by planimetry or by an appropriate arithmetical interpolation procedure (e.g. using Simpson's formulae). Procedures which are close to this, in fact, have been used by Rodhe (1958), Rodhe, Vollenweider & Nauwerck (1958), Findenegg (1964), and others; for convenience, experiments were run from sunset to sunset. As has been discussed in 3.31d, the exposure time of enclosures, in order to prevent secondary effects, should not exceed a few hours. Many investigators—without considering primarily the empirical side of the question—shortened their exposure times for purely practical reasons. Some adopted half-day expositions, others made their exposures during the middle of the day, and still others did not follow any particular criterion. With regard to the conversion applied, some used to multiply their experimental data with a factor equal to the ratio 'duration of the light day/duration of the experiment', others who tried to refine their calculations, used the ratio 'total irradiance per day/irradiance during the exposure time', etc. The inadequacy of all these attempts has been shown by the studies of Vollenweider & Nauwerck (1961), but only a theoretical analysis of the problem, as first attempted by Talling (1957a) and later by Vollenweider (1965b), could give guide-lines as to how to tackle the problem of conversion. Though progress has been made along these lines, the problem is as yet not entirely solved.

(i) *The theoretical background*

For a correct though simplified description of the problem, a distinction must be made between '*instantaneous rates*' (which is a theoretical notion) and '*exposure rates*' (which are the entities measured experimentally over a particular interval of time). It is obvious that any practical rate measurement represents already an integrated value (integrated over the time interval of exposure). If P_{S,t_n} denotes the '*instantaneous rate integral per unit of lake surface'* at time t_n (another theoretical entity), which may be considered to remain constant over the short time interval Δt_n, then the *'exposure rate integral per unit of lake surface over any interval t_s–t_r of time'* (for convenience denoted shortly as *'surface time rate integral'*) is given by,

$$\text{Ps},_{t_s\text{-}t_r} = {}^{s}\underset{r}{\Sigma}\ \text{Ps},_{t_n} \cdot \Delta t_n = \int_{t_r}^{t_s} \int_0^\infty (p_z \cdot dz)\, dt \tag{1}$$

where p_z is the instantaneous rate at depth z, and t_n refers to clock time. In particular, P is called *'surface day rate integral'* if t_r and t_s refer to the time of sunrise and sunset respectively; this is the integral which will ultimately be calculated. Its dimension is 'g C_{ass}/m². day', or any corresponding quantity.

Under the condition (and only under this) that phytoplankton is homogeneously distributed with depth, and the p_z's are dependent on light only, the inner integral of the above equation can be approximately solved analytically, i.e.

$$\int_0^\infty p_z \cdot dz = F(i) \cdot \frac{p_{max}}{\varepsilon} \tag{2}$$

p_{max} represents the rate maximum either at the (light independent) saturation plateau or at the light optimum (cf. Fig. 3.7); in this last case, it may also be symbolized by p_{opt}. ε is the extinction coefficient of the photosynthetically active energy of the spectrum (cf. chapter 5). This coefficient, at suboptimal light intensities, coincides fairly well with that of the most penetrating spectral block, $\varepsilon_v^{\lambda max}$ (Talling 1957a; Vollenweider 1960, 1965b; Rodhe 1965). $F(i)$ is a function of the ratio i_0'/i_k, i.e. the sub-surface light intensity i_0' (referred to the photosynthetically active energy), and the intensity i_k present at a certain depth. This last term, introduced by Talling (1957a,b) and sometimes also symbolized by I_k, can be interpreted in several ways. First, it represents the intensity-determined from a linear rate-light intensity graph— at the intersect between the initial linear slope and the height of the saturation plateau of the photosynthesis-light curve. Then it refers to the integral (2) in as far as the area under the photosynthesis-depth curve (cf. Fig. 3.7) is equal to the rectangle given by p_{max} and the depth z' at which the light intensity is about $0.5\ i_k$. Finally, as discussed by Talling, the intensity i_k can also be considered as measure of a light-temperature adaptation property of the phytoplankton community at the time of measurement; this property may vary seasonally (Steemann Nielsen & Hansen 1959; Ichimura 1960), as well as over shorter periods (Ichimura 1960).

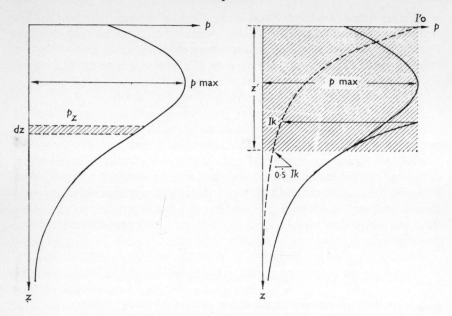

Figure 3.7. Simplified photosynthesis–depth curves; see text.

The possible numerical variations of the function $F(i)$ ranges between 0 and 3·5 during the course of a day, and, to some extent, may be approximated by $1n\,(2\,i_0'/i_k)$ (Talling 1957a; Vollenweider 1965).

The analytical integration of equation (1), on the other hand, is considerably more complicated. Assuming that the instantaneous rate p_i, relative to a definite light intensity remains constant, it can be shown that the surface day rate integral has the following form,

$$P_{S,\,day} = \sum a = F(I) \cdot \frac{a_{opt}}{\varepsilon} \qquad (3)$$

which, in fact, is proved by experience. The essential difference between equation (3) and equation (2) lies in the fact that a_{opt} refers to the assimilation optimum under natural conditions, and is the sum over all variations of p at the optimum depth, i.e.

$$a_{opt} = \int_{t_r}^{t_s} p_{z_{opt,\,t}} \cdot dt,$$

and F(I) is a function of the ratio of the total subsurface irradiance I_0' and an average I_k value over the whole day. Normally F(I) ranges between about 2 and 3·5 but shows a frequency maximum between 2·5 and 3·0.

On this basis, it has also been possible to calculate a conversion function for laboratory, or constant-temperature bath exposure,

$$P_{s,\,day} = (0.83 \text{ to } 0.67) \cdot p_{opt}/\text{hr.} \; \lambda/\varepsilon \cdot \ln[(1.26 \text{ to } 1.54) \, I_0'/I_k] \qquad (4)$$

where λ is the day length (in hours) between sunrise and sunset; the other terms corresponding to those defined above. The principal value of the integral, which is a generalized form of Steemann Nielsen's equation (cf. 3.62), results from the fact that it defines a confidence range. Accordingly, day rate estimates from laboratory measurements cannot be better than $\pm10\%$, even under the best conditions, but in most instances they are worse. This is also true for estimates made from *in situ* exposures (see below).

In this connexion, it should also be mentioned that light extinction measurements are not always available. No reliable calculation can be made under such conditions. However, if transparency is known from Secchi disc readings, then at least a certain approximation is possible, assuming F(I) equal to 2·5–3; for the extinction coefficient needed the relation given in 5.44 can be used (Vollenweider 1960).

(ii) *Application and limitations*

The theoretical frame-work outlined has proved to be reasonably valid if the boundary conditions, i.e. homogeneous distribution of phytoplankton with depth, and constant light intensity-rate relationship over the experimental time, are sufficiently fulfilled in nature. In order to calculate daily production from exposures *in situ* a 'surface rate curve' is determined from equation (2) and a recorded irradiance curve for the day in question. The area under this curve as well as that fraction of it during which the exposure was made is found by planimetry, and the ratio between these two areas is used as conversion factor for the integrated measurements of a depth-profile. It is evident that this conversion factor is similar to that calculated from the solar irradiance curve provided that both curves are fairly parallel; this is almost true up to a midday i_0'/i_k ratio of 5. At higher i_0'/i_k ratios the departures can no longer be neglected. Under natural conditions i_0'/i_k ratios as high as 25 have been observed.

In most, or at least in many circumstances the conditions are more complex. Firstly phytoplankton is seldom homogeneously distributed with depth, particularly during thermal stratification. A way to account for this for calculating surface integrals over the time of exposure has been discussed in 3.62, but the problem of conversion to daily estimates remains open. In fact, little is known, as yet, about the time course of photosynthesis in populations located at different depths, and how they behave with regard to adaptation characteristics, such as i_k, light-independent saturation level and linear slope at low light intensities. If these characteristics were known (which, of course, can be studied but need much work), the total integral could be split, and calculations made for each fraction separately.

This is not possible yet. Probably the best we can do at present is to proceed from the assumption of a fairly homogeneous distribution and to calculate surface rate curves, as discussed above. The biggest difficulty will arise from the selection of a reasonable midday i_0'/i_k ratio, but it can be assumed that the most important, with regard to the whole integral, will be that of the population present in sub-surface layers at the time of measurement. It may also be possible to study simultaneously the light-dependence characteristics from two or three populations with the response obtained when samples are distributed over the same period of time at various depths.

Secondly, another difficulty, not less a pitfall than the above, results from variations of the photosynthetic rate with time that are not due to light variations or changes in phytoplankton density. It is a common pattern that rates decrease with increasing experimental time, or, more precisely, in dependence upon the cumulative effects of exposure. Such effects may be due to nutrient depletion, storage of assimilation products, phase of synchronization, etc. High differences between early morning and late afternoon rates have been reported, e.g. by Ohle (1958), Doty (1959), and Vollenweider & Nauwerck (1961). Provided the decrease of rates with time of day is regular, it has been suggested (Vollenweider 1965b) that day rate estimates from short exposures would be facilitated if the duration of standard exposures, instead of being constant, was chosen proportional to the day length, e.g. by dividing the light day (sunrise to sunset) into five equal periods, and exposures were made over the periods II + III. Calculation has shown that over these two periods about 55—60% of the total daily production is measured, regardless of the magnitude of the rate decrease during the day; the deductions were confirmed from experiments. Accordingly, the uncertainty introduced in estimating daily production would not be larger than about $\pm 10\%$; this is less than in any other procedure.

Thirdly it is also possible that rate fluctuations during the course of a day are irregular (cf. e.g. Ohle 1961); the reasons for this are not quite clear.

However, as has been shown recently (cf. Nauwerck 1963; Soeder 1967) certain phytoplankton constituents, particularly flagellates, can actively migrate vertically over a 24-hour period. It is obvious that such migrations can be revealed only by frequent sampling and sets of short term exposures, under such conditions any calculation of daily production from *one* standard exposure would be unrealistic.

Summarizing the experience up to the present shows that standard exposures are but a limited source of information on daily production in phytoplankton. Therefore it is positively suggested that there is need for studying in much more detail the daily course of photosynthesis, considering distribution phenomena, adaptation phenomena, nutrient depletion, and the effects of cell division and synchronization.

(b) Periphyton and macrophytes

D F WESTLAKE

If such plant material is enclosed at a series of depths for oxygen or carbon dioxide exchange studies, the problem of obtaining surface dayrate integrals is probably even more complicated than for the phytoplankton. The depth distribution of the plants is most unlikely to be homogeneous and it will not be easy to fit a mathematical function to it. Accurate day rates will only be obtained if the results of series of short-period exposures at different depths are used to obtain depth-integrals (graphical or mathematical) for each short period and then depth-time integrals for all the short periods making up the day. The graphical model described by Westlake (1966a) uses calculated short period rates, but observed rates could be substituted. Ultimately, given theoretical knowledge at present lacking, it may be possible to justify some assumptions and extrapolations which could reduce the labour involved.

However, it is implicit in the procedures recommended in Sections 3.33 and 3.34 that the whole community upon a unit area will normally be enclosed, so that there is no need for a series of exposures at different depths and the experimental values are already integrated with respect to depth. This means that each exposure period requires much less work and often it will be possible to make short-period exposures throughout the day. If these can be made continuously, the day rate can be obtained by simple summation, otherwise smooth curves can be prepared for graphical integration, with a minimum of interpolation.

If it is not possible to make frequent determinations, rough day rates can be obtained by multiplying the value obtained by a factor (visible radiation received during day/visible radiation received during period of determination). These rates will be subject to all the errors arising from the non-linearity of the relation between incident light and photosynthesis of the community, and from variations in the rate of photosynthesis not directly due to changes in light intensities. Such errors are discussed in 3.72a and by Wetzel (1965b). He presented some evidence that the average of exposures from 10.00 to 14.00 hrs on several days would give a good approximation to directly determined day rates, provided that there were not large diurnal changes in the environment.

These methods will give gross photosynthesis or net photosynthesis over the period of daylight. Twenty-four hour net photosynthesis can only be determined by subtracting the overnight respiration of the plants alone. Daytime determinations of the rate of respiration may need correction for night-time changes of temperature (cf. 3.41) before application for this purpose.

3.73   Conversion from daily rates of photosynthesis to annual production
YU I SOROKIN

In large lakes and reservoirs great changes in the rate of primary production usually occur in different parts of the basin as well as in the different seasons of the year.   In order to obtain the value of the average annual production under 1 m^2, it is therefore necessary to carry out a series of expeditional cruises at numerous stations during different times of the vegetation period of phytoplankton (Sorokin 1958). Such expeditional surveys of primary production should be done with 15–30 day intervals (or closer) in accordance with the general trend of the phytoplankton development in the basin. The stations must be selected on the basis of the distribution of main water masses, biotopes and shallow waters.

For the evaluation of the annual production, the average daily production for the whole basin must be calculated for each survey. For this the area of the basin is divided into a number of sections having comparable values of daily production. The area of each part is found by planimetry. Then the total daily production of each single part can be found by multiplying the dimensions of its area with the mean daily production, and the total daily production of the whole basin at the time of survey is calculated as a sum of the production of its different parts. These last values are plotted against the time (Fig. 3.8). The curve so obtained corresponds to the current state of production for the annual cycle and it is not difficult to find the annual production P of the basin by graphical methods. The value of P divided by the area in m² of the basin surface gives the average annual production per 1m², which is one of the main characteristics of the primary trophic level of a basin.

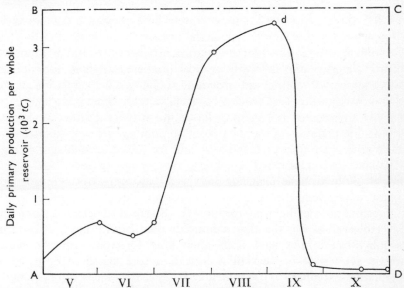

Figure 3.8. Curve of total daily primary production (in 10^3t C_{ass}/surface.day) in the Rybinsk Reservoir (USSR) 1955. Original Yu I Sorokin.

3.74   Relations between primary production and population density ('standing crop')

J F TALLING

These relationships are varied, and can be viewed in several ways. Examples are given below.

If both *production rate* and *population density* refer to the same unit of habitat (e.g. 1 m³, or 1 m²), division of the first by the second gives a *mean specific rate* per unit of population. This specific rate—equivalent to the German 'Aktivitätskoeffizient', or Production/Biomass (P/B) quotient used by many Russian authors—may vary from zero (completely inactive population) to an upper limit determined by inherent properties of the organisms (e.g. maximum specific growth rate) and environmental regulation (e.g. by temperature, energy input and nutritional factors).

The significance of the mean specific rate will depend upon the heterogeneity encompassed by the populations and the environmental segment under study. Sources of heterogeneity include mixed populations of species, healthy and moribund cells, and state of synchronization of cells with respect to growth stages; such variation can rarely be expressed quantitatively in ecological work. Other factors include the time-variation in rates during long (e.g. 24 hours) experiments; depth-variation in rates when the environmental unit is a water-column involving vertical gradients of light intensity and possibly temperature, etc.; and pronounced changes in population density during measurements (best avoided by using suitably short periods).

The *index* chosen to measure population quantity (cf. chapter 2) may also affect the interpretation of specific rates. Cell numbers are only suitable when a single species strongly predominates, and for mixed assemblages of algae cell volume and chlorophyll *a* content are commonly used. Although a principal photosynthetic pigment, the special advantages of chlorophyll as an index lie largely in the calculation of specific rates at low light intensities and in estimations of light interception (cf. Steemann Nielsen & Jørgensen 1962). However, as it is the most commonly used general index of material, chlorophyll-based rates have been often used to express specific photosynthetic activity at or near light-saturation (the classic A.Z. value, or 'Assimilation Number', is here included). Such rates can vary widely in general, but may be reasonably uniform for measurements conducted over a restricted area or period (e.g. Gessner 1949; Talling 1965).

If production rates *per unit area* for the entire trophogenic zone are considered, the correspondence with population density *per unit volume* of water is often very poor, particularly at higher densities. This apparent 'uncoupling' may originate by the consequences of self-shading, and by a more indirect association between population density and other pigments (e.g. 'Gelbstoff') in the water. In these (and other) situations, it may be more useful to compare production rates with the population content per unit area of the euphotic zone. It is, of course, possible that denser populations may tend to exhibit lower specific rates for other reasons (e.g. nutrient depletion), although this is not a universal feature.

When a production increment is expressed in the same units as the population density, the specific rate has the dimensions of $time^{-1}$ only, and can be recalculated as an exponential growth constant k (see below). Thus a specific rate of 0·1 gC/gC · day equals a k value of 0·095 $\log_e$ units/day or 0·041 $\log_{10}$ units/day. Other examples are provided, from work on algal cultures, by McAllister, Shah & Strickland (1964). In favourable examples, therefore, and especially when a single species is predominant, a link can be established with a fundamental characteristic of population growth. However, in nature, significant rates of depletion are usually opposed to the measured rates of production, so that effects of the latter on a stationary population can be expressed by an average 'turn-over time'. Although this approach to production has been widely used (e.g. Juday 1940; Rodhe 1958; Rodhe *et al.* 1958) and emphasizes the replacement of population components, it seems to be less suited than the approach based on specific production rates for describing the general case, which may include exponential growth.

The following examples illustrate the calculation of specific production rates.

(a) initial gradient, at low intensities, of the relation between specific photosynthetic rate and light intensity

e.g. $\dfrac{\text{mg C/m}^3.\text{h. kilolux}}{\text{mg chlorophyll } a/\text{m}^3} = \text{mg C/mg chlorophyll } a \cdot \text{h. kilolux}$

(b) photosynthetic capacity measured at light-saturation:

e.g. $\dfrac{\text{mg C/m}^3. \text{ h}}{\text{mg chlorophyll } a/\text{m}^3} = \text{mg C/mg chlorophyll } a \cdot \text{h (from a volume basis!)}$

(c) average photosynthetic rate per unit of euphotic population

e.g. $\dfrac{\text{mg C/m}^2. \text{ h}}{\text{mg chlorophyll } a/\text{m}^2} = \text{mg C/mg chlorophyll } a \cdot \text{h (from a surface basis)}$

(d) specific or relative growth rate, 'activity coefficient'

e.g. mg C/mg C · day (calculated either from a volume or a surface basis)

(e) exponential growth constant (K_b) from

$$^b\log C_t = {}^b\log C_o + K_b \cdot t,$$

$$\text{or,} \quad K_b = \frac{1}{t} \, (^b\log C_t - {}^b\log C_o),$$

Whereby K_b may be expressed as

$\log_e$ units/day, $(b = e = 2·718 \ldots)$

$\log_{10}$ units/day, $(b = 10)$, or,

$\log_2$ units/day, (cell divisions), $(b = 2)$

Note: $^b\log$ means logarithm to the base b $(^{e, \ 10, \ or \ 2})$

4

Bacterial Production

Methods of water bacteriology have been described in a series of manuals and monographs on general and aquatic microbiology (Fred & Waksman 1928; Omelanskii 1940; ZoBell 1946; Rasumov 1947; Rippel-Baldes 1947; Kuznezov 1959; Frobisher 1962; Kuznezov & Romanenko 1963; Rodina 1965; *a.o.*).

It is not intended to give a full account of bacterial methods in this Manual. Readers who are particularly interested in the subject of water bacteriology are referred to the text books mentioned above and also to pertinent text books in soil science and related subjects, where many cross references of general interest and common ground with water bacteriology can be found.

This chapter deals briefly with a selected number of methods useful for obtaining direct and indirect data on total number and biomass of natural bacterial populations, their production rates, on the metabolic activity of some specific groups and its spatial localization in a water body.

PART I: GENERAL METHODS
YU I SOROKIN*

4.1 SAMPLING PROBLEMS, FILTRATION APPARATUS AND OTHER DEVICES

For sampling bacteria special bacteriological water bottles are usually required. However, for eutrophic and mesotrophic waters, water sampling for estimating total number and biomass of bacteria can often be done using a clean plastic water bottle commonly employed in productivity and hydro-chemistry work without introducing significant errors in the final results.

* The editor does not agree entirely with all parts of Dr Sorokin's exposition. Nevertheless, apart from editorial changes only slight modifications at the original text were applied.

Special microbiological water samplers are necessary in oligotrophic waters, and for samples in which the bacteria are to be enumerated by plate counts; in both cases contamination from the walls of an ordinary water bottle may easily cause erroneous estimates.

The principal part of a microbiological water sampler consists either of a sterile evacuated glass container (balloon, matrass, cylinder or flask) or of a sterile rubber bulb closed by end capillaries, and the whole is attached to a frame fastened to a cable (cf. e.g. Butkevich 1932; ZoBell 1946; Issachenko 1951; Sorokin 1960c; Sieburth 1963; Rodina 1965). At the desired depth the end capillary is crushed by a messenger and the glass container and the bulb is filled with water. It might be mentioned here that the use of glass containers is preferable to that of rubber bulbs because from the porous walls of the latter bacteria-like particles are likely to be washed off which hinder direct microscope countings.

Below, two different models of microbiological water samplers are described in more detail; both have been successfully used in fresh waters and in the sea, and are convenient for routine work.

(a) Model using a one-neck bottle

This model can be used up to a depth of 60—70 m. The scheme of the apparatus is shown in Fig. 4.1 (Sorokin 1960c): An evacuated sterile bottle (3) having a volume of 0·25–0·5 l is fastened in a heavy frame (1) with the aid of a clamp (2). The bottle is closed with a rubber stopper (8) through which a curved glass tube (4) passes; the latter is connected to a thick walled rubber tube (5) of 10 to 15 cm length which is stoppered with a sealed glass capillary (9). This capillary is pinched by a clamp with sharp edges (6) which in turn is connected to the plate (7) receiving the blow of the messenger.

The whole apparatus is lowered to the required depth; at the moment when the messenger crushes the capillary, the rubber tube (5) straightens, and water is sucked into the bottle from some distance away.

For prolonged expeditions a number of sterile bottles plugged with cotton are prepared beforehand; the rubber stoppers fitted with the tubes as described above are separately autoclaved in paper covers. Connection to the bottle is done immediately before sampling (replacing the cotton plug by the tubed stopper), and the bottle is evacuated by a manual vacuum pump; finally the glass capillary is sealed in the flame of an alcohol burner, and the frame of the sampler is cleaned with alcohol.

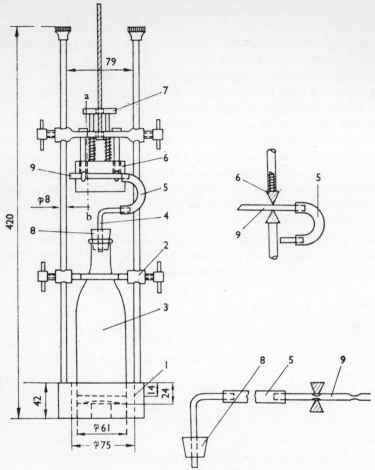

Figure 4.1. Microbiological water-sampler, see text.

During short surveys it is more convenient to evacuate the bottles previously in the laboratory but a last external cleaning with alcohol must be done on board ship.

(b) Model using a gas-cylinder-like two-neck flask
In this model (Sorokin 1964) the sample is sucked into a cylindric glass container having end openings at the top and the bottom side respectively (cf.

Figs. 4.2 and 4.3). To each end tube (external diameter 2 mm) a piece of vacuum rubber tubing (internal diameter about 2 mm, external diameter about 8 mm) is attached and their ends are fitted with capillaries of about 1·5–2 mm internal diameter, one of which is bent as shown in Fig. 4.3. A set of such capillaries are prepared before the expedition.

During prolonged expeditions it may happen that the cylinders have to be used several times. In this case it is necessary to sterilize the device by steaming as follows. The cylinders needed are fitted with open capillaries and rubber tubings, and the whole is connected to a source of steam (cf. Fig. 4.3); several cylinders may be attached simultaneously at the same source. After ten minutes of steaming the end tubes are closed by clamps, and both capillaries of each cylinder are sealed. Vacuum is automatically produced after the vapour in the cylinders has condensed.

The sterile cylinder is fastened to the supporting frame and the whole attached to the cable (cf. Fig. 4.2). The end of the upper capillary is placed so that (after the blow of the messenger) it will be broken on the side opposite the point of the bend, and the apparatus is ready for sampling.

After the sampler is withdrawn on board the ship, the broken upper capillary of the cylinder is replaced by a sterile capillary fitted with a rubber tube and a clamp, and the cylinder is removed from the frame and fastened to a suitable support. Then the lower capillary is flamed and broken, and the water of the cylinder is collected (by opening the upper clamp) for analysis into a sterile flask.

Simultaneous sampling at various depths can be done by using several samplers attached to the same rope at appropriate distances. The frame of each sampler has a device which—after arrival of a first messenger—automatically releases a second one which drops to the next lower sampler. In this manner sampling in series up to 1000 m and more is possible.

Also in this case, for short surveys, it is more convenient to prepare cylinders and capillaries in the laboratory before the expedition in order to reduce work on board the ship to the minimum absolutely necessary (set-up of the sampler(s) and external sterilization).

4.2 CHEMICAL AND PHYSICAL CHARACTERISTICS OF THE ENVIRONMENT

At this place, it may be remembered that microbiological studies—just as any other productivity study—must be supplemented with the necessary data on

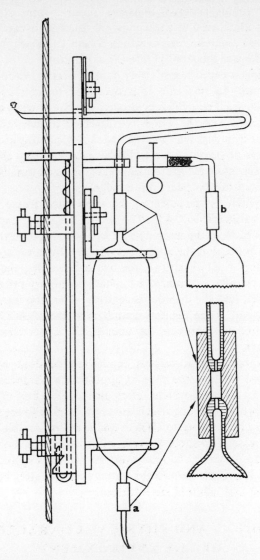

Figure 4.2. Modified bacteriological water sampler, see text.

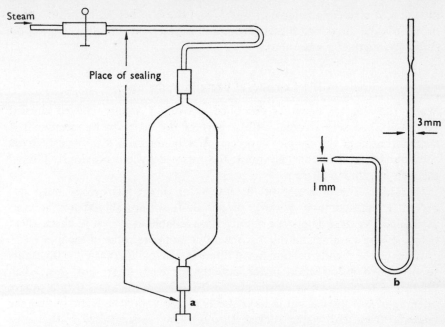

Steam

Place of sealing

3 mm

1 mm

a

b

Figure 4.3. Sterilization device for modified bacteriological water sampler (Figure 4.2).

environmental characteristics of the water body (bodies) in question at the time of sampling. For suggestions see chapter 5.

4.3   DIRECT MICROSCOPIC COUNTS OF BACTERIA IN WATER AND IN SEDIMENTS; ESTIMATION OF BACTERIAL BIOMASS

It is now generally recognized that direct countings of the total amount of bacteria is a most important method for the quantitative study of the microflora, and its reproduction, in a natural water body.* Only by this method can all the bacterial cells present in a given volume of water or silt be enumerated with sufficient accuracy (Razumov 1947; Davey & Wilde 1955; Kusnezov 1959). The bacteria in water are counted on membrane filters after

* Cf. also, e.g., Collins 1963; Jannasch & Jones 1959; Jannasch 1965.

filtration of a suitable volume of water, and those in bottom deposits either on membrane filters or on preparations of suspensions of silt which are on slides (Winogradsky's method).

4.31   Counting of bacteria in the water

Water samples are taken as described above, or simply in well cleaned bottles washed several times with a part of the water to be examined. If transportation of the samples is necessary they are fixed with formaldehyde solution (1 % at final concentration); the formaldehyde is previously filtered through membrane filters.

Filtration. The pore size of the filters for direct microscopy must not exceed 0·5 μ, and their working (upper dull) surface should not be contaminated. As clean filters are not always available, it is best to check them before use by staining and microscopically examining some of them.

If the use of slightly contaminated filters is unavoidable then it is advisable to determine a correction factor directly for each filter. For this, when filtering, a round piece of plastic film of 0·1–0·2 mm thickness with a square opening of 1–2 cm² cut out in its centre is placed under the filter, so that the bacteria from the water sucked through are concentrated within this 'window'; the rest of the filter can be examined for contamination.

For filtration, an apparatus of the type shown in Fig. 4.4 is used.

The volume of water to be filtered will, of course, depend upon the trophic level of the water body investigated. In an oligotrophic basin 10–15 ml of water pass through the working surface of the filter (see above); in meso-trophic lakes the volume can be 5–10 ml, in eutrophic ones 2–5 ml, and in contaminated waters 0·5–1 ml.

If only a small volume of water is to be filtered, then, as a precaution, additional filtered water must be added beforehand to the funnel to provide equal distribution of bacteria on the surface of the filter.

Storage. After filtration the bacteria on the filters are fixed in formaldehyde fumes, by placing the filters in a Petri dish to which a few drops of concentrated formaldehyde are given inside the cover. The filters are then dried and stored.

Staining. For this purpose a sector of the filter is cut out, marked with a pencil and brought into a Petri dish at the bottom of which a round piece of 2–3 layers of plankton netting, moistened with 3 % erythrosin solution in 5 % phenol, is placed. Staining takes one day. After this the filters must be decolourised; hence, they are transferred to a beaker, filled with water, and

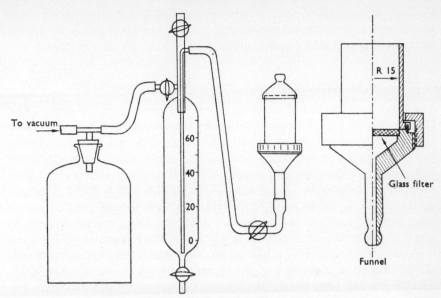

Figure 4.4. Microbiological filtration device, see text.

laid on the surface of some plankton netting stretched across the surface of the water, and left there until they are pale pink in colour. The filters are then dried and prepared for microscopic examination.

Examination. For this purpose the prepared filter sectors are placed on top of a drop of immersion oil on a microscope slide; another drop of oil is put on the surface of the filter and the whole is covered with a cover slide. The slides are ready for examination when the filters have become transparent.

Examination is usually made with an immersion objective $\times 90$ and ocular $\times 15$ using a micrometer disc in one of the oculars ruled with 25 sections in an area of 25–35 mm². It is normally sufficient to count only the nine diagonally placed squares of the total 25 on each of 20 counting grids. If there are less than five bacteria per cell of the grid it is necessary to count more fields for higher accuracy.

The number of bacteria (N) in the initial sample can be calculated using the formula,

$$N = \frac{S \cdot n \cdot 10^6}{s \cdot V} \text{ cells/ml},$$

where S is equal to the area of the 'working' surface of the filter (mm²), s is the area of one cell of the micrometer disc (measured in μ^2 with a stage micrometer at the same magnification), n is the average number of bacteria per cell of the grid, and V is the volume (ml) of water which was filtered.

4.32   Direct microscopic count of bacteria in sediments

The most usual method of counting bacteria in sediments is by microscopic examination of preparations of sediment suspensions dried on slides and stained. This method was proposed by Winogradsky and has subsequently been borrowed from soil microbiology. The preparations are made in the following way. The sample of sediment (0·5 ml) is taken with marked glass tubes and transferred to a flask with 50–100 ml of 0·0005 N KOH. The flask is stoppered and shaken strongly for several minutes to separate the bacteria from detritus particles. The suspension is left for half a minute in order to allow large particles to sediment. A portion of the suspension (0·1–0·2 ml) is placed on the surface of a microscope slide which has been cleaned with alcohol and ether. To a drop of the suspension is added one drop of 0·05% agar which has been previously filtered through a membrane filter. The mixture is carefully and equally spread over the surface area of a slide (6 cm²). The preparation is dried, fixed by flaming or by absolute alcohol and stained with erythrosin and dissolved fuchsin ($^1/_{300}$). Erythrosin is poured on the surface of the preparation and the latter is heated up until the erythrosin begins to vaporize. The dye is then washed off, and dissolved fuchsin is poured on the preparation. After the same washing procedure the preparation is dried, a drop of immersion oil is placed on its surface, and the slide is ready for microscopic examination under the immersion objective × 90. The bacterial count is made with a micrometer disc as described above.

The number of bacteria in the sediment suspension can also be counted on a membrane filter. The suspension is left standing for 3—4 minutes, for optimum sedimentation of large particles. 0·1–0·2 ml of the suspension are then transferred into the filtration funnel filled with water from which the bacteria have been removed by previous filtration. The subsequent analysis is carried out as described above.

4.33   Calculation of the bacterial biomass

The biomass of bacteria in a given water sample is determined similarly to that of phytoplankton (cf. 2.13). For this, the average cell volume and the total number of cells present must be known. In contrast to phytoplankton biomass determinations where every species is evaluated separately, the biomass of bacteria is obtained considering the principal morphological groups only, i.e. long rods, short rods, coccoid forms, and yeast-like forms. Discrimination in these various forms is made while doing the direct counts of the total number of bacteria.

The average volume of the various groups is obtained from special wet preparations; due to shrinking, the volume of dried bacteria is considerably smaller than that of living ones.

In order to make suitable preparations the bacteria must be concentrated in a small volume of water. For this, as much of the sample as possible is filtered through a membrane filter. Filtration is interrupted at the moment when 0·5—1·0 ml of water remain in the funnel. Then the vacuum in the filter device is offset, and the liquid left in the funnel is mixed with the sediment on the filter surface by stirring with the aid of a microbiological loop. This suspension may be fixed with filtered formaldehyde for the following studies.

The bacterial cells are stained by adding several drops of a standard microbiological dye carbol fuchsin solution (1/100) to 0·5–1 ml of the suspension. Then a drop of the suspension is placed on a microscope preparation slide, to which several drops of a warm concentrated solution of agar or gelatine (previously cleaned by filtration through a membrane filter) are added. After careful mixing the liquid is covered with a cover slide. Examination is preferably made under a phase contrast microscope and the bacteria are measured with the aid of a calibrated screw ocular micrometer.

Dry preparations may be used occasionally but a somewhat uncertain factor of 2·5 must be applied to convert dry volume to wet volume to account for shrinkage.

Another method to get the necessary data for size determination is to take photomicrographs of the bacteria and obtain their size from greatly enlarged prints.

The average cell volume of each morphological group is calculated using the formulae for cylinders, spheres, and ellipsoids. For this the linear parameters needed are averaged from a sufficient number of individual measurements; the mean values may be arithmetic, or better geometric. The biomass B can be obtained by multiplying the total number N of bacteria of each group by the average volume V of their cells ($B = N.V$), and summing over the various B's. The dimension of B is mg/l if N is taken per ml, measured V in μ^3, and the whole divided by 10^6.

4.4 RATE OF REPRODUCTION AND PRODUCTION OF BACTERIAL BIOMASS

The multiplication rate of bacteria can be measured by the average generation time, i.e. the time needed for the total number of bacteria to double. Razumov (1947), Ivanov (1954, 1955), *a.o.* suggested a bottle method for measuring the generation time of natural planktonic bacteria.

The experiments are carried out in the following manner. A sample, collected as outlined above, is poured into two 250 ml bottles or balloons. One of the bottles is filled through a funnel in which a large pore size membrane filter or a fine plankton netting is inserted to remove phyto- and zooplankton. The funnel (see Fig. 4.5a) can be directly attached to a sampler. Another possibility is to use a glass tube with 2–3 layers of plankton netting closing one of its ends (Fig. 4.5b).

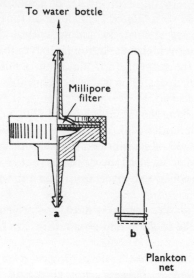

Figure 4.5. Microbiological filtration funnel, see text.

The second bottle is filled with unfiltered water. The bottles are exposed *in situ* or in similar conditions in an incubator. The optimum exposure time is 12–30 hours in the warm season, and 1–7 days in the cold season. At the beginning and at the end of the experiment the total number of bacteria in both bottles is determined by direct counting (see 4.3).

The generation time g can be calculated from the formula,

$$N_t = N_0 \cdot 2^{t/g},$$

i.e. $\quad g = \dfrac{t \cdot \log 2}{\log N - \log N_0}.$

N_0 is the initial number, N the final number of bacteria/ml, and t the exposure time in hours.

The daily production of bacterial biomass in the filtered sample, where no grazing of bacteria by zooplankton does take place, may be calculated as

$$P = 24/g \cdot N_0 \text{ cells/ml} \cdot \text{day*}$$

Production in the non-filtered sample in presence of zooplankton can be calculated by the formula (Ivanov 1955),

$$P' = 24 \, (N_0/g + (N_0 - N)/t) \text{ cells/ml} \cdot \text{day}\dagger$$

In units of biomass, $PB = P \cdot V \cdot 10^{-6}$ mg/l . day, if V, the average cell volume, is measured in μ^3, and P in cells/ml . day.

.The other methods of calculating bacterial biomass production are indirect, and are based on analyses of the rate of *in situ* $^{14}CO_2$ uptake by the natural microflora (cf. 4.7, 4.8).

4.5 RATE OF IN SITU DESTRUCTION OF ORGANIC MATTER

The *in situ* destruction of organic matter usually does not markedly vary within a water column. Experience shows that in shallow waters two samples, one from the surface and the other from the near-bottom layer, are sufficient for these measurements. In basins deeper than 20 m *in situ* destruction should be measured at three or more depths, and particularly include measurements in the layers where organic matter is concentrated by gradients of temperature, water density, and redox potential.

---

* Note by the editor: The formula proposed by Sorokin is valid only for measurements in a turbidistatic continuous culture. In a closed culture the correct treatment, of course, is given by

$$P = N - N_o = N_o \, (2^{t/g} - 1).$$

Accordingly, all deductions further made are of limited value. For general treatment of growth problems, see e.g. Volterra (in: d'Ancona 1939), Riley, Stommel & Bumpus 1949, *a.o.*

† This formula is a very arbitrary treatment of the problem (editor).

Experiments on the rate of bacterial destruction *in situ* are done in the following manner. The water sampled is poured into four bottles of 150–200 ml volume through a funnel with a large pore size filter, or through a glass tube, the end of which is covered with plankton netting (Fig. 4.5). In two of the bottles the oxygen content is measured immediately after filling; the two other bottles are darkened and exposed for one or two days *in situ* or in an incubator at *in situ* temperature.

At the end of exposure dissolved oxygen is measured, and the average decrease of oxygen per day is calculated. This rate is considered as due to bacterial decomposition of organic matter. However, it must be emphasized that the method gives reliable values (i.e. confrontable values comparable with the natural destruction) only in relatively productive waters (cf. Vollenweider 1959).

Other methods are respirometric; they have been recently reviewed by Montgomery (1967).

Destruction of organic matter also occurs, of course, in bottom sediments. The techniques for assessing this destruction were described by Hayes & Macaulay (1959), Gambaryan (1962), and further refinements were discussed by Edwards & Rolley (1965). Oxygen consumption in sediments is measured in plastic or glass tubes attached to a corer. Samples are taken directly in the tubes or from the sediments collected by a dredge or grab. The water is poured out from the tube, and replaced with previously aerated natural water, the oxygen content of which is known. The tubes are stoppered, care being taken to exclude air bubbles, and are exposed for 10–20 hours. In the control tube the same water without sediment is exposed. In order to provide a turnover of water inside the tube, one side of it is attached to a wire slightly heated by an electric current. At the end of exposure several portions of water are siphoned out of the tube into small bottles to measure the final concentration of oxygen. The rest of the water is then poured off and the experiment can be repeated with a new portion of water*.

The comparison of the value of daily destruction (D) and the production of biomass shows that the ratio of destruction (Δ mg O_2/l) to production of raw biomass (mg/l) under the natural conditions of a lake usually varies between 0·5 and 1; the value of this relation (K) is mainly influenced by the type of disintegrated organic matter. It must be stated for each type of biotope of the water basin and for different periods of the year. To obtain

* This method may underestimate the bacterial metabolism in the deposits of polluted waters (Bayley, personal communication to D.F.Westlake).

approximate values for the production of bacteria from destruction data, the K-value may be accepted as roughly 0·8. The production of bacterial biomass must then be equal to,

$$P \approx 0.8 \times D \quad \text{mg (raw biomass)/l . day,}$$

or, expressed as carbon,

$$P \approx 0.06\text{--}0.08 \times D \quad \text{mg } C_{org}/\text{l . day.}$$

4.6 DARK ASSIMILATION OF CO_2, HETEROTROPHIC ASSIMILATION OF CO_2, CHEMOSYNTHESIS AND BACTERIAL PHOTOSYNTHESIS

The biomass production of bacteria of all metabolic types is connected, in various degrees, with the utilization of external CO_2 for biosynthesis. At present, these processes can be detected with the very sensitive radiocarbon method, although there are still problems with regard to the correct interpretation of the results of this method. Different groups of bacteria need quite different amounts of external CO_2 for biosynthesis (Sorokin 1961). Heterotrophs generally assimilate 3–5% of their total carbon metabolism from the external CO_2. This group causes the bulk of the 'dark assimilation' of CO_2 in the surface layers of eutrophic and mesotrophic lakes, and in the whole water mass of oligotrophic lakes. Bacteria belonging to an intermediate metabolic type between true heterotrophy and true chemoautotrophy, and which oxidize low molecular weight products resulting from the anaerobic decay of organic matter (methane, methanol, formic acid, etc.) may require as much as 30–90% from the external CO_2 for biosynthesis.

The third group which is the most active in the broad layer between the aerobic and the anaerobic zones of a water, and/or at the surface of bottom sediments, consists of chemoautotrophs utilizing the oxidation energy of reduced inorganic end products of the anaerobic decay, i.e. H_2, H_2S, $NH_4^{\cdot}$, $Fe^{\cdot\cdot}$.

Considering what has been said above it is possible to estimate approximately that fraction from the total dark assimilation of CO_2 which is due to heterotrophic bacteria. If PB is the heterotrophic biomass produced (expressed in mg C/l . day), and H denotes the CO_2 carbon incorporated, then $H = F . PB$ mg C/l . day. The F value can be determined by comparing the microscopically measured bacterial biomass production and the total CO_2 assimilation measured by the ^{14}C method. As already stated above

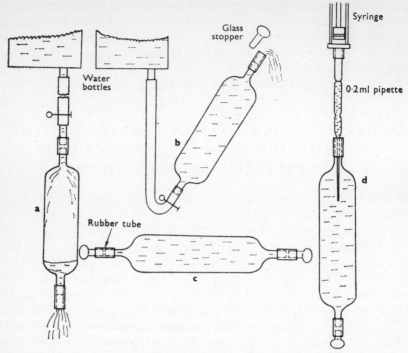

Figure 4.6. Experimental flasks for microbial techniques, see text.

Sorokin (1961) found values from 3–5% (F = 0·03–0·05; average = 0·04); Romanenko (1964) assumes a somewhat higher value of 0·06.

Vice versa, if the measurement of total CO_2 uptake in the dark is made in waters where chemoautotrophic CO_2 assimilation is practically absent, it is also possible to estimate approximately the biomass production of hetero-trophs, PB = H/F mg $C_{biomass}$/l . day, or, expressed as mg/l . day of raw biomass, PB = 14H/F*. This procedure has been used by Romanenko (1965) and Kusnezov & Romanenko (1967).

The total dark assimilation of CO_2, using the ^{14}C technique, is performed according to the procedures described in chapter 3. A suitable kind of experimental vessel, and its filling, is shown in Fig. 4.6. The experimental water has

* Note by the editor: Romanenko assumes a dry weight/raw biomass ratio of 0·15, and a carbon/dry weight ratio of 0·5; accordingly, the conversion factor from carbon to raw biomass results as 1/0·15×0·5 = approx. 13–14.

to be cleaned from zoo- and phyto-plankton by pouring it through a funnel with a large pore size (3–6 μ) membrane filter directly attached to the sampler. It is important to ensure a complete absence of air bubbles inside the funnel in order to keep the CO_2 of the water unaltered.

The ^{14}C 'working' solution (0·2 ml giving $2–5 \times 10^6$ counts per minute) is inserted into the flask using a small pipette of the Mohr type. The flask is stoppered and darkened, and then kept in a water bath at *in situ* temperature for 1 (or rarely 2) day(s).

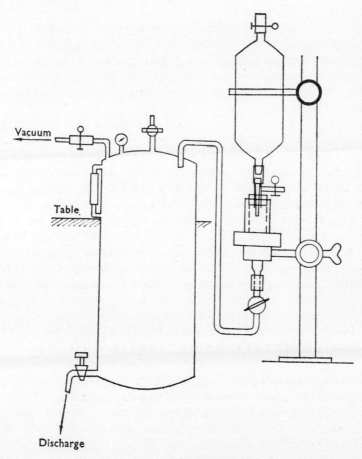

Figure 4.7. Filtration device for bacteria, see text.

After exposure 20–40 ml are filtered through membrane filters with a pore size of 0·3–0·5 μ. A convenient filter device is shown in Fig. 4.7. The filters are washed just after filtration with 1 ml of 0·05 N HCl placed directly in the funnel; then they are dried, and their radioactivity is measured, and calculations are made according to the formulae of chapter 3. It is to be remembered here that the total CO_2 content of the water examined is usually determined by titration; however, in anaerobic zones, where the presence of H_2S is possible, a distillation procedure is preferable([ef. 3, 12]).

Bacterial photosynthesis
Bacterial photosynthesis is measured by a ^{14}C technique analogous to the one described in chapter 3. The difference lies only in the omission of the preliminary filtration of the samples. It may be remembered here that bacterial photosynthesis proceeds only under strongly anaerobic conditions; accordingly, the water must not be allowed to come in contact with air during the sampling and filling operation.

Bacterial photosynthesis becomes a real possibility if anaerobic conditions exist in the deeper layers of the euphotic zone. As this latter normally extends down to a depth which corresponds very roughly to three times that of the actual Secchi disc reading, samples for *in situ* measurements should be collected down to this depth, at intervals of 0·2–0·5 m, starting from the depth of beginning anaerobiosis. 'Light bottles' to which suitable amounts of [14]C 'working solution' have been added are exposed *in situ* at the sampling depth simultaneously with darkened control bottles to measure CO_2 dark uptake. After exposition the photosynthetic production by bacteria is then determined, calculated from filtered subsamples of corresponding 'light' and 'dark bottles' according to standard procedures of radiocarbon estimates.

4.7 MEASUREMENT OF THE METABOLIC ACTIVITY OF SPECIALIZED BACTERIAL GROUPS

The method for evaluating the potential activity of specific metabolic groups of the natural microflora is based on a bioassay technique, in which the increase of the metabolic activity after the addition of selected specific substrates to samples of natural waters is measured. As criteria for the biochemical activity of the microflora can be used: the biological oxygen demand (BOD), the rate of [14]CO_2 assimilation, or the rate of assimilation of low molecular weight organic substances, such as glucose or acetate labelled with ^{14}C (Parsons & Strickland 1962; Sorokin 1964; Romanenko 1965; Wright & Hobbie 1965, *a.o.*). Experience in aquatic microbiology shows that attempts to localize, within a water basin, the specific metabolic groups by measuring their potential biochemical activity *in loco*, are often preferable to the usual methods of counting these bacteria in nutrient media. Normally, the number of bacteria in the natural environment is maximal when the specific substrates are already completely oxidized. However, bacteria in the inactive latent stage can easily be transported by water movements from the places of their normal activity (in the water column, or near or in the sediments) to other places where they hardly can exist because of inadequate environmental conditions. Therefore, using artificial media as a counting technique, a misleading picture concerning their spatial distribution may be obtained. The potential biochemical activity, on the other hand, can be maximal only in the sites of their natural habitats.

The potential activity of methane- and hydrogen-oxidizing bacteria can be measured, using BOD as parameter, in the following manner. Four bottles or balloons are filled with water samples previously aerated in a flask. In one of these bottles the initial oxygen content is measured, and into the second and third 1–2 cm^3 of hydrogen and methane gas are inserted with a syringe; the fourth bottle serves as a control. The bottles are then exposed in a water bath for one to three days, at the end of which their oxygen content is analysed. The criterion for the activity of the microflora in question is the difference of BOD between the bottles with H_2 and CH_4, and the control (Kuznezov 1959).

The potential activity of thiobacilli is determined by measuring the oxidation rate of thiosulphate added to a water sample (the additions in amounts of 10 mg per 100 ml of the water examined); the same water, sterilized by boiling, serves as a control. At the end of a suitably selected exposure time the remaining thiosulphate in both the experimental and the control flask is measured by iodometry. The potential activity of thiobacilli is then proportional to the rate of biological oxidation of thiosulphate calculated by difference.

The potential activity of the autotrophic microflora can be measured by estimating $^{14}CO_2$ uptake in the water or sediment samples examined, in the presence or absence of a specific substrate. For this a sufficient number of bottles or balloons are filled with the experimental water from which the phytoplankton has been removed. A suitable amount of ^{14}C 'working solution' ($0.5-1 \cdot 10^6$ counts per minute of actual activity) is added to all bottles, and suitable amounts of the specific substrate (H_2, CH_4, S_2O_3'', H_2S, $NH_4^{\cdot}$) to all except controls. After exposure of the darkened samples in a water bath for 1–2 days subsamples are filtered through membrane filters, and the radio-activity of the latter is determined according to standard procedures. The potential activity of the autotrophic microflora, accordingly, is proportional to the difference of bacterial radioactivity between the substrate-containing sample and the control.

The potential activity of heterotrophs can be determined in a corresponding manner. Further to this, Parsons & Strickland (1962) have suggested the use of trace amounts of labelled low molecular weight organic substances, such as glucose or acetate. The rate of incorporation of the ^{14}C of these labelled substances into the cells is used as an index of their biochemical activity. The same technique was also used to estimate organic substrates dissolved in the water. Particulars of this method are outlined in Part II of this chapter.

PART II. A METHOD FOR STUDYING HETEROTROPHIC BACTERIA

J E HOBBIE

The heterotrophic bacteria in natural waters are extremely difficult to study. While an estimation of their type and number is possible, their rate of produc-tion of cellular material under natural conditions is almost impossible to measure. In contrast to the photosynthetic algae, which use only carbon dioxide or bicarbonate, the heterotrophic bacteria may use tens or hundreds of different substrates. A study of the uptake of a single substrate, therefore, does not give the productivity. This type of study, however, does give valuable information about the substrates that are being used, the rates of turnover of the substrate, and the activity and probable number of the bacteria. This section describes a method for measuring the uptake of organic compounds by heterotrophic bacteria and discusses the interpretation of the results.

Essentially, the technique resembles the ^{14}C measurement of primary production with an organic substrate substituted for the $^{14}CO_2$. When primary production is measured, it is assumed that the amount of CO_2 added in the experiment is an insignificant part of the total CO_2 and the uptake velocity found is equal to the natural uptake rate. These assumptions are not valid for a measure of heterotrophic uptake, however, as the substrate added experimentally is often many times larger than the amount initially present. For example, 4 μC of glucose-^{14}C added to a 50 ml water sample gives 0·122 mg glucose/litre (at the specific activity of glucose-^{14}C supplied by the Radiochemical Centre, England). In nature, glucose has been found in lakes at a concentration of less than 0·010 mg/l (Vallentyne & Whittaker 1956; Hobbie & Wright 1965). In order to find the velocity of uptake at the low substrate concentration found in nature, a back extrapolation must be made. Because the curve relating uptake velocity to substrate concentration might take several different forms, the uptake must be measured at a number of substrate concentrations in order to determine the shape of the curve.

An added complication is that the actual substrate concentration in nature is difficult to determine. The real velocity of uptake of the substrate, therefore, is not feasible to measure. Instead, a number of other kinetic parameters may be found because the velocity of uptake follows an adsorption isotherm or Michaelis-Menten kinetics (Parsons & Strickland 1962).

METHODS

The technique presented here is illustrated with glucose-^{14}C, but other compounds may be used. The method is flexible and should be changed to fit various situations.

As soon as the water sample is enclosed in a bottle, the bacterial activity begins to fall. At 20°C, the activity of one sample decreased by 40% within 4 hours. However, at 3°C little decrease was found after 4 hours. It is important, therefore, to begin the experiment as soon as possible after sampling and to keep the experimental time short. The activity is sensitive to temperature change and experiments should be run at the environmental temperature. It is easiest to use a constant temperature room for the incubation, but the samples can be incubated *in situ* in darkened bottles.

Fifty ml aliquots of a water sample are poured into 5 bottles (125 ml reagent bottles are convenient). Next, various amounts of a 1 μc/ml solution of glucose-^{14}C in distilled water are added to each bottle with a micropipette. With high specific activity glucose, additions of 50, 100, 200, 400, and 200 μl give 0·0015, 0·0031, 0·0061, 0·0122, and 0·0061 mg glucose/l. The last sample is immediately killed with 4 drops of Lugol's acetic acid solution and used as a blank after incubation alongside the others. The incubation time will vary from 1/2 to 6 hours, depending upon the bacterial activity and the temperature. Generally, the time needed for the organisms to accumulate several thousand counts/min is sufficient. At 20°C this may be only 1/2 hours in a rich pond, and at 2°C it may be 6 hours. Shaking during incubation seems to have little effect on the uptake.

The exact times of inoculation and filtration should be noted, and the bottles should not be allowed to warm up or cool down before the filtration. It is often convenient to kill the samples before filtration, but there is a possibility that labelled material may leak from the killed cells. After incubation, the samples and the blank are filtered onto membrane filters (less than 0·5 μ pore size), the bottles and filters rinsed with filtered lake water, and the activity measured.

CALCULATIONS

If the natural substrate concentration (S) is known, then the velocity of uptake by the bacteria (*v*) may be experimentally measured

$$v = \frac{f}{t} (S + A) \tag{1}$$

Here, f is the fraction of the available isotope that is taken up, t is the incubation time (hr), and A is the amount of substrate added in the experiment (mg/l).

When the *v* is measured over a series of substrate concentrations (Fig. 4.8), the uptake velocity soon reaches a maximum velocity (V) and then is unaffected by a further increase in the amount of substrate. This type of uptake follows the Michaelis-Menten equation

$$V = v \frac{(K + S + A)}{(S + A)} \tag{2}$$

The constant, K, resembles the Michaelis constant and is the substrate concentration when *v* is V/2.

As has been mentioned, S is very difficult to determine in nature. Even if the S is unknown, the V may still be measured using the Lineweaver-Burk form of equation (2).

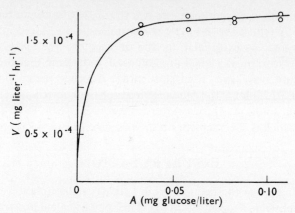

Figure 4.8. The velocity of uptake of glucose–^{14}C by bacteria; see text.

$$\frac{S + A}{v} = \frac{A}{V} + \frac{K + S}{V} \tag{3}$$

Combining equations (1) and (3)

$$\frac{t}{f} = \frac{A}{V} + \frac{K + S}{V} \tag{4}$$

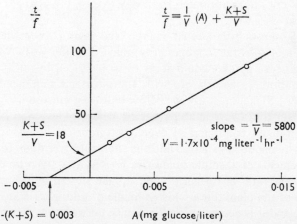

Figure 4.9. Uptake of glucose by bacteria at 19 m, Lake Erken. Data from Table 4.

Data from a typical experiment are given in Table 4 and plotted in Fig. 4.9 as t/f versus A (equation (4)). The maximum velocity is the inverse of the slope of this line. By extrapolation, the intercept on the abscissa (K+S) is found. In this case, it was 0·003 mg glucose/l, indicating that the concentration of glucose was lower than this value. Another piece of information obtained from this plot is the time required for the bacteria to remove all the substrate from solution. This turnover time equals S/v or, from equation (2), $(K + S)/V$, which is the intercept on the ordinate in Fig. 4.9 (here, 18 hours).

INTERPRETATION

The best indicator of the heterotrophic activity is the uptake velocity (v) at the natural substrate concentration (S). This may be calculated from equation (2) but only when S is known. When S is unknown, then the maximum velocity (V) may be used as an indicator of heterotrophic activity. In the laboratory, V is proportional to biomass. At 3°C, a population of 10^7 bacteria/l had a V of 5×10^{-5} mg/l.hr. The kinetics of different cultures vary, however, so at the present time it is not possible to find bacterial numbers in nature by this method. In Lake Erken, Sweden, there was an annual range for V of from 7 to 500×10^{-6} mg glucose/l.hr, and the total range in all the lakes studied was from 1 to 10,000 $\times 10^{-6}$ mg/l.hr. Most of the measurements above 10^{-3} were in polluted lakes, and V is an extremely sensitive indicator of relative amounts of pollution. In contrast to primary productivity determinations, V does not vary much from day to day, but changes slowly from week to week.

The (K+S) shows little annual change, and there is no evidence that the concentration of substrate changes very much over the year. Any change in the rate of glucose uptake would seem to be balanced by an increase in the rate of formation. In accordance with the direct measurements previously noted, the (K+S) is almost always below 0·010 mg glucose/l.

The turnover times vary as the V varies. Values of less than 1/2 hour were found in a polluted pond, and of over 5,000 hours in oligotrophic lakes in winter. This tremendous variation and the short turnover times found indicate that measurements of absolute quantities present at a given time are of little use. Rather, the rates of formation and uptake should be determined.

The algae of the plankton are also capable of taking up dissolved organic compounds, and it is necessary to distinguish between the uptake of bacteria and algae if the bacteria alone are to be studied (Wright & Hobbie 1965a).

This is easily done (Wright & Hobbie 1965b), because the mechanisms of uptake of the algae and of the bacteria are very different, and may be separated by kinetic analysis. As shown in Fig. 4.8, the uptake mechanism of the bacteria (called a permease system by Cohen & Monod 1957) is effective at very low substrate concentrations. That of the algae, on the other hand, is only effective at higher substrate concentrations, as the velocity of uptake is directly proportional to the substrate concentration. At the very low substrate concentrations used in this method, the uptake of the algae is very low and can be ignored even though the algal biomass is greater than the bacterial. For this reason, it is important to use low quantities of added substrate in these experiments.

A number of conditions must be fulfilled in order for the equations and interpretations to apply. First of all, the uptake must be constant over time (see Wright & Hobbie 1965a, Fig. 3) and not all occur in the early minutes of the incubation. Secondly, the substrate concentration must not vary appreciably during the experiment. As indicated in Table 4, the greatest amount taken up should be less than 10% of the total available isotope. Finally, the respiration should be low enough so little labelled material is lost from the cells as CO_2. Short incubation times are important for this reason, but further studies are needed to determine the amount of error introduced in this way.

The method described here is of great potential importance because it is a way to study the dynamic aspects of aquatic bacteriology. With this method, the rates of uptake and formation of individual substrates can be measured. In addition, the maximum velocity of uptake is a useful indicator of the heterotrophic activity and a relative measure of the bacterial population. So far, only glucose and acetate have been studied, but the method should work with sugars, fatty acids, and amino acids. In order to evaluate the method, measurements in a number of different lakes must be made, and, most important, comparisons made with other methods of aquatic bacteriology.

TABLE 4 Data for glucose uptake at 19 m, Lake Erken, 14 October 1964.
1 μc = 8.77×10^5 CPM in the counter used, time (t) = 2.0 hours, sample size = 50 ml.

μl added	CPM added		CPM taken up by plankton	$\dfrac{t}{f}$	A (mg/l)
0·05	4·38	10⁴	3108	28·2	0·00153
0·10	8·77	,,	4933	35·6	0·00306
0·20	17·54	,,	6360	55·2	0·00612
0·40	35·08	,,	7929	88·5	0·0122

5

Environmental Factors linked with Primary Production

R A VOLLENWEIDER

General

In order to achieve a more profound understanding of the scientific basis of primary production, it is highly desirable to design pertinent research programmes as large as possible, and to combine production analyses with appropriate analyses of the physical, chemical, and biological properties of the environment(s) in question. The number of possible features for selection is, of course, almost unlimited, but it is a matter of common sense to focus efforts on those from which we reasonably can expect to improve our knowledge. Nevertheless, establishing a generally applicable list of priorities remains difficult.

In the following, some suggestions are given, primarily for the use of beginners in the field. Little attempt is made to discuss theory or motivation, as this belongs to pertinent text books or to the senior researcher of a research team.

In addition to these suggestions (which do not include methodological recommendations), the methodology of light measurements is treated in the last subchapter (cf. 5.4), because light measurements may be needed to calculate integral production per surface area from indirect or incomplete estimates of photosynthesis (*in situ*, or laboratory measurements; cf. 3.6, 3.7).

For the preparation of published papers, it is positively recommended to include always a certain number of general records apart from geographical information. Many of these items—needed for identification, general description, and comparison—can be summed up from available data, or the literature. They may be presented in tabular or graphical form, whereby discussion largely can be restricted to those features which do not clearly appear for themselves, and/or which have a particular bearing on the central subject. According to the writer's experience, it is tedious to search through the literature for such elementary information as surface extension, mean depth, volume, catchment area, discharge rates, etc., but which are often indispensable for a full appreciation of the paper, or for the purpose of comparison. Therefore, it is also recommended to indicate clearly if some important information is still unknown.

5.1   DESIRABLE GENERAL RECORDS

As desirable records are considered:

(a) All data and elements needed to identify and to describe the basic properties of the water in question: geographical position, altitude, morphometry (surface extension, volume, mean depth and maximal depth or depths, formation and division in sub-basins, shore line and horizon development, etc.). In addition to surface and depth charts, hypsographic curves (which show the depth-distribution of lake volume) may often be instructive. If running waters are in question, the reach and the particular transects have to be adequately described.

(b) Data describing the basic hydrographical conditions of the water body, such as replenishment time (theoretical replenishment time = lake volume/ average yearly water discharge, or preferably more elaborated estimates; cf. Piontelli & Tonolli 1964), water budget (if available), currents, or stream velocities.

More specific questions, such as the hydrological cycle, are preferably considered in connection with the climatic and meteorological conditions.

(c) Data and information regarding the drainage area. It is obvious—considering the many individual situations existing in nature—that no generally valid list of items can be proposed. Such a list, however, may include: extension of the catchment area, mean altitude, geology, climatology and meteorology, total rainfall and water discharge rates, glaciation, etc. Further to this, useful information may be: land utilization (agriculture, forests, natural rocks, etc.), urbanization, population density, industrialization, state of river pollution, etc.

(d) Any further information which may appear relevant to the understanding of lake and river productivity, e.g. sewage discharge from human settlements and industries, existence of engineering works, particularly with regard to level control, importance of navigation and tourism, fishing, water birds, etc.

For marine environments, of course, the above list does not apply.

5.2 DESIRABLE PARTICULAR RECORDS

Factors which are not of general nature but variable from season to season, or from year to year, such as meterological conditions, irradiation, water temperature, stratification and mixing cycles, light extinction, etc., should be individually recorded and elaborated for the particular research period, and be possibly discussed in relation to standard conditions (averages from long term records, if available).

Particular attention should be paid to chemical factors, especially nutrients. Some research suggestions are outlined below.

A detailed discussion of the relevant methodology pertinent to this section is beyond the direct scope of the manual; readers who are not sufficiently acquainted with standard limnological and oceanographical methods are invited to consult handbooks on these subjects, e.g.,

—Welch, P.S., Limnological Methods. The Blakiston Company, Philadelphia 1948.
—Schwoerbel, J., Methoden der Hydrobiologie. Franck'sche Verlagsbuchhandlung, Stuttgart 1966. (also English Translation, Pergamon, 1969)

5.3 CHEMICAL FACTORS

It is not intended to discuss, or to recommend here, any particular method; once more, readers are invited to consult for this either the IBP Manual on Chemical Methods (edit. Golterman & Clymo 1968), or any handbook pertinent to the subject (e.g. the American 'Standard Methods', Haase 1954; 'Deutsche Einheitsverfahren', etc.).

The main purpose of this section is to draw attention to some of those factors from which—at the present stage of knowledge—we may expect to obtain significant results, for comparison and correlation analyses. The selected list of components does by no means pretend to be complete, and further, it is up to the individual research teams to decide whether or not efforts should be put into this or that direction, and how much effort should be devoted to the single items, particularly if time and logistic resources are restricted. Some examples may help for finding criteria from the basis of which such decisions can be made: if, e.g., primary production of an oligotrophic water (where dissolved oxygen changes but little during an annual cycle) is in question, then probably more meaningful data will result from tracer analyses—although tedious and time consuming—than from oxygen determinations. In eutrophic waters, on the contrary, the oxygen metabolism may give additional information about community respiration, net and gross production, etc., and pertinent analyses will be indispensable to discuss chemical equilibria, etc. In certain environments, mineral turbidity needs to be considered because of its bearing on nutrient adsorption phenomena, and on light attenuation. In all dystrophic waters, but also in less coloured ones, 'coloured substances' (humic acids, fulvic acids, *a.o.*) play a role as chelators, or may be involved in a concurrent metabolism (cf. e.g. Ryhanen 1967), and, in any case, are an important parameter of the optical properties of the water (cf. e.g. Åberg & Rodhe 1942; Schmolinsky 1954; Vollenweider 1961; *a.o.*), etc.

From the biological point of view, the chemical factors may be allocated to three main groups, although such a sharp distinction is of but limited significance: (i) inorganic components characterizing the ionic environment; according to relative composition and concentration, fresh, brackish and marine waters are distinguished; (ii) nutritional factors *sensu stricto*, including also microelements and organic stimulators; (iii) toxic factors (inorganic and organic ones).

The spatial and temporal sampling programme has to be designed according to the general conditions of the water(s) in question. Large lakes, especially shallow ones, lagoons, etc., are likely to show strong horizontal differentiation. In running waters, but also in lakes, occasional day-night samplings are recommended.

(a) Scheme for a basic programme
(i) *Ionic composition (major constituents)*
Fresh waters are adequately defined in most instances by the following components (listed according to relative importance, and separately for cations and anions; cf. e.g. Rodhe 1949): $Ca^{..}$, $Mg^{..}$, $Na^{.}$, $K^{.}$; $CO_3^{''} + HCO_3^{'}$, $SO_4^{''}$, $Cl^{'}$. In some cases also $NH_4^{.}$, $Sr^{..}$, $NO_3^{'}$ and $F^{'}$ have to be considered. Waters showing a different scheme of the relative composition are not infrequent, and are of particular interest.

Further to this, the following hints for practical performance may be useful: the sum of $Ca^{..} + Mg^{..}$ is known as 'total hardness', and the sum of $CO_3^{''} + HCO_3^{'}$ ($+ OH^{'}$) as carbonate alkalinity; both can be determined directly. It is not recommended to use the term 'temporary hardness' any longer. If 'hardness' terms are used at all (which is not particularly recommended), then it should clearly be stated to which hardness scale figures are referred to.

Electrical conductivity is a most useful measure in any kind of water, and it is recommended to accompany all ionic analyses with electrical conductivity records for construction of correlation diagrams, from which useful additional information can be retrieved (cf. Rodhe 1949, Vollenweider 1963, 1965b). If no specific analyses can be performed at all, then dry weight (total salt content measured on filtered samples evaporated on a water bath, and dried at 180°C) may serve as preliminary measure.

Efforts on the above components can be restricted to some occasional analyses, unless there are reasons to suppose that strong temporal variations do occur. Such variations are often due to dilution, or biogenic decalcification, and then can easily be recorded by frequent conductivity and alkalinity measurements.

In mono- and dimictic lakes the most favourable period to perform a full analysis is the time of spring overturn, i.e. after complete mixing; this gives also the possibility to judge if a water is holo- or meromictic (cf. e.g. Findenegg 1933; Vollenweider 1964). For polymictic waters, of course, no particular period can be indicated generally.

pH should be recorded frequently in all kinds of waters.

The same kind of analyses may also be performed on *brackish waters*, but particular attention should be paid to local and seasonal variations of Cl′, and eventually of SO_4''. Sodium carbonate waters are defined by frequent alkalinity analyses.

The relative ionic composition of *marine waters*, in general, remains almost constant, and salinity (referred to chlorinity records) is a sufficient measure for their concentrations.

(ii) *Nutritional factors*

Routine analyses will be similar in all kinds of waters (fresh, brackish, marine), and should preferably include:

Total phosphorus from unfiltered samples, and phosphate phosphorus from filtered samples; if practicable, also total phosphorus from filtered samples is recommended (cf. Ohle 1938).

Total nitrogen (Kjeldahl) from unfiltered, and from filtered samples, inorganic nitrogen (nitrate, nitrite and ammonia determined separately) from filtered samples.

Total silica from unfiltered and filtered samples, molybdate-reactive silica from filtered samples.

As far as possible, these analyses should be performed at regular intervals of time on samples collected according to an appropriate spatial sampling programme. If this is impracticable, then at least one such complete analysis may be located during spring overturn, and a second one possibly at the end of the summer stratification.

(iii) *Additional analyses of other factors*

Fe, Mn, and other microelements (esp. Co, Mo, Cu, etc.), organic compounds and toxic factors, of course, are desirable supplements but it may be difficult to include them in a routine programme. Further, it remains up to the decision of the individual research group, if they wish to extend their programme to the overall metabolism of the water body (bodies) in question, including factors such as oxygen, free CO_2, H_2S, CH_4, etc.

Running waters, in any case, require special programmes which give particular emphasis to day-night variations apart from spatial and seasonal overall variations.

(b) Enlarged programmes

The programme suggestions made under (a) are primarily intended for relatively small research teams having a limited working capacity, and/or limited logistic possibilities. From various points of view, these suggestions can be criticized as too 'classical' and restrictive. Nevertheless, studies along the given line are justified in any case where research starts *ex novo*, i.e. where no information about the chemical properties of a water is available at all.

At an advanced stage of research, this basic programme has to be supplemented, or replaced by a conceptually more elaborated one which gives more emphasis to the dynamic nature of production. Particular attention has to be paid to nutrient consumption and replenishment (re-cycling from extracellular products, death, secondary producers, etc., and from the sediments), and to nutrient supply from the drainage area.

To approach these questions properly, great research efforts and co-operation in specialized research teams are required. In many instances this may not be feasible yet, but already much could be learnt from tentative nutrient budgets of lakes and river transects, particularly if this can be done on a comparative basis, by considering, e.g., income, retention and loss of total and mineral nitrogen and phosphorus. Interesting studies in this direction were undertaken, e.g. by Thomas (1955, 1956, 1957), Ambühl (1960, 1966), Bachofen (1960), Edmondson (1961), Kliffmüller (1960), *a.o.*, but they now need to be supplemented by direct primary production measurements.

At this point it may be useful to remember that the IBP offers a unique possibility to tackle these problems—which can be considered as among the most urgent in limnology—at an extensive comparative level. Any progress towards a better insight into the qualitative and quantitative relationship between primary production and nutritional conditions of waters will improve our possibilities to effectively controlling and managing them with regard to the many and varied practical demands (fish production, eutrophication, pollution and water quality, etc.). The particular aspects concerned with eutrophication have been recently discussed by Vollenweider (1968).

5.4 THE METHODOLOGY OF LIGHT MEASUREMENTS

This section is a short introduction to the principles of light measurement techniques used in field studies for the purpose of supplementing studies on primary production. As further reading on the subject, the following papers are particularly recommended:

Strickland J.D.H., 1958. Solar radiation penetrating the ocean. A review of requirements, data, and methods of measurement, with particular reference to photosynthetic productivity. *J.Fish.Res.Board Can.*, 15.

Sauberer F., 1962. Empfehlungen für die Durchführung von Strahlungsmessungen an und in Gewässern. *Mitt. Int. Ver. Limnol.*, *Communications No.* 11.

Westlake D.F., 1965. Some problems in the measurement of radiation under water: a review. *Photochemistry and Photobiology* 4, Pergamon Press.

Generally speaking, the photic conditions of a natural water body are a function of the local radiation climate (which is defined by geographical parameters), and of the transmission properties of the water in question. Accordingly, the 'underwater light climate' can be defined either by considering the total radiant energy at various depths received during a certain time interval, or by considering the relative spectral extinction (attenuation*) of the light flux between two arbitrarily selected depth levels.

* The term 'attenuation' is used sometimes synonymously with the term 'extinction' as defined in the following (cf. e.g. Westlake 1965).

Both expressions are equally useful in studying the relationship between primary production and light conditions. Total production and production rates may be referred to total light energy and energy rates (intensities), whereas extinction refers to a general optical property used for calculating energy fluxes and photosynthesis integrals, but which must also be considered for the interpretation of various biological phenomena (photosynthetic efficiency in relation to spectral composition, adaptation phenomena with regard to species and pigment composition, etc.).

5.41 Definitions and units

(a) The total quantity of radiation energy, received on a unit area of (lake) surface over a particular period of time, is called **'total irradiance'**, and if referred to unit time, it is called **'intensity'**, or simply **'irradiance'**.

Solar radiant energy covers a spectral wavelength range from about 300 to 3,000 mμ, but most of the energy is between 400 and 1,000 mμ. **'Light'** is a physiological, not a physical expression, and refers to the sensitivity of the human eye (the sensitivity ranges between 380 and 760 mμ, with a maximum at about 580–590 mμ). The rate of incident light per unit area is called **'illuminance'**, or light intensity, and is normally measured in lux, or foot-candles.

The photosynthetically active part of the solar spectrum ranges from about 390 to 710 mμ; accordingly the usage of the term 'light' in primary production studies does not fully coincide with its general usage.

As light travels away from its source the intensity falling on a unit area diminishes with distance. For an artificial point source the main cause of the diminution is divergence of the light rays, which follows the inverse square law. For natural light fields under water there are two main causes; **'absorption'** of the radiant energy by the water itself and any solutes present (A), and **'scattering'** by particles suspended in the water (S, which involves deflection of the light rays from their original path as well as absorption by the particles themselves and absorption along increased path lengths). The sum of these processes is called **'extinction'** (E), and **'transmission'** (T) is the complementary term; accordingly:

$$E = A + S \; (\%)$$
$$T = 100 - E \; (\%)$$

Further to this, one has to distinguish between **'vertical'** and **'horizontal'** extinction (or transmission). The first term takes account of the fact that the 'natural light field' is not composed of parallel 'light beams' but of the integral over all possible light beams having any angular distribution between 0–180° relative to a horizontal plane. On theoretical grounds it is possible to calculate the 'mean path length' along the vertical axis (perpendicular to the water surface plane) which, according to Whitney (1938), is about 115–120 cm/1 m under average light conditions, but, depending on the sun elevation, varies between about 100 and 150 cm.

In practical measurements of the natural underwater light flux, therefore, expressions refer to 'vertical transmission' and 'vertical extinction' (Poole & Atkins 1926), whereas the corresponding terms for horizontal measurements (for which a parallel light beam is used) relate to 'turbidity' (*sensus latus*). In primary production studies, turbidity measurements may be useful to detect vertical stratifications of phytoplankton; a simple instrument for this purpose was described by Sauberer (1962).

(b) Energy quantities are expressed in various units, and selection is merely a matter of convenience. The most appropriate units for radiant energy are the (gram) calorie, the erg and the watt-sec. These three units are related by the following conversion factors:

$$1 \text{ (gram) calorie} = 4 \cdot 185 \times 10^7 \text{ ergs*} = 4 \cdot 185 \text{ watt-sec.}$$

Accordingly, the energy flux per a unit of surface and a unit of time (intensity!) can be expressed as:

$$X \text{ cal/cm}^2 . \text{sec} = 4 \cdot 185 \times 10^7 \text{ X ergs/cm}^2 . \text{sec} = 4 \cdot 185 \text{ X watts/cm}^2.$$

In meteorological practice, however, intensity measurements are preferably given in millical/cm^2 . min (note the difference of units!).

The gram cal/cm^2 (i.e. without the time dimension) was called a 'langley' (1 gram cal/cm^2 = 1 langley); accordingly, the total quantity of radiant energy received on a unit area during a day can be expressed, e.g., as

$$Y \text{ gram cal/cm}^2 . \text{day, or Y ly/day, etc.}$$

The photosynthetically available energy of the natural daylight radiation, considering the fraction between 400—700 mμ, varies, according to Talling (1957b) from 43·5% (cloudy day, no sun), to 53% (cloudless day, sun elevation 65°), with an average of 46—48%. Recently, a somewhat different range has been reported (38–51%, average 41%), and no, or almost no, influence of the sun height and the cloudiness was observed (Szeicz 1966); however, these findings need confirmation. In any case, records of total radiation from

---

* 10^7 ergs is also called 1 Joule.

pyranometers must be corrected if used for calculating, e.g., the efficiency of photosynthesis.

5.42   Measurement of the natural light field above the water

(a) Direct measurements

(i) The radiation received at the surface of a lake can be split into two parts: (1) the **direct solar radiation**, (2) the **diffuse radiation** from the sky. In meteorological practice, normally the sum of both is reported as **'total radiation'** (comprehending UV, 'light', and IR).

The instruments commonly used for recording total radiation (called **'pyranometers'**) are designed either on a thermo-electric principle (thermopiles), on on a mechanical principle (differential bending of black and white metal strips). Electrical pyranometers, such as the Moll-Gorczynski (Kipp & Zonen), the Eppley pyranometer, the star pyranometer of Linke (Schenk-Sauberer), etc., give more precise readings than bimetal pyranometers (e.g. the Robitzsch's), and their scale can be expanded by appropriate amplifying millivolt recorders. Accordingly, they are suitable also for short time measurements (intensity readings), whereas bimetal pyranometers are but little suited for this purpose.

Instruments for measuring direct solar radiation (**pyrheliometers, actinometers**) are specialized meteorological equipment, and are employed for the calibration of pyranometers.

(ii) Light (see above) is measured and recorded by means of **photometers.** The most widely used devices are self-sufficient (silver selenite) barrier layer instruments (photoelements connected to a suitable microammeter). Silicon and germanium elements, photo-tubes (needing a suitable potential between the electrodes), and photo-resistances are less often used for measuring purposes.

Barrier layer instruments are particularly useful because their spectral sensitivity coincides reasonably well with the sensitivity range of the human eye, and that part of the spectrum which is important in photosynthesis. These instruments are normally calibrated directly in units of lux or foot-candle (1 lux = 0·0929 foot-candle), but it should be borne in mind that these units are only meaningful relative to natural daylight. In this case (and only in this), rough conversion of lux units to energy units of photosynthetically available energy (400–700 mμ) can be made considering that

$$1 \text{ lux} = \text{approx. } 4 \text{ ergs/cm}^2 \cdot \text{sec}$$

(cf. Talling 1957b).

For artificial light sources which are sometimes employed for studies in the laboratory, the following hints may be of use:

According to Hill & Whittingham (1955) a tungsten lamp emits a total radiant energy equivalent of about 60 ergs/cm². sec per lux (or 86×10^{-6} cal/cm² . min per lux); about 9% of this energy is at wavelengths less than 700 mμ, so that the photosynthetically active energy is about 5·4 ergs/cm² . sec per lux (or 8×10^{-6} cal/cm² . min per lux).

The corresponding values for white fluorescent lamps are (cf. Westlake 1965): (1) total radiation equivalent about 3·5 ergs/cm² . sec per lux (or 5×10^{-6} cal/cm² . sec per lux); photosynthetic radiation equivalent about 2·8 ergs/cm² . min per lux (or 4×10^{-6} cal/cm² . min per lux).

Beside direct reading and recording instruments, integrating instruments are also available on the market; they are particularly indicated in photosynthesis studies for exposures of relatively short duration.

All instruments equipped with barrier layer elements need checking from time to time against an absolute instrument, and further they should never be exposed to excessive intensities (see below).

(b) Indirect estimates

It is not always possible to have absolute radiation records made at the time of primary production experiments. Nevertheless, even in this case, some reasonable approximation can be made from local meteorological standard tables, and the formula:

$$Q = Q_0 (0{\cdot}3 + 0{\cdot}7 \, S_r)$$

(cf. Ångstrom 1924; Sauberer & Ruttner 1941; Thams & Wierzejewski 1958). Q_0 signifies the total irradiance to be expected at a cloudless day at the time of interest, and S_r is an estimate of the relative sunshine (estimated as fractions of $1 : 1 = $ cloudless, $0 = $ sky fully covered; estimated visually, or better with a glass sphere pyrheliograph). As an example: If the day considered was July 15th, and the local standard insolation at a bright day of that period be normally 600 cal/cm² . day, and the sunshine duration was 5 hours from a 15 hour day (accordingly $S_r = 0{\cdot}33$), then the total irradiation at the day in question was likely to be some 320 cal/cm² . day.

Such approximations, in reporting primary production experiments, are more meaningful than the bare information that the weather was 'variable'.

The above estimates fail, however, if S_r is below 0·1–0·2; on very cloudy days the irradiance may be much below 30% of the full possible irradiation.

5.43   Measurement of the natural light field in water

The underwater light field is characterized by two vectors: (1) a vertical gradient (attenuation; quantitative change), (2) a concomitant shifting of the radiation spectrum (qualitative change). The first can be measured directly by means of a pyranometer (e.g. a star pyranometer enclosed in a waterproof box) which gives absolute values, or is calculated indirectly from relative measurements (see below). The qualitative change of the spectrum, on the other hand, is more easily estimated from relative measurements, for which barrier layer instruments are most suitable. The employment of pyranometers (particularly for routine measurements) is limited by their relatively small current output.

The following outline is restricted to the methodology of relative measurements, and their interpretation. For more specialized techniques readers are referred to the already mentioned publications.

(a) Instrumentation

Relative measurements of the underwater light field are best performed using a photoelement in combination with an appropriate set of colour filters. For construction of such an instrument the following guide lines should be observed:

(i) Photoelements (silver selenite barrier layers*) of any kind can be used, yet, the spectral sensitivity curve must be known, either obtained from the manufacturer, or measured in a physics laboratory. Cells of 50–60 mm diameter, normally, give a reasonable current output.

For protection, the photocell is built into a waterproof metallic container, and fixed below a transparent front glass (strong enough to resist against water pressure) as close as possible. To reduce shading, the diameter of the front glass should be somewhat larger (1 to 2 cm) than the diameter of the photocell.

Colour filters (see (iii))—which should have about the same diameter as the front glass—are fixed removably and must be covered with an opal glass or Plexiglas (Perspex) disc which preferably rises a little above the rim of the

---

* Barrier layer elements are manufactured, e.g. by: Lange, Berlin; Falkenthal & Presser, Nurtingen, Germany; Megatron, London N4; Evans Electroselenium, Halstead, England.

filter holder. Opals help to ensure that light from all angles of incidence is correctly measured and to reduce the light intensity received by the photocell to the desired level (see below).

(ii) The photocell is connected—by means of a tightly built-in cable of desired length (15–25 m about for lakes, less in rivers and ponds)–to a microammeter of low internal resistance, preferably not more than 500 ohms, ideally not more than 100 ohms, because otherwise the intensity-current relationship is no longer linear. Shunts (designed to keep the total external resistance constant) for range expansion can be applied, but in no case should the intensity at the photocell surface (i.e. after the attenuation by the overlying filters) exceed the equivalent of 1000 lux. Reduction of the intensity to this level may be obtained by appropriate neutral filters.

The linearity range can be easily checked by the two light source method of Sauberer (1962): An ammeter deflection (about 20 to 30 μA) is produced by switching on a first light source appropriately located, and the reading is recorded; then a second light source which gives an additional deflection of some 20 μA (record this precisely!) is added; the location of this latter source is kept constant subsequently. Now the whole operation is repeated by bringing the first light source nearer to the photocell to produce a higher initial deflection, and so on. Linearity of the intensity-current relationship exists as long as the difference of deflection between light sources 1 + 2 and light source 1 remains constant. Checks should be repeated individually on every filter combination, and only the respective linearity ranges found should be used later on in the field for measurement.

(iii) The following filters are recommended for combinations with photo-elements of standard sensitivity:

Schott filters (Manufacturer: Schott & Gen., Mainz, Germany*):

RG 5 (far red)	thickness	2 mm
RG 2 (red)	,,	2 mm
OG 2 + BG 18 (yellow orange)	,,	1 + 1 mm
VG 9 (green)	,,	2 mm
BG 12 (blue)	,,	2 mm
UG 1 + BG 12 (near ultra violet)	,,	1 + 1 mm
NG 5 (neutral)	,,	for 10 and 1 % attenuation

* Of course, corresponding filters from other manufacturers may be used as well, e.g. from: Chance Pilkington, St Helens, England.

The numbers underlined indicate the basic filter set needed to define the principal blocks of the underwater spectrum.

The spectral range effectively covered by each filter must be calculated from the combination of the respective transmission curve with the sensitivity curve of the photoelement; this is achieved by multiplying the percentage transmission by the percentage sensitivity at various points along the transmission range of the filter (the specific curves are normally furnished by the manufacturer). An example for the basic set, and a Weston photronic cell, is given in Fig. 5.1.

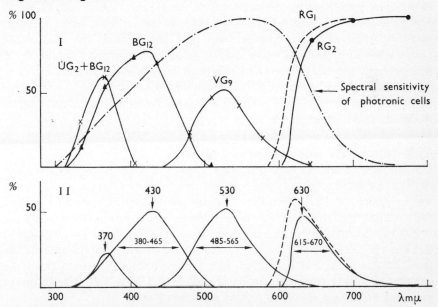

Figure 5.1. I. Filter transmission curves (Schott & Gen., Mainz), and spectral sensitivity curve of a typical barrier layer photocell (Weston photronic cell). II. Spectral response of the mounted photocell in air, calculated from the combination of the sensitivity curve of the photocell and the various filter transmission curves. Further to this the sensitivity centre and the 50% band width of each combination in air are indicated by arrows. After Vollenweider 1961.

For more details consult Sauberer (1962), and Westlake (1965).

(b) Performance of measurement on board ship
The light attenuation of each spectral part is measured separately by lowering the mounted photocell at preselected depth intervals (normally from meter to

meter; in very transparent water from 5 to 5 m, and *vice versa*, in shallow or very turbid waters, e.g. from 0·1 to 0·1 m).

It is advisable to mark the cable at appropriate distances (e.g. at meter intervals) starting from zero at the level of the photocell. The support of the photocell should enable it to be held horizontal (e.g. by three wires leading to the cable; in rivers a rigid support will be needed). To avoid shading from the boat, the cell is exposed toward the most luminous part of the sky using an outrigger.

The reading operation at various depths should be performed as quickly as possible (yet letting the ammeter adjust for at least one minute at every depth) in order to avoid noticeable changes of the incident light; this can easily be achieved after some practice. The best periods for underwater photometry are either on cloudless days, or on fully overcast days, at about noon in both cases. If light conditions are strongly variable all the time, then it is advisable to use a second photocell (mounted on gimbals on board ship) as a reference. The time and prevailing weather conditions should always be recorded.

(c) Elaboration and interpretation of data

The microammeter readings recorded from the various depths are best plotted on a semilogarithmic paper (separately for each filter), starting from a reading taken at 0·1 m; subsurface readings are not representative because of the so-called 'surface effect' (cf. Berger 1961). Under normal conditions the points can be fitted by a straight line which is extrapolated to zero depth; this value is taken as 100%, and all values from the various depths are recalculated on this basis, and re-plotted. If a surface photocell is used the ratio submerged/surface (records) can be plotted in the same way. The intersept may include surface effects as well as reflection losses.

Of course, if strong vertical stratification of turbidity does exist, the whole procedure becomes less simple.

On the basis of such diagrams (an example is given in Fig. 5.2) the optical properties of the water can be derived, considering the following relations:
(i) The transmission between depth 1 and 2 at a wavelength λ is given by
$$T^\lambda_{(z_2 - z_1)} \% = i_2/i_1 \times 100$$
(i_1 = intensity measured at depth z_1, i_2 = intensity measured at depth z_2).

In particular, if $z_2 - z_1 = 1$ m, then T is called the transmission coefficient (T^λ_k) which is used for constructing spectral transmission curves; this is done by plotting the various T^λ_k (λ represents the sensitivity centres of the various

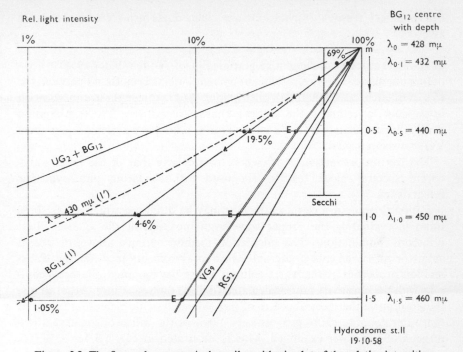

Figure 5.2. The figure shows a typical semilogarithmic plot of the relative intensities measured at various depths with the filters specified in figure 5. Individual measuring points are indicated only for BG_{12} measurements (blue).
The percentage transmission (E) of the visible part of the spectrum (approximately between 400–700 mu) was calculated according to the formula given in 5.43d.
Further to this the theoretical sensitivity centres of BG_{12} measurements at various depth (accounting for the filter effect of the water column above the lowered photocell) are indicated at the right-hand side of the diagram (cf. also figure 5.3). The dashed line (1′) indicates the corrected 'true' relative transmission at 430 mμ; for further discussion see text. Original.

filter-photocell combinations as determined according to 5.43a) at the proper wavelength positions (see also below) and relating the various points by a continuous curve. Such transmission curves represent the optical conditions of the water studied at the time of measurement, and can be used for comparisons of variations during a year, or for comparisons between different waters.

(ii) The 'vertical extinction coefficient' is defined according to

$$\varepsilon_v^{\lambda} = \frac{1}{z_2 - z_1} (\ln i_1 - \ln i_2)$$

For practical reasons, calculations are often made using ^{10}log; ε_v is then given by*

$$\varepsilon_v = 2 \cdot 3 \; \varepsilon_v{}',$$

or ε_v values can be estimated also graphically (cf. Vollenweider 1955).

In a number of waters a significant correlation has been found between the ε_v^λ's of different wavelengths (Vollenweider 1961); under these conditions it is possible to estimate the optical characteristics (ε_v^λ, T_k^λ, transmission curves) approximately from measurements at a unique wavelength (e.g. from VG 9 measurements).

The 'vertical extinction coefficients', particularly that of the most transparent spectral block ($\varepsilon_v^{\lambda\,\mathrm{max}}$), are used for calculating photosynthesis integrals (cf. 3.7).

(iii) At this point, a certain difficulty may be discussed which arises some times in evaluating the proper wavelength position of the various filter-photocell combinations. The calculation method outlined above, in fact, is valid for measurements in air only. For measurements in water the transmission properties of the water column above the mounted photocell combine with the sensitivity range calculated like an additional filter. Accordingly, the position of the spectral centre of measurement, with increasing height of the water column, shifts progressively towards the range of greatest transmission of the water examined. This is illustrated in Fig. 5.3 for a BG 12 measurement: the centre of measurement in air was found to be at 428 mμ, but at 1 m depth it was at 440 mμ, and at 1·5 m depth already at 460 mμ.

Ideally, it is necessary to account for this 'shifting effect'; the problem has been discussed by Sauberer (1962) who gives also correction tables. Practically, the question is less simple.

As shown from Figs. 5.2 and 5.3, the current output of the photocell, at any depth, is proportional to the area below the various curves which result from combination of the photocell sensitivity, the BG 12 transmission, and the approximately estimated transmission of the water examined, and the attenuation is perfectly fulfilling the relationship given above (cf. (ii)). On the other hand, the depth curve resulting after correction (dashed line) appears to be distorted, and hence, less reliable than the original plot.

This is a common experience using the above recommended filter set in combination with a photocell of standard sensitivity, but may be different,

---

* Sometimes, the extinction coefficient calculated on the ^{10}log basis is called 'absorption coefficient'; this usage is not recommended (nobody would use different terms for 'lake surface' because some measure in km^2, and others in sq. mi.!).

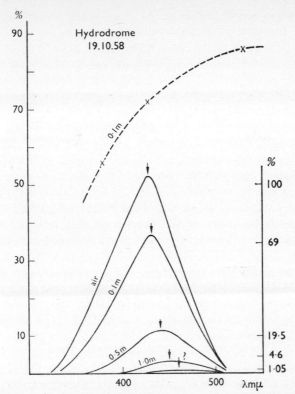

Figure 5.3. The diagram explains the effect of the transmission properties of the water column (indicated for the depth 0·1 m only; dashed line) on the actual sensitivity response of the photocell-filter combination (calculated for BG_{12} measurements reported in figure 5.2; solid lines) and the shifting of the sensitivity centre (indicated by arrows) with depth.

As resulting from comparison of this diagram with figure 5.2 the current output of the photocell at any depth is directly proportional to the areas under the curves calculated taking the area of the photocell-filter combination in air equal to 100%. Original.

if other filters (having larger transmission ranges) and other cells are used. In these latter cases, a systematic bending of the original plots with depth is likely to be observed, and it is recommended to adjust only such kind of curves.

The problem can be overcome by using filters of very narrow band width, such as interference filters. However, in this case, the whole measuring device becomes more complicated.

(d) Calculation of energy fluxes
In spite of the limitations discussed above (indicating that photometric measurements in water are but only approximate to reality) energy fluxes for a given time interval can be approximately estimated from transmission curves.

For this purpose, transmission curves for various depths are calculated from a T_k curve, considering that,
$$T_z^\lambda = (T_k^\lambda/100)^z$$
The T_z^λ's are then multiplied, for every wavelength range and depth considered, by the energy function, i.e. the spectral energy distribution of the incident radiation above water (corrected for surface reflection losses which approximately can be considered as 10%; cf. Sauberer 1962) according to meteorological standard tables, and these values are plotted against wavelength separately for every depth. The energy flux referring to a selected wavelength range (e.g. between 400 and 700 mµ) is then found by planimetric procedures.

Evaluations of this kind are tedious, and are required only for particular considerations. It has been found that a simpler, although less accurate procedure gives reasonable estimates too (cf. Åberg 1943; Vollenweider 1959, 1961). In this procedure the assumption is made that the percentage energy at depth z, is made up as
$$T_z^E \% = 1/3 \, (T_z^{red} + T_z^{green} + T_z^{blue})$$
where the various T_z's are determined directly from the plots discussed previously. To estimate the energy flux at depth z during a given time interval, $T_z^E/100$ is multiplied by the approximately corrected irradiance during that time. As an example: To find the photosynthetically available energy at depth z during a given exposition time—if T_z^E was found to be 10%, and the total irradiance was 250 cal/cm² and considering that about 10% were lost due to back reflection at the surface—the following calculation applies:
$$T_z^{400-700 \, m\mu} = (250 - 25) \times 0{\cdot}46 \times 0{\cdot}1 = 10{\cdot}3 \text{ cal/cm}^2$$
(0·46 refers to the fraction between 400–700 mµ of the total irradiance). Accordingly, 10 cal/cm² is approximately the radiation energy between 400–700 mµ which passed through a horizontal plane at depth z during the time interval considered; the average intensity is found by dividing the above value by the number of minutes in the time interval.

5.44   Secchi disc readings as an auxiliary measure
to characterize the optical conditions

Secchi disc readings have been used for a long time to characterize the transparency of a water. For lack of other possibilities, this simple measure was also applied to the interpretation of primary production measurements; an account of the suitability and limits was given earlier by Vollenweider (1960).

According to the findings of several authors (Poole & Atkins 1929; Clarke 1941; Ichimura 1956; Beeton 1957) the order of magnitude of the light intensity at the limit of visibility of the disc (s) is about 15 % of the subsurface intensity, and hence,

$$\varepsilon_v \cdot s = (1n\ i_1 - 1n\ i_2) = (1n\ 1 - 1n\ 0\cdot 15) = 2\cdot 2.$$

However, as shown by experience, this product is not constant but varies—depending on local conditions as well as on the observer—from 1·4 to 3 and more. It is therefore impossible to compare the results from different localities, and different authors absolutely. This is also due to the fact that Secchi disc readings probably do not refer to the 'vertical extinction coefficient' but rather to the 'horizontal', or more likely to the turbidity integral

$(\int_{o}^{s} S(z)dz)$ above the disc; (Szczepański 1958). Accordingly, if 'turbidity' is

due primarily to phytoplankton, then Secchi disc readings may be closely related to primary production rates (Vollenweider 1960).

A better way to use Secchi disc readings for the purpose of defining 'vertical extinction coefficients' is systematic combination with photometer readings taken at the same time. In this case, correlation diagrams can be constructed (individually for every water body examined) which then may be used for conversion of further Secchi disc readings. As shown by Vollenweider (1960) the correlations are of the form,

$$(\varepsilon_v^\lambda)^n \cdot s = \text{const.},$$

where $n \gtrless 1$ depending on the wavelength range considered.

The use of Secchi disc measurements in primary production calculations has been discussed above (cf. 3.72).

6
Appendix

6.1 ALGAL CULTURES
C J SOEDER

The aim of this brief chapter is to provide the reader who is unfamiliar with the subject with some references to basic literature on algal culture.

Cultures of algae are widely used to solve taxonomic, developmental and physiological problems in phycology. Unialgal cultures which are free from bacteria or other microorganisms are required for most of the physiological studies. A classic description of methods for isolating algae, and for their cultivation under sterile conditions, has been given by Pringsheim (1949). Modern techniques are reviewed by Provasoli & Pintner (1960).

The difficulties encountered with the isolation of algae and the establishment of pure cultures vary with regard to the different taxonomic groups, and sometimes from species to species. Many green algae, like *Chlorella*, *Ankistrodesmus*, or *Scenedesmus*, are easy to handle. Other groups (e.g. many Chrysophyceae) are much more delicate, and in numerous cases attempts to obtain pure cultures have not yet been successful. Peculiar requirements of certain algae are referred to by Chu (1943), Rodhe (1948), Pringsheim (1949), Provasoli & Pintner (1960), and in a vast number of special articles in the literature.

Myers (1962) summarized the techniques involved in the handling of laboratory cultures. The detailed article by Kuhl & Lorenzen (1964) gives a complete survey of methods for culturing *Chlorella*, including synchronous and continuous cultures. Proper adjustment of nutrient concentrations, pH, light intensity, and temperature are essential prerequisites for the successful cultivation of algae. The evaluation of their specific optimum conditions is therefore desirable and may be of ecological significance (Chu 1943; Rodhe 1948). Many algae will not grow unless they are supplied with minute concentrations of vitamins, especially of vitamin B_{12} (Provasoli 1958; Droop

1962). Moreover, the addition of chelating agents to the medium may be stimulating or essential (Provasoli & Pintner 1960).

In many cases, it is advantageous or necessary to grow the algae under the conditions of alternating light and dark periods. This leads to a more or less pronounced synchrony of cell division and growth (cf. Kuhl & Lorenzen 1964), which can also be induced by the natural day-and-night regimen and is hence of ecological importance (Soeder 1965).

Some algae are known to require a continuous supply of acetate (Danforth 1962) which can in special cases only be metabolized in the light (Pringsheim & Wiessner 1960).

A culture medium which is suitable for many freshwater algae has been developed by Chu (1942). The composition of his nutrient solution No. 12 is:

1000 ml quartz-distilled water

30 mg $Ca(NO_3)_2$	5 mg KCl
5 mg K_2HPO_4	20 mg Na_2CO_3
75 mg $MgSO_4 . 7 H_2O$	0·5 mg $FeCl_3 . 6 H_2O$
25 mg K_2SiO_4	1 ml trace element solution

The addition of soil extract to a medium of this kind does often considerably improve its versatility (Pringsheim 1949), but the composition of the solution is then no longer well defined.

For vigorously growing organisms of the Chlorella type, the medium of Kuhl (1962) can be recommended. Per litre it contains:

1011·10 mg KNO_3	0·061 mg H_3BO_3
621·0 mg $NaH_2PO_4 . 1 H_2O$	0·169 mg $MnSO_4 . 1 H_2O$
89·0 mg $Na_2HPO_4 . 2 H_2O$	0·287 mg $ZnSO_4 . 7 H_2O$
246·5 mg $MgSO_4 . 7 H_2O$	0·00249 mg $CuSO_4 . 5 H_2O$
14·7 mg $CaCl_2 . 2 H_2O$	0·01235 mg $(NH_4)_6Mo_7O_{24} . 4 H_2O$
6·95 mg $FeSO_4 . 7 H_2O$ Fe-EDTA complex	

To prepare the Fe-EDTA complex, 0·69 gm $FeSO_4 . 7 H_2O$ and 0·93 gm Na_2EDTA are dissolved in 80 ml distilled water by boiling for a short time. After cooling to room temperature, the solution is made up to 100 ml. It is stored in a cool and dark place. 1 ml will contain the above iron concentration.

The media of Chu and of Kuhl are phosphate buffered. For growing organisms that are sensitive to inorganic phosphate other buffering substances like glycylglycine have to be employed together with organic phosphates (Provasoli & Pintner 1960). The composition of most culture media is extremely different from natural environments. For the sake of better simulation of ecological conditions in the laboratory, Vollenweider &

Saraceni (1964) developed a nutrient solution which resembles the water of certain lakes in northern Italy.

Several thousand algal strains are available as pure cultures from the culture collections all over the world; these institutions also give instructions for the cultivation of the respective algae.

Some of the larger culture collections are:
    Culture Collection of Algae;
        Department of Botany, Indiana University,
        Bloomington, Indiana, USA.
    Collection of the Institute of Applied Microbiology;
        University of Tokyo,
        Bunkyo-ku,
        Tokyo, Japan.
    Sammlung von Algenkulturen des Pflanzenphysiologischen Instituts
    der Universität Göttingen;
        34 Göttingen, Germany,
        Nikolausberger Weg 18.
    Culture Collection of Algae and Protozoa;
        The Botany School of the University of Cambridge,
        Downing Street,
        Cambridge, Great Britain.
    Collection of Algal Cultures;
        Department of Botany of the Hebrew University of Jerusalem,
        Algal Laboratory,
        Jerusalem, Israel.
    Collection of Autotrophic Organisms;
        Czechoslovak Academy of Sciences,
        Viničná 5,
        Praha 2, Czechoslovakia.

6.2 STATISTICAL ASPECTS OF SAMPLING
AND RECORDING DATA

R M CASSIE

There are to-day so many good texts on basic statistics for biologists that a comprehensive statistical section within this volume would be either inadequate or superfluous. The scope of this chapter is, therefore, restricted to a simple exposition of two aspects: firstly, what statistics can do for the biologists (Sections 1–6); and secondly how the biologist can best aid the statistician (and himself) by collecting and recording his data in an appropriate manner (Sections 7 and 8). The arithmetic of statistics is relatively easy, and, with increasing availability of mechanical calculators and electronic computers, very large sets of data can be manipulated in seconds or minutes, where previously weeks or even years would have been required. Thus the ecologist has a very powerful tool which he may be tempted to use indiscriminately and without proper regard for the validity of the tests and estimates he wishes to make. It is always best to consult a statistician (or at least a good text) before, rather than after conducting a quantitative investigation. Since scientists who combine both biology and statistics in their training are few, it is a considerable advantage for the biologist to understand enough about the principles of statistics to know what sort of questions he can ask the statistician.

The first product of a field investigation is usually a large and cumbersome table of data. Each row in the table will probably represent a single sample (or station) and each column a single biological or physical variable. Within the limits of accuracy of the techniques of measurement being used and the range of variables measured, this table contains complete information about the samples. However, the samples themselves are interesting only insofar as they represent the *population*. 'Population' here is a statistical term with a slightly different meaning to that commonly implied in ecology. It may be briefly defined as being the totality of measurements of any given kind which might have been made (given infinite resources) in the section of the environment under investigation. (Thus we may, for example, have a population of temperatures or weights as well as a population of organisms). It is the first task of the statistician to extract from the data the information which is representative of the population and to discard that which represents only chance variations in individuals. Also, since the human mind can assimilate only a limited number of figures at any one time, this information should be expressed in as small a series of numbers as possible.

1 The condensation of data—single variable methods

In the process of condensing the data to manageable proportions, the mass of numbers is converted to a smaller set of numbers or *statistics*, which are estimates of essential properties or *parameters* of the population. It is convenient practice to designate statistics by Latin and parameters by the corresponding Greek letters, e.g. m and μ, s and σ. The simplest statistic is the average or arithmetic mean. Each of the original columns of data, i.e. each variable, may be represented by a mean which is designated by the symbol m, with an appropriate subscript: m_1, m_2, m_3, etc. These are statistics estimating the parameters μ_1, μ_2, μ_3, etc. of the population. The m's by themselves do not give complete information since they do not indicate the range of variation of individual sample measurements. A second statistic, almost invariably the standard deviation, s (and estimating the population parameter, σ), must be calculated to measure *dispersion* or spread of observations around their mean. In some cases the two statistics m and s will give a complete summary of the column of data (though not of its relation to other columns). This, however, can not be taken for granted. For a two-statistic summary to give complete information, it must be assumed that the individual sample figures are symmetrically distributed about the mean (or, more specifically, that they take the mathematical form known as the *Normal* distribution). However, there may be, for example, a large number of moderately small values on one side of the mean balanced by a few extremely large values on the other. This may be illustrated by the numbers: 3, 10, 25, 45, 63, 141, 252, 448, 1,000, 3,990, which have a mean of 598. Eight of the numbers are less than the mean and only two greater. In such a skewed distribution, a third or even a fourth statistic may be necessary to give full information. When the data consist of counts of individual organisms, these are almost invariably asymmetrically distributed about the mean. Fortunately, however, it is usually possible to convert most sets of data to a relatively symmetrical form by means of a *transformation*. By far the most useful transformation in ecological work is the logarithm. Thus the logarithms of the set of five numbers are: 0·48, 1·00, 1·40, 1·65, 1·80, 2·15, 2·40, 2·65, 3·00, 3·60 with a mean of 2·01 which now divides the distribution symmetrically. Barnes (1952) discusses this and other transformations useful to the aquatic ecologist and Cassie (1962) discusses some of the concepts underlying logarithmic transformations.

Once a sufficient number of statistics (hopefully 2) has been calculated, it would be possible, if one wished to do so, to construct a set of figures from the statistics alone, which will closely resemble the original data. The resemblance will not be exact, but will be as good as could be produced by returning to the field and repeating the same set of measurements. Thus, in relation to the population, the two statistics give as much information as the original data which may have contained hundreds or even thousands of separate numbers.

2   Errors of estimates

A statistic is only an *estimate* of the true population parameter. The quantitative ecologist will want to know more about the reliability of this estimate, i.e. to give a numerical value to the error. If the error is a systematic one (e.g. if an instrument or technique always gives too high, or too low, a result), the statistician can supply no answer. The error, better known in this case as *bias*, can only be detected by a careful review of technique. However, many errors in measuring and recording are equally likely to be positive or negative, and in a large series of measurements will tend to be self-cancelling. These are amenable to statistical treatment. In most field biological measurements, by far the greatest source of error arises, not from the technique, but from the biological material itself. Indeed, errors (as opposed to biases) in technique can often be ignored since they are relatively trivial.

One realises intuitively that, the larger the number of samples, the smaller the error of estimate will be, provided, of course, that the samples are taken in such a way that they are representative of the population. If a sample can be adequately summarized by the two statistics, m and s, a standard error, s_m, can be estimated which becomes smaller as the number of samples, n, becomes larger.

$$s_m = s/\sqrt{n}$$

Use of this statistic is dependent on a number of theoretical considerations which we do not have space to consider, but, provided n is fairly large (say 50 or more) and the data are not grossly asymmetrical about their mean, the standard error may be used to set upper and lower *fiducial limits* within which the population mean, μ, may be assumed to lie with a specified degree of certainty. We might say, for example, that:

$$\mu = m \pm s_m$$

This would be true for about 2 in every 3 sets of samples. Most scientists would consider such limits inadequate, because, although the statement is more often right than wrong, nevertheless, every third set of data will be misrepresented. Thus, in biological investigations, it is common practice to use the limits:

$$\mu = m \pm 2\,s_m$$

This will be wrong only once in about 20 trials, or the probability (of being wrong) is:

$$P \sim 0.05$$

Other limits can, of course, be chosen, e.g. for $m \pm 2.6\,s_m$, $P \sim 0.01$, leaving only one chance in 100 of an incorrect statement.

3   Tests of significance—the null hypothesis

Scientific thought is commonly divided into two processes, induction and deduction. The estimation of parameters and errors of these estimates is inductive statistics. In a deductive process, the scientist sets up an hypothesis and then conducts experiments (or collects data) of a type which would be likely to disprove this hypothesis if it were untrue. One set of data may be sufficient for disproof, whereas proof can never be considered absolute until all possible sets of data have been examined. For example, the 'law' of conservation of matter remained 'true' only until the discovery of atomic fission. A related concept in statistics is known as the *null hypothesis*. This is best illustrated by an example:

In a population of animals it is believed that the number of females exceeds the number of males. In a sample of 100 individuals, 45 were found to be males and 55 female, a distribution which at first sight would seem to confirm the hypothesis. However, the null hypothesis is set up: that males and females are equal in number and that departure from equality in the sample is merely an accident of sampling. Under the null hypothesis, the 'expected' number of each sex is 50. We thus calculate the statistic:

$$\chi^2 = \frac{(45 - 50)^2 \, (55 - 50)^2}{50}$$
$$= 1.000$$

Clearly, the greater the departure from a 50:50 distribution, the higher will be the value of χ^2. The distribution of this statistic is known and can be obtained from statistical tables. In examples of this type, χ^2 may be expected by chance alone to be equal to or greater than 3.84 once in every 20 trials. (i.e. $\chi^2 = 3.84$ has a probability, $P = 0.05$.) Clearly $\chi^2 = 1.0$ is not a particularly unusual value, and in fact this value has an exact probability (of being exceeded by chance) of 0.32. Thus, in samples of 100 from a population with males and females equal in numbers; about $^2/_3$ of the trials would give a higher χ^2. We accept the null hypothesis and consider that we have failed to demonstrate any real difference between the numbers of the sexes in the population. Note, however, that we have not 'disproved' the original hypothesis. A real departure from the 50:50 sex ratio may still exist, but a larger sample would be required to demonstrate the difference. Conversely, we have not 'proved' the null hypothesis. We might consider that a 50:50 ratio was a sufficiently accurate estimate upon which to base further calculations and predictions, but only after the entire population had been sampled could we consider that the exact ratio has been finally demonstrated.

4 Relationship between two variables

So far, the methods discussed concern single variables, i.e. the columns of the table of data are considered entirely separately from one another. An important task of the ecologist is to seek relationships between the columns, say between different species, or between species and properties of their environment. The simplest form of relationship between two columns is the linear regression equation:

$$Y = a + bX \qquad\qquad (1)$$

where X and Y are any pair of values (taken in the same row of the two columns), and a and b are constants which may be either positive or negative. b is known as the regression coefficient and is a statistic estimating the parameter β which measures the rate of change of X relative to Y. Since, in the equation, the value of Y is determined by that of X, the Y column is known as the dependent variable and the X column the independent variable. X might, for example, be the amount of chlorophyll a, and Y the rate of carbon-14 uptake in a series of water samples. Since Y can not be predicted exactly from X, a further term, ε, the error is added, and the equation becomes:

$$Y = a + bX + \varepsilon$$

The geometric form of the equation is shown in Fig. 6.1. Two sets of X, Y and ε values (subscripted 1 and 2) are labelled. a, sometimes known as the *intercept*, is the point at which the regression line intercepts the Y axis, while b is the increase in Y for unit increase in X as shown by the regression line. The equation does not permit the prediction of any particular value of ε, but is computed in such a way that the algebraic mean of all ε's is zero. The standard deviation of ε can be estimated from the data, and is usually designated $s_{y \cdot x}$ which signifies 'standard deviation of Y independent of X', or (in a somewhat oversimplified definition) the standard deviation that Y would have had if X had been constant.

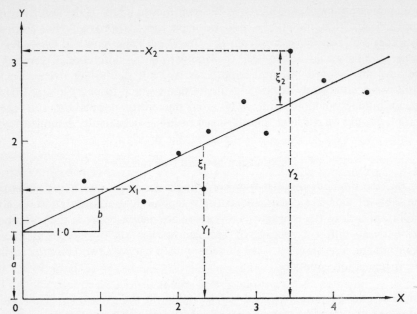

Figure 6.1. The regression line, $Y = 0\cdot84 + 0\cdot47X + \varepsilon$, fitted to 10 pairs of values of X and Y (black circles). The coordinates X_1, X_2, Y_1, Y_2 and errors, ε_1, ε_2, are shown for two pairs. $b = 0\cdot47$ is the regression coefficient, and a $0\cdot84$ is the intercept of the regression line on the Y axis.

Just as with the standard deviation, s, of X, $s_{y\cdot x}$ may be employed in setting fiducial limits or tests of significance. $s_{y\cdot x}$ is always smaller than the standard deviation, s_y, of Y taken on its own. Thus, by measuring X we obtain more precise information about Y. Taking the chlorophyll example, we can specify the mean carbon-14 for the water represented by the samples more accurately in relation to chlorophyll a content than we can without such a reference standard. This is a concept which has received little recognition in ecological sampling, though the technique of 'regression sampling' is well-known in other disciplines. A simple example will serve to illustrate the principles underlying this technique. Imagine we have taken a series of fish samples from a lake, and are attempting to estimate the total fish population. Certain areas are found to be unusually barren of fish and on investigation we find that these are close to factories discharging toxic wastes into the lake. Clearly we would be able to make a better estimate of the fish if we plotted the position of the polluted waters and treated samples from these areas separately instead of lumping them in with the rest of the lake. This division into polluted and unpolluted waters would be a simple but effective form of stratified sampling. Even better (since pollution is a graded effect) would be to plot the concentration of toxic material throughout the lake and find the regression of fish density, Y, on pollutant, X. Even in regions where we had taken no fish samples, we could make an estimate of the fish abundance from the toxicity of the water, by using the regression equation. We have, in fact, more information than that resulting from the fish samples alone, and the resulting regression estimate is correspondingly more precise.

It is also possible to estimate the standard deviation, s_b, of b and thus to make comparisons with other estimates or hypothetical values of the parameter β. Commonly, the ecologist is interested, not so much in the actual value of b, as in its 'reality', or, in statistical language, the null hypothesis: $\beta = 0$. This information can be readily obtained by regression methods, but it is common practice (though not always the best practice) to make use of the *correlation* coefficient.

Correlation is most appropriate when there is no basis upon which to decide which of the two variables is dependent and which independent. For example, two species may have a similar pattern of distribution, though there is no clear indication that either is truly controlled by the other. (Note, however, that, if we wanted to *predict* the number of species Y from the number of species X, regression would still be appropriate). The correlation coefficient (or, more specifically the product moment correlation coefficient), r, is a number which may have any value between -1 and 1. Just as b estimates β, so r estimates a parameter ρ. When $\rho = 0$ there is no correlation; when $\rho = 1$ the correlation is 'perfect'. The geometrical meaning of correlation, which is rather different from that of regression, can be expressed in various ways, one of which is shown in Fig. 6.2. We may imagine the points representing the data as enclosed by an elliptical envelope. The slope of the major axis of the ellipse indicates the sign of r, negative in this case, since Y decreases as X increases. The shorter the minor axis, the higher the correlation, becoming unity when the ellipse collapses to a straight line. Correlation is zero when the major axis is parallel to the X or Y axis, or when the ellipse becomes a circle and thus has no major axis. Biological measurements seldom produce correlations close to the limiting values, 1 or -1. This is not necessarily attributable to deficiencies in measuring techniques, but simply a manifestation of the complexity of biological phenomena— only rarely can an effect be attributed to one cause alone. On the other hand,

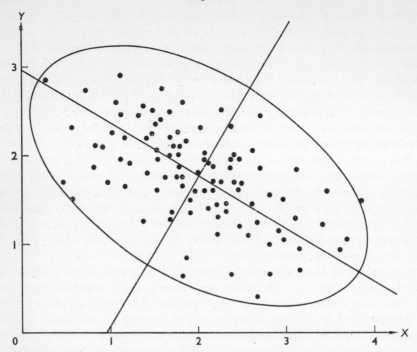

Figure 6.2. The elliptical envelope with major and minor axes for 100 pairs of $X - Y$ values which have a correlation coefficient, r, of approximately 0·6.

even a small correlation, say $\rho = 0·1$, may be perfectly real, even though several hundred pairs of observations would be necessary to demonstrate its existence with any degree of confidence. The correlation coefficient can be used a little more easily than the regression coefficient since the null hypothesis, $\rho = 0$ (exactly equivalent to $\beta = 0$) can be tested by reference to tables. If the null hypothesis has a low probability (less than 0·05 is a common standard) the correlation is judged 'significant' i.e. there is a real relationship between the two variables.

Unfortunately, correlation is one of the most abused of the statistical techniques. In the first place, it should be clearly understood that no correlation, no matter how formally significant, can tell us anything about the train of cause and effect between two variables. We may find that carbon-14 uptake and chlorophyll *a* are highly correlated, but this does not 'prove' that chlorophyll *a* controls carbon uptake. For this conclusion we may perhaps use our biochemical knowledge, but *not* statistics. On the other hand, the absence of significant correlation between any reasonably comprehensive set of paired measurements would certainly cast some doubt on the validity of the $^{14}C/$ chlorophyll association. If experiment A produces a higher correlation than experiment B of the same type, this does not necessarily show that A is the better experiment. A colleague and I conducted similar experiments to determine the ^{14}C / chlorophyll correlation. His correlation was 0·6 and mine 0·9. My higher correlation was obtained simply because I used about a 100 times greater range of chlorophyll *a* concentrations; in fact my standard deviation from regression was several hundred times larger than his.

One requirement, sometimes overlooked in interpretation of correlation and regression analyses, is that all the observations in any column of data should be independent of one another. This is seldom true in ecological data. Observations which are close together either in space or time tend to resemble each other more than those which are widely separated. The changes which take place may be in the form of simple trends (the numbers consistently increasing or decreasing as one moves down the column) or of a more complex variation known as serial correlation (or autocorrelation), in which the similarity between adjacent samples is preserved even though there is no simple trend. Such situations often lead to spurious, or at least highly misleading correlations which may baffle the mathematician, let alone the biologist.

Bearing in mind the many pitfalls which may be found in correlation analysis, the biologist is well advised to plot his data in a simple $X - Y$ graph before calculating correlation coefficients. Ideally, the graph should have a form similar to Fig. 6.2, the points falling within an elliptical envelope with their greatest concentration near the centre of the ellipse. Points representing observations which are close together in space or in time should be more or less randomly scattered through the graph with no tendency for adjacent samples to be adjacent in the graph. Departure from these conditions may not always invalidate correlation analysis, but they will always indicate that the interpretation should be treated with the greatest of care. Chapters 1–3 (Graphical analysis) and 11 (Time series analysis) of Quenouille (1952) are helpful reading in amplifying some of the comments in this section.

5 More than two variables

Most of us are well aware that ecology involves the interaction, not of two, but of many variables. The ecologist will ultimately want to digest all the columns of his data table in the one analysis. Where one variable is judged to be dependent on several others, multiple regression is appropriate, and methods are readily available to construct equations of the form:

$$Y = a + b_1X_1 + b_2X_2 + b_3X_3 \ldots + \varepsilon \qquad (3)$$

With three variables (Y, X_1 and X_2) the equation represents a plane in a three

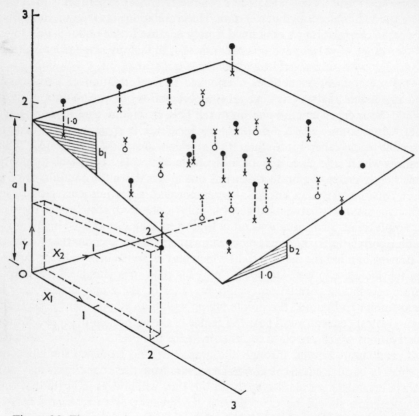

Figure 6.3. The regression plane, $Y = 0.82 - 0.47X_1 + 0.21X_2 + \varepsilon$ fitted to 26 triplets of values of X_1, X_2 and Y. (Note that the subscripts are not used in the same sense as in Fig. 1). The points are shown as black circles except when they lie behind the regression plane, when the circles are left open. The ε's are shown as dotted vertical lines, the point at which these meet the regression plane marked with a cross. The hatched right angled triangles have their horizontal sides equal to unity and their vertical sides equal to the regression coefficients, $b_1 = -0.47$, and $b_2 = 0.21$. $a = 0.82$ is the intercept of the plane on the Y axis. The coordinates on the three axes for one of the points are shown as broken lines delineating a rectangular figure with the dimensions: $X_1 = 1.8$, $X_2 = 0.2$, $Y = 0.8$.

dimensional space. This is represented geometrically in Fig. 6.3. The individual ε values are represented as dotted lines connecting the data points with the regression plane. With four or more variables, the equation can not be represented geometrically, but the mathematical procedures follow extensions of the same principles. Equivalent correlation methods are available but are usually less useful. However, the multiple correlation coefficient, R, is of some interest. This coefficient summarizes the effectiveness of equation (3) by measuring the correlation of Y with X_1, X_2, X_3, etc., all combined. R (which has no sign) always has a larger value than any individual r and thus illustrates the multiplicity of effects in accounting for any biological phenomenon. Even so, $R = 1$ would be a rare occurrence, since some ecological causes (one of which is chance) will probably always remain unmeasured.

Less commonly found in texts are the various methods of multivariate analysis which are still very much in the developmental stages, particularly in ecological applications. Various mathematical models have been used, but basically an attempt is made to place the entire biotic and environmental complex in a series of equations of the type:

$$c_1Y_1 + c_2Y_2 + c_3Y_3 + \ldots = a + b_1X_1 + b_2X_2 + b_3X_3 \ldots \qquad (4)$$

where the X's are the environmental (independent) and the Y's the various biotic (dependent) variables. The c's are coefficients comparable to the regression coefficients. The techniques and concepts may seem esoteric to the beginner, but are nevertheless relatively easily understood in their general principles. Elementary accounts are given by Quenouille (1952) and Cassie (1963), the latter referring particularly to interpretation of plankton data. For those who are prepared to master the rudiments of matrix algebra, a more advanced and comprehensive exposition is given by Seal (1964).

6 Non-linear relationships

Equations (1) to (4) above all describe straight lines, flat planes and other mathematical forms which are essentially linear. Many correlation and regression relationships, however, are better described by curvilinear figures. For example the equation:

$$Y = Ae^{bX} \quad (A \text{ and } b \text{ are constants}) \qquad (5)$$

describes an exponential curve such as might be traced by the number of organisms in a new culture of unicells when plotted against time. This relationship as it stands is relatively difficult to handle either graphically or arithmetically. However, transforming both sides of the equation to natural logarithms:

$$\ln Y = a + bX \quad (a = \ln A) \tag{6}$$

we have once again a linear relationship comparable to (1). Other common relationships which use transformations for linearity are:

$$\log Y = a + b \log X \tag{7}$$

$$Y = a + bX + cX^2 + dX^3 \ldots + \varepsilon \tag{8}$$

Note that (8) contains two expedients, firstly transformations of X to various powers, and secondly the appearance of different transformations of the same variable as separate terms of a multiple regression equation. It is not possible to set down precise instructions as to what transformations should be employed under what circumstances, since the application may often be purely empirical. However, the three above seem to cover a wide range of circumstances effectively and at least sometimes can be reconciled with what is known of the principles controlling animal and plant behaviour and metabolism. In general it is often appropriate to use logarithmic transformations (6 and 7) for data such as counts of organisms and no transformation or a power transformation (3) for physical properties of the environment. It is interesting to note that the logarithmic transformation in regression is fully compatible with the use of the same transformation for 'normalizing' frequency distributions as in section 1.

7   The collecting of data

In field biology, lip service is often paid to the concept of random sampling, but this is seldom achieved in practice. In simple random sampling (for the estimation, say of mean population density, or of a mean property of the environment) a list is made (at least in principle) of *all possible samples* and a smaller number of samples is selected from these by a random process, usually mechanical, such as drawing from a table of random numbers. The only simple alternative which is acceptable is systematic sampling. Here the position of samples follows a regular and predetermined pattern, usually based on a randomly selected origin. The commonest form is a square grid with a sample taken at every point of intersection. It is not always realised that these are *not* random samples, though intuitively they seem to represent the population in much the same way as the random sample.

Random sampling has a single advantage over systematic—it permits a valid estimate to be made of the standard error, because every possible sample has an equal and independent probability of being selected. On the other hand, it does not necessarily produce the best estimate of the parameters—indeed, in most natural populations the error of simple random sampling will be considerably greater than that which could be achieved by systematic or other methods. The systematic sample, on the other hand will almost always produce an estimate with less error than the random, because the sampling area is covered more evenly. However, the error itself can not be estimated because all possible samples do not have an independent probability of being selected. Some efforts have been made to estimate the errors of systematic sampling, at least under certain circumstances, but no comprehensive theory has yet been presented. Logistically, random sampling is difficult to achieve in the field. For example, a research vessel operating in a lake might have little difficulty in making a series of parallel traverses and sampling at equally spaced intervals, whereas a series of random positions might present a fine problem in navigation.

Thus the investigator is faced with a dilemma—whether to have a large but known or a small but unknown error, and whether logistic expediency or statistical rigour should be his aim. In the matter of error, a satisfactory compromise may sometimes be reached by *stratified random sampling*. Here the area is divided into a number of smaller areas, or *strata*, which could, if necessary, have a similar pattern to that of a systematic sampling series. Within each stratum at least two samples are selected at random. With proper sampling design, the combined errors arising from the individual strata will be considerably less than those of simple random sampling of the entire area. Methods for use in ecology are relatively poorly developed, but those who wish to pursue the problem further should consult an appropriate text, e.g. Cochrane, in the final chapter of Snedecor (1962). Note, however, that stratification in itself provides no solution to logistic problems, though these can be taken into account in the design of stratified sampling.

From the last three paragraphs, it might appear that statistics should immediately be abandoned if sampling is not randomized. Nevertheless, a perusal of the literature shows that there are a great many statistical tests in use by ecologists which produce meaningful results, without strict randomization. Methods such as analysis of variance, regression, correlation, the various tests involving χ^2, multivariate analysis, etc. are all dependent upon some type of model involving the concept of randomness. It is often almost impossible to determine whether or not the requirements of the model are realised. For example, are two water samples, taken in quick succession at 'the same station' in a lake, truly random replicates? The investigator should not be too discouraged by the demands made by the theory of statistics, but at the same time he should realise that he is working very much on the unexplored border of this field, and that the elegant techniques available, say to the agricultural experimenter, may not necessarily be applicable without modification to field ecology.

8   Recording of data

Since it will not always be obvious at the beginning of an investigation what methods will be applied to the data, it is particularly important that data should be recorded and reported in the original form and units of measurement, or, if conversion to another form seems essential, the original raw data should be recoverable. With measurements of continuous variables (usually physical properties, or biological properties expressed in physical form), probably the worst that can happen is that errors of conversion will be made. However, where numerical counts of organisms or discrete events are converted, say, to a constant volume basis (often with a variable conversion factor), certain statistics immediately become unavailable or invalid. The χ^2 test discussed in section 3 can not be applied except in terms of the original sample counts. We might, for example, have reason to multiply by 10, thus converting the sample to a 'per thousand' basis, i.e. 450: 550. It is easily verified that χ^2 becomes 10·000 which is well above the level (3·84) for a probability of 0·05. Clearly, χ^2 could be raised or lowered to any value at all by such a process, and it is only the raw data which are valid for the test. In many analyses it is necessary to transform data, such as sample counts, to logarithms. When some of the counts are zero, an appropriate transformation is $\log (X + C)$, where X is the count, and C a constant, usually unity. If, for example, sample counts are converted from a litre to a cubic metre basis, using the factor 1,000, the transformed data could differ considerably depending on whether the factor was applied before or after transformation.

$$\text{e.g. } \log (1000 \times 0) + 1 = \log 1 = 0$$
$$\log 1000 \times (0 + 1) = \log 1000 = 3$$

9   Statistical texts

It would be invidious to recommend any 'best' statistical text—in fact the ideal manual for the ecologist has not yet been written. The following are listed for those who do not already have a favourite of their own. Snedecor (in English) has been my own basic text since my first venture into statistics, and I still refer to it frequently. The others (in other languages) have been recommended to me by various colleagues.

Cavalli-Sforza, L. 1961. Analisi statistiche per medici e biologi e analisi del dosaggio biologico. Edizioni Universitarie Boringhieri, Torino.

Linder, A. 1964. Statistische Methoden für Naturwissenschafter, Mediziner, und Ingenieure. Verlag Birkhäusser, Basel.

Lison, L. 1958. Statisque appliquée à la biologie expérimentale. La planification de l'expérience et l'analyse des resultats. Gaulthier Vellons, Paris.

Snedecor, G.W. 1962. Statistical methods applied to experiments in agriculture and biology. Iowa State University Press, Ames, Iowa.

References

ÅBERG B. and RODHE W. (1942) Über die Milieufactoren in einigen südschwedischen Seen. *Symb. Bot. Upsal.* **5** (3), 1–256.

ÅBERG B. (1943) Physiologische und ökologische Studien über die pflanzliche Photomorphose. *Symb. Bot. Upsal.* **8** (1), 1–189.

AGG A.R., MITCHELL N.T. and EDEN C.E. (1961) The use of lithium as a tracer for measuring rates of flow of water or sewage. *J. Inst. Sew. Purif.* 1961, 240–245.

AMBÜHL H. (1960) Die Nährstoffzufuhr zum Hallwilersee. *Schweiz. Z. Hydrol.* **22** (2), 563–597.

AMBÜHL H. (1966) Der Einfluss chemischer Düngung auf stehende Oberflächengewässer. *Gas u. Wasserfach.* **107** (14), 357–363.

AMERICAN PUBLIC HEALTH ASSOCIATION *et al.* (1965) *Standard Methods for the Examination of Water and Wastewater, including Bottom Sediments and Sludges,* 12th edition. American Public Health Association, New York.

AMERICAN SOCIETY OF CIVIL ENGINEERS, COMMITTEE ON SANITARY ENGINEERING RESEARCH (1961) Thirty-first progress report. Effect of water temperature on stream reaeration. *J. sanit. Engng. Div., Am. Soc. civ. Engrs.* **87** (SA6), 59–71.

ÅNGSTROM A. (1924) Solar and terrestrial radiation. *Quart. J. Roy. Met. Soc.* **50**.

ANTIA N.J., MCALLISTER C.D., PARSONS T.R., STEPHENS K. and STRICKLAND J.D.H. (1963) Further measurements of primary production using a large-volume plastic sphere. *Limnol. and Oceanogr.* **8**, 166–183.

ARNON D.I., WHATLEY F.R. and ALLEN M.B. (1958) Assimilatory power in photosynthesis. *Science*, **127**, 1026–1034.

ASSMAN A.V. (1951) Rol vodoroslevykh obrastanii v obrazovanii organicheskogo veshchestva v vodoeme (The role of algal periphyton in the production of organic matter in a body of water). *Dokl. Akad. Nauk SSSR*, **76**, 905–908 (in Russian).

ASSMAN A.V. (1953) Rol vodoroslevykh obrastanii v obrazovanii organicheskogo veshchestva v Glubokom ozere (The role of algal periphyton in the production of organic matter in Lake Glubokoje). *Trudy vsesoyuz. gidrobiol. Obshch.* **5**, 138–157 (in Russian).

ASSOCIATION OF OFFICIAL AGRICULTURAL CHEMISTS (1965) *Official methods of analysis of the Association of Official Agricultural Chemists,* 10th Ed. Washington D.C.

BACHMANN R.W. and ODUM E.P. (1960) Uptake of Zn^{65} and primary productivity in marine benthic algae. *Limnol. and Oceanogr.* **5**, 349–355.

BACHMANN R.W., SAUNDERS G.W. and TRAMA F.B. (1961) Investigations in lake metabolism-photosynthesis: a modified C-14 technique for estimation of photosynthesis in large lakes (Abstr.). *Proc. 4th Conf. Great Lakes Res., Great Lakes Res. Div., Univ. Mich., Ann Arbor, Publ.* **7**, 163.

BACHOFEN R. (1960) *Stoffhaushalt und Sedimentation im Baldegger-und Hallwilersee.* Diss. Juris-Verlag, Zürich, 1–118.

References 191

BACKHAUS D. (1967) Ökologische Untersuchungen an den Aufwuchsalgen der obersten Donau und ihrer Quellflüsse. *Arch. Hydrobiol.* (*Suppl.*) **30** (4), 364–399.

BAKER D.N. and MUSGRAVE R.B. (1964) Photosynthesis under field conditions. V. Further plant chamber studies of the effects of light on corn (Zea mays). *Crop. Sci.* **4**, 127–131.

BALLANTINE D. (1953) Comparison of the different methods of estimating nanoplankton. *J. Mar. Biol. Ass. UK*, **32**, 129–147.

BARBER D.A. (1961) Gas exchange between *Equisetum limosum* and its environment. *J. Exp. Bot.* **12**, 243–251.

BARNES H. (1952) The use of transformations in marine biological statistics. *J. Cons. Int. Explor. Mer*, **18**, 61–71.

BAUER G. (1957) *Die Ausnützung der Sonnenenergie durch das Phytoplankton eines eutrophen Sees.* Diss. Univ. München (Ph.D. Thesis).

BEETON A.M. (1957) Relationship between Secchi disk readings and light penetration in Lake Huron. *Trans. Amer. Fish. Soc.* **87**, 73–79.

BELCHER R. and INGRAM S. (1950) A rapid micro-combustion method for the determination of carbon and hydrogen. *Analytica chim. Acta*, **4**, 118–129.

BERARDI G. and TONOLLI V. (1952) Clorofilla, fitoplancton e vicende meteorologiche (Lago Maggiore). *Mem. Ist. Ital. Idrobiol.* **7**, 165–187.

BERGE G. (1958) The primary production in the Norwegian Sea in June 1954, measured by an adapted C-14 technique. *Rapp. Cons. Explor. Mer*, **144**, 85–91.

BERGER F. (1961) Über den 'Taucheffekt' bei Lichtmessung über und unter Wasser. *Arch. Meteorol.* (*B*), **11**, 224–240.

BERNATOWICZ S. (1960) Metody badania roslinnosci naczyniowej w jeziorach (The methods of investigations of vascular plants in lakes: in Polish with English and Russian summaries). *Roczn. Nauk Roln.* **77** (B1), 61–78.

BEYERS R.J. (1963) A characteristic diurnal metabolic pattern in balanced microcosms. *Publs. Inst. Mar. Sci. Univ. Tex.* **9**, 19–27.

BEYERS R.J. and ODUM H.T. (1959) The use of carbon dioxide to construct pH curves for the measurement of productivity. *Limnol. and Oceanogr.* **4**, 499–502.

BEYERS R.J., LARIMER J.L., ODUM H.T., PARKER R.B. and ARMSTRONG N.E. (1963) Directions for the determination of changes in carbon dioxide concentration from changes in pH. *Publ. Inst. Mar. Sci. Univ. Tex.* **9**, 454–489.

BORUTSKII E.V. (1950) Data on the dynamics of the biomass of the macrophytes of lakes (in Russian). *Trudy vses. gidrobiol. Obshch.* **2**, 43–68.

BORUTSKII E.V. (1959) Metodika izucheniya dinamiki biomass'i makrofitov vodokhranilishch (Methods for the study of the dynamics of the biomass of macrophytes in reservoirs: in Russian). *Trudy VI Sovetschchaniya problemam biologii vnutrennikh vod*, 580–588.

BOURN W.S. (1932) Ecological and physiological studies on certain aquatic angiosperms. *Contr. Boyce Thompson Inst. Plant Res.* **4**, 425–496.

BRAY J.R. (1961) Measurement of leaf utilisation as an index of minimum level of primary consumption. *Oikos*, **12**, 70–74.

BROCK T.D. and BROCK M.L. (1967) The measurement of chlorophyll, primary productivity, photophosphorylation and macromolecules in benthic algae. *Limnol. and Oceanogr.* **12**, 600–605.

BRUINSMA J. (1963) The quantitative analysis of chlorophylls *a* and *b* in plant extracts. *Photochem. Photobiol.* **2**, 241–249.

BUCH K. (1945) Kolsyrejämvikten i Baltiskahavet. *Fennia,* **68** (5), 1-208.

BUNT J. (1965) Measurements of photosynthesis and respiration in a marine diatom with the mass spectrometer and with carbon-14. *Nature,* **207**, 1373–1375.

BUTKEVICH W.S. (1932) An apparatus for the collection of water samples for microbiological investigations (in Russian). *Mikrobiologiia,* **1** (3).

CASSIE R.M. (1962) Frequency distribution models in the ecology of plankton and other organisms. *J. Anim. Ecol.* **31**, 65–92.

CASSIE R.M. (1963) Multivariate analysis in the interpretation of numerical plankton data. *N.Z. J. Sci.* **6**, 36–59.

CASTENHOLZ R.W. (1960) Seasonal changes in the attached algae of freshwater and saline lakes in the Lower Grand Coulee, Washington. *Limnol. and Oceanogr.* **5**, 1–28.

CASTENHOLZ R.W. (1961) An evaluation of a submerged glass method of estimating production of attached algae. *Verh. int. Verein. Limnol.* **14**, 155–159.

CAVALLI-SFORZA L. (1961) *Analisi Statistiche per Medici e Biologi e Analisi del Dosaggio Biologico.* Edizioni Universitario Boringhieri, Torino.

CHU S.P. (1942). The influence of the mineral composition of the medium on the growth of planktonic algae. I. Methods and culture media. *J. Ecol.* **30**, 284–325.

CHU S.P. (1943) The influence of the mineral composition of the medium on the growth of planktonic algae. II. The influence of the concentration of inorganic nitrogen and phosphate phosphorus. *J. Ecol.* **31**, 109–148.

CHURCHILL M.A., ELMORE H.L. and BUCKINGRAM R.A. (1962) The prediction of stream reaeration rates. *Int. J. Air Wat. Pollut.* **6**, 467–504.

CLARKE G.L. (1941) Observations on the transparency in the South Western section of the North Atlantic Ocean. *J. Mar. Res.* **4**, 221–230.

COHEN G.N. and MONOD J. (1957) Bacterial permeases. *Bact. Rev.* **21**, 169–194.

COLE H.A. and KNIGHT-JONES E.W. (1949) Quantitative estimation of marine nannoplankton. *Nature,* **164**, 694–696.

COLLINS, VERA G. (1963) The distribution and ecology of bacteria in freshwater. *Proc. Soc. Water Treatment and Examination,* **12**, 40–73.

COOKE W.B. (1956) Colonisation of artificial bare areas by microorganisms. *Bot. Rev.* **22**, 613–638.

COPELAND B.J. and DUFFER W.R. (1964) The use of a clear plastic dome to measure gaseous diffusion rates in natural waters. *Limnol. and Oceanogr.* **9**, 494–499.

CUSHING D.H. (1957a) Production of carbon in the sea. *Nature,* **179**, 876.

CUSHING D.H. (1957b) Some experiments using the C-14 technique. *Rapp. Cons. Explor. Mer,* **144**, 73–75.

CONSEIL INT. EXPLOR. MER. (1958) *Rapp., Proc. Verb.* **144**, 1–158.

DANFORTH W.F. (1962) Substrate assimilation and heterotrophy. In: *Physiology and Biochemistry of Algae,* R.A. Lewin (ed.). Academic Press, New York and London, 99–124.

DAVEY C.B. and WILDE S.A. (1955) Determination of the numbers of soil microorganisms by the use of molecular membrane filters. *Ecology,* **36**, 760–761.

DAVIS C.C. (1967) Circulation of matter versus flow of energy in production studies. *Arch. Hydrobiol.* **63**, 250–255.

DEEVEY E.S. (1957) Limnological studies in Middle America. *Trans. Conn. Acad. Arts Sci.* **39**, 213–328.

DEPARTMENT OF SCIENTIFIC AND INDUSTRIAL RESEARCH (1964) Effects of polluting discharges on the Thames estuary. *W.P.R. Technical Paper No.* 11. H.M. Stationery Office, London, 354–360.

DOBBINS W.E. (1964) BOD and oxygen relationships in streams. *J. sanit. Engng. Div. Am. Soc. civ. Engrs.* **90** (SA3), 53–78.

DOTY M.S. (1959) Phytoplankton photosynthetic periodicity as a function of latitude. *J. Mar. Biol. Ass. India,* **1**, 66–68.

DOTY M.S. and OGURI M. (1957) Evidence for a photosynthetic daily periodicity. *Limnol. and Oceanogr.* **2**, 37–40.

DOTY M.S. and OGURI M. (1958) Selected features of the isotopic carbon primary productivity techniques. *Rapp. Cons. Explor. Mer,* **144**, 47–55.

DOTY M.S. and OGURI M. (1959) The carbon-14 technique for determining primary plankton productivity. *Pubbl. Staz. Zool. Napoli,* **31** (Suppl.), 70–94.

DOUGLAS B. (1958) The ecology of the attached diatoms and other algae in a small stony stream. *J. Ecol.* **46**, 295–322.

DOWNING A.L., MELBOURNE K.V. and BRUCE A.M. (1957) The effect of contaminants on the rate of aeration of water. *J. appl. Chem., London,* **7**, 590–596.

DUGDALE R.C. and WALLACE J.T. (1960) Light and dark bottle experiments in Alaska. *Limnol. and Oceanogr.* **5**, 230–231.

DROOP M.R. (1962) Organic micronutrients. In: *Physiology and Biochemistry of Algae,* R.A. Lewin (ed.), 141–160. Academic Press, New York and London.

DYSON N., JITTS H.R. and SCOTT B.D. (1965) Techniques for measuring oceanic primary production using radioactive carbon. *Tech. Pap. Div. Fish. Oceanogr. CSIRO. Aust. No.* 18.

EATON J.W. and MOSS B. (1966) The estimation of numbers and pigment content in epipelic algal populations. *Limnol and Oceanogr.* **11**, 584–595.

EDEN G.E. (1959) Some uses of radioisotopes in the study of sewage-treatment processes. *J. Inst. Sew. Purif.* 1959, 522–538.

EDMONDSON W.T. (1961) Changes in Lake Washington following an increase in the nutrient income. *Verh. Int. Verein. Limnol.* **14**, 167–175.

EDMONDSON W.T. (ed., in prep.) *Methods for Assessment of Secondary Production in Freshwaters.* Blackwell Scientific Publications, Oxford.

EDWARDS R.W. (1962) Some effects of plants and animals on the conditions in freshwater streams with particular reference to their oxygen balance. *Int. J. Air Wat. Pollut.* **6**, 505–520.

EDWARDS R.W. and BROWN M.W. (1960) An aerial photographic method for studying the distribution of aquatic macrophytes in shallow waters. *J. Ecol.* **48**, 161–163.

EDWARDS R.W. and OWENS M. (1960) The effects of plants on river conditions. I. Summer crops and estimates of net productivity of macrophytes in a chalk stream. *J. Ecol.* **48**, 151–160.

EDWARDS R.W., OWENS M. and GIBBS J.W. (1961) Estimates of surface aeration in two streams. *J. Instn. Wat. Engrs.* **15**, 395–405.

EDWARDS R.W. and OWENS M. (1962) The effect of plants on river conditions. IV. The oxygen balance of a chalk stream. *J. Ecol.* **50**, 207–220.

EDWARDS R.W. and OWENS M. (1965) The oxygen balance of streams. In: *Ecology and the Industrial Society,* Goodman G.T., Edwards R.W. and Lambert J.M. (eds.). *Symp. Brit. Ecol. Soc.* **6**, 149–172. Blackwell Scientific Publications, Oxford.

EDWARDS R.W. and ROLLEY H.L.J. (1965) Oxygen consumption of river muds. *J. Ecol.* **53**, 1–19.

EGLE K. and SCHENK W. (1952) Untersuchungen über die Reassimilation der Atmungs-kohlensäure bei der Photosynthese der Pflanzen. *Beitr. Biol. Pflanz.* **29**, 75–105.

EICHELBERGER H.H. (1963) Ecological investigation of the periphyton ('Aufwuchs') community in the Ohio River at Louisville, Kentucky. M.Sc. Dissertation, University of Louisville.

EINSELE W. and GRIM J. (1938) Über den Kieselsäuregehalt planktischer Diatomeen und dessen Bedeutung für einige Fragen ihrer Ökologie. *Z. Bot.* **32**, 545–590.

EL-SAYED S.Z. and LEE B.D. (1963) Evaluation of an automatic technique for counting unicellular organisms. *J. Mar. Res.* **21**, 59–73.

ELSTER H.-J. and MOTSCH B. (1966) Untersuchungen über das Phytoplankton und die organische Urproduktion in einigen Seen des Hochschwarzwalds, im Schleinsee und Bodensee. *Arch. Hydrobiol. Suppl.* **28**, 291–376.

FAGER E.W., FLECHSIG A.O. *et al.* (1966) Equipment for use in ecological studies using SCUBA. *Limnol. and Oceanogr.* **11**, 503–509.

FELFÖLDY L.J.M. and KALKO Z.F. (1958) A vizalatti fenyviszonyok es a fotoszintezis összefüggese a Balatonban, 1957 nyaran (The rate of photosynthesis and underwater radiation in Lake Balaton. Observations of summer 1957). *Annal. Biol. Tihany,* **25**, 303–329 (in Hungarian, English summary).

FINDENEGG I. (1933) Alpenseen ohne Vollzirkulation. *Int. Rev. ges. Hydrobiol.* **28**, 295–311.

FINDENEGG I. (1964) Produktionsbiologische Planktonuntersuchungen an Ostalpenseen. *Int. Rev. ges. Hydrobiol.* **49**, 381–416.

FINDENEGG I. (1966) Die Bedeutung kurzwelliger Strahlung für die planktische Primär-produktion in Seen. *Verh. Int. Verein. Limnol.* **16**, 314–320.

FOGG G.E. (1963) The role of algae in organic production in aquatic environments. *Brit. Phyc. Bull.* **2**, 195–205.

FOGG G.E., NALEWAJKO C. and WATT W.D. (1965) Extracellular products of phytoplankton photosynthesis. *Proc. Roy. Soc. B.* **162**, 517–534.

FORSBERG C. (1959) Quantitative sampling of sub-aquatic vegetation. *Oikos,* **10**, 233–240.

FOX H.M. and WINGFIELD C.A. (1938) A portable apparatus for the determination of oxygen dissolved in a small volume of water. *J. Exp. Biol.* **15**, 437–445.

FRED E.B. and WAKSMAN S.A. (1928) *Laboratory Manual of General Microbiology.* New York and London.

FREY D.G. and STAHL J.G. (1958) Measurements of primary production on Southampton Island in the Canadian Arctic. *Limnol. and Oceanogr.* **3**, 215–221.

FROBISHER M. (1962) *Microbiology,* 7th edition. W.B. Saunders, Philadelphia and London.

GAMESON A.L.H., TRUESDALE G.A. and DOWNING A.L. (1955) Reaeration studies in a lakeland beck. *J. Instn. Wat. Engrs.* **9**, 57–94.

References   195

GAMBARYAN S. (1962) On the method of estimation of the intensity of destruction of organic matter in silts of deep water bodies (in Russian). *Microbiologiia*, 31, 895.

GESSNER F. (1944) Der Chlorophyllgehalt der Seen als Ausdruck ihrer Produktivität. *Arch. Hydrobiol.* 40, 687–732.

GESSNER F. (1949) Der Chlorophyllgehalt im See und seine photosynthetische Valenz als geophysikalisches Problem. *Schweiz. Z. Hydrol.* 11, 378–410.

GESSNER F. and PANNIER F. (1958) Influence of oxygen tension on respiration of phytoplankton. *Limnol. and Oceanogr.* 3, 478–480.

GESSNER F. and PANNIER F. (1958) Der Sauerstoffverbrauch der Wasserpflanzen bei verschiedenen Sauerstoffspannungen. *Hydrobiologia*, 10, 325–351.

GESSNER F. (1959) *Hydrobotanik. Band II.* Stoffhaushalt VEB Deutscher Verlag, Berlin.

GESSNER F. (1960) Die Photosynthese des Phytoplanktons. In: *Handbuch der Pflanzenphysiologie* (edited by W. RUHLAND), 5 (2), 521–567.

GILLBRICHT M. (1962) Über das Auszählen von Planktonschöpfproben. *Helgoländer Wiss. Meeresunter.* 8, 203–218.

GOLDMAN C.R. (1960) Primary productivity and limiting factors in three lakes of the Alaska Peninsula. *Ecol. Monogr.* 30, 207–230.

GOLDMAN C.R. (1962) A method of studying nutrient limiting factors in situ, in water columns isolated by polyethylene film. *Limnol. and Oceanogr.* 7, 99–101.

GOLDMAN C.R. (1963) Measurement of primary productivity and limiting factors in freshwater with C-14. In: *Proc. Conf. on primary productivity measurement, marine and freshwater* (edited by M.S. DOTY). Univ. Hawaii, Aug.–Sept. 1961. *U.S. Atomic Energy Commission Div. Tech. Inf. T.I.D.* 7633, 103–113.

GOLDMAN C.R., MASON D.T. and WOOD B.J.B. (1963) Light injury and inhibition in Antarctic freshwater phytoplankton. *Limnol. and Oceanogr.* 8, 313–322.

GOLTERMAN H.L. and CLYMO R.S. (1969) *Methods for Chemical Analysis of Freshwaters.* IBP Handbook No. 8. Blackwell Scientific Publications, Oxford.

GORSKI F. (1929) Récherches sur les méthodes de mesure de photosynthèse chez les plantes aquatiques submergées. *Acta Soc. Bot. Poloniae*, 6, 1–29.

GORSKI F. (1935) Gas interchange in aquatic plants during photosynthesis. *Bull. Int. Ac. Polon. Sci. Lett., Cl. Sci. Math. Nat. Ser. B*, 177–198.

GRASSLAND RESEARCH INSTITUTE STAFF (1961) Research techniques in use at the Grassland Research Institute, Hurley. *Bull. Commonw. Bur. Past. Fld. Crops.* No. 45.

GRIEG-SMITH P. (1964) *Quantitative Plant Ecology.* 2nd edition. Butterworth, London.

GRIM J. (1939) Beobachtungen am Phytoplankton des Bodensees (Obersee), sowie deren rechnerische Auswertung. *Int. Rev. ges. Hydrobiol.* 39, 193–315.

GRIM J. (1950a) Ein Vergleich der Produktionsleistung des Bodensee-Untersees, des Obersees und des Schleinsees. *Abhandlg. Fischerei Hilfswissensch.* 4, 787–841.

GRIM J. (1950b) Versuche zur Ermittlung der Produktionskoeffizienten einiger Planktophyten in einem flachen See. *Biol. Zentralblatt*, 69 (3/4), 147–174.

GRIM J. (1952) Vermehrungsleistungen planktischer Algenpopulationen in Gleichgewichtsperioden. *Arch. Hydrobiol., Suppl.* 20, 238–260.

GRONTVED J. (1957) A sampler for underwater macrovegetation in shallow waters. *J. Cons. Int. Explor. Mer*, 22, 293–297.

GRØNTVED J. (1960) On the productivity of microbenthos and phytoplankton in some Danish fjords. *Medd. Danmarks Fiskeri og Havundersøgelser N.S.* **3**, 55–92.

GRØNTVED J. (1962) Preliminary report on the productivity of microbenthos and phytoplankton in the Danish Wadden Sea. *Medd. Danmarks Fiskeri og Havundersøgelser N.S.* **3**, 347–378.

GUNNERSON C.G. and BAILEY T.E. (1963) Oxygen relationships in the Sacramento River. *J. sanit. Engng. Div., Am. Soc. Civ. Engrs.* **89**, 95–124.

GUTKNECHT J. (1963) Zn^{65} uptake by benthic marine algae. *Limnol. and Oceanogr.* **8**, 31–38.

HAASE L.-W. (1954) *Deutsche Einheitsverfahren zur Wasser-Abwasser und Schlammuntersuchung*. Verlag. Chemie, Weinheim.

HARROD J.J. and HALL R.E. (1962) A method for determining the surface areas of various aquatic plants. *Hydrobiologia,* **20**, 173–178.

HART I.C. (1967) Nomograms to calculate dissolved oxygen contents and exchange (mass transfer) coefficients. *Wat. Res.* **1**, 391–395.

HARTMAN R.T. and BROWN D.L. (1967) Changes in the composition of the internal atmosphere of submerged vascular hydrophytes in relation to photosynthesis. *Ecology,* **48**, 252–258.

HASTINGS J.W., SWEENEY B.M. and MULLIN M.M. (1962) Counting and sizing of unicellular marine organisms. *Ann. N.Y. Acad. Sci.* **99**, 280–289.

HAMMANN A. (1957) Assimilationszahlen submerser Phanerogamen und ihre Beziehung zur Kohlensäureversorgung. *Schweiz. Z. Hydrol.* **19**, 579–612.

HAYES F.R. and ANTHONY E.H. (1959) The standing crop of bacteria in lake sediments and its place in the classification of lakes. *Limnol. and Oceanogr.* **4**, 299–315.

HAYES F.R. and MACAULAY M.A. (1959) Lake water and sediment. V. Oxygen consumed in water over sediment cores. *Limnol. and Oceanogr.* **4**, 291–298.

HENDLER R.W. (1959) Self absorption correction for carbon-14. *Science,* **130**, 772–777.

HEPHER B. (1962) Primary production in fishponds and its application to fertilisation experiments. *Limnol. and Oceanogr.* **7**, 131–136.

HILL R. and WHITTINHAM C.P. (1955) *Photosynthesis. Methuen's Monographs*. John Wiley, New York.

HOBBIE J.E. and WRIGHT R.T. (1965) Bioassay with bacterial uptake kinetics: glucose in freshwater. *Limnol. and Oceanog.* **10**, 471–474.

HOLMES R.W. and WIDRIG T.M. (1956) The enumeration and collection of marine phytoplankton. *J. Cons. Int. Explor. Mer,* **22**, 21–32.

HOLMES R.W. (1962) The preparation of marine phytoplankton for microscopic examination and enumeration on molecular filters. *U.S. Fish and Wildlife Serv., Spec. Sci. Rep. Fish,* **433**, 6 pp.

HOLM-HANSEN O., LORENZEN C., HOLMES R.W. and STRICKLAND J.D.H. (1965) Fluorometric determination of chlorophyll. *J. Cons. int. Explor. Mer,* **30**, 3–15.

HOSKIN C.M. (1959) Studies of oxygen metabolism of streams in North Carolina. *Publs. Inst. mar. Sci. Univ. Texas,* **6**, 186–192.

HUTCHINSON G.E. (1957) *A Treatise on Limnology,* Vol. I. *Geography, Physics and Chemistry*. John Wiley, New York and London.

HUTCHINSON G.E. (1967) *A Treatise on Limnology,* Vol. II. *Introduction to Lake Biology and the Limnoplankton*. John Wiley, New York and London.

IBP News No. 2 (February 1965). IBP Central Office, London.

ICHIMURA S. (1956) On the ecological meaning of transparency for the production of matter in phytoplankton community of lake. *Bot. Mag., Tokyo,* **69,** 219–226.

ICHIMURA S. (1960) Photosynthesis pattern of natural phytoplankton relating to light intensity. *Bot. Mag., Tokyo,* **73,** 458–467.

ICHIMURA S. and SAIJO Y. (1958) On the application of C-14 method measuring organic matter production in the lake. *Bot. Mag., Tokyo,* **71,** 174–180.

ICHIMURA S., SAIJO Y. and ARUGA Y. (1962) Photosynthetic characteristics of marine phytoplankton and their ecological meaning in the chlorophyll method. *Bot. Mag., Tokyo,* **75,** 212–220.

ISSACHENKO B.L. (1951) Selected works. *Acad. Sci. USSR, Moscow,* **1** (in Russian).

IVANOV M.W. (1954) Estimation of the duration of one generation of aquatic bacteria. *Trans. Inst. Microbiology, Acad. Sci. USSR.* **3,** 213 (in Russian).

IVANOV M.W. (1955) The method of the estimation of biomass of bacteria in a water basin. *Microbiologiia,* **24** (1), 79–89.

JAAG O, AMBÜHL H. and ZIMMERMANN P. (1956) Über die Entnahme von Wasserproben in fliessenden Gewässern. *Schweiz. Z. Hydrol.* **18,** 156–160.

JANNASCH H.W. and JONES G.E. (1959) Bacterial populations in sea water as determined by different methods of enumeration. *Limnol. and Oceanogr.* **4** (2), 128–139.

JANNASCH H.W. (1965) Biological significance of bacterial counts in aquatic environment. *Proc. Atmospheric Biol. Conf.* 127–132.

JAVORNICKY P. (1958) Revise některych metod pro zjišťovani kvantity fytoplanktonu. *Sbornik vys. školy chem.-technol. v Praze,* **2,** 283–367 (Czech, English summary).

JENKIN P.M. (1937) Oxygen production by the diatom *Coscinodiscus excentricus* Ehr. in relation to submarine illumination in the English Channel. *J. Mar. Biol. Ass. UK.* **22,** 301–343.

JENKINS R.V. (1959) An airflow planimeter for measuring the area of detached leaves. *Pl. Physiol.* **34,** 532–536.

JITTS H.R. and SCOTT B.D. (1961) The determination of zero thickness activity in Geiger counting of C-14 solutions used in marine productivity studies. *Limnol. and Oceanogr.* **6,** 116–123.

JITTS H.R. (1963) The simulated *in situ* measurement of oceanic primary production. *Austr. J. mar. Freshwat. Res.* **14** (2), 139–147.

JITTS H.R., MCALLISTER C.D., STEPHENS K. and STRICKLAND J.D.H. (1964) The cell division rates of some marine phytoplankters as a function of light and temperature. *J. Fish. Res. Bd. Canada,* **21,** 139–157.

JOERIS L.S. (1964) A horizontal sampler for collection of water samples near the bottom. *Limnol. and Oceanogr.* **9,** 595–598.

JOYET G. (1949) Méthodes de travail biologique à l'aide d'isotopes radioactifs. Le dosage relatif dans les cendres de tissus. *Bull. Acad. Suisse Sciences Médicales,* **5** (5/6), 361–404.

JUDAY C. (1940) The annual energy budget of an inland lake. *Ecology,* **21,** 438–450.

KALLE K. (1949) Fluoreszenz und Gelbstoff im Bottnischen und Finnischen Meerbusen. *D. Hydrogr. Ztschr.* **2,** 117–124.

KALLE K. (1959) Chlorophyll, organised and free fluorescence—three counteractors in the biochemical cycle of the seas. *Intern. Oceanogr. Congr.,* Preprints, 947–949.

198 *References*

KANWISHER J. (1963) On the exchange of gases between the atmosphere and the sea. *Deep-Sea Res.* 10, 195–207.

KEVERN N.R. and BALL R.C. (1965) Primary productivity and energy relationships in artificial streams. *Limnol. and Oceanogr.* 10, 74–87.

KEVERN N.R., WILHM J.L. and VAN DYNE G.M. (1966) Use of artificial substrata to estimate the productivity of periphyton. *Limnol. and Oceanogr.* 11, 499–502.

KIMBALL J.F. and FERGUSON WOOD E.J. (1964) A simple centrifuge for phytoplankton studies. *Bull. Mar. Sc. Gulf Caribbean*, 14, 539–544.

KING D.L. and BALL R.C. (1966) A qualitative and quantitative measure of Aufwuchs production. *Trans. Amer. Microsc. Soc.* 85, 232–240.

KLIFFMÜLLER R. (1960) Die in den Bodensee-Obersee eingebrachten Schmutz und Düngstoffe und ihr Verbleib. *Int. Rev. ges. Hydrobiol.* 45, 359–380.

KOBAYASI H. (1961) Productivity in sessile algal community of Japanese mountain river. *Bot. Mag., Tokyo*, 74, 331–341.

KOSICKA A. and KOSICKI S. (1959) Zdjecie florystyczne jeziora Skonal przy zastosowaniu metody nurkowej (A floral sketch of Skonal Lake done by diving method). *Polskie Arch. Hydrobiol.* 6, 133–153. (In Polish with English and Russian summaries.)

KOZMIŃSKI Z. (1938) Amount and distribution of chlorophyll in lakes of North Eastern Wisconsin. *Trans. Wisconsin Acad. Sci.* 31, 411–438.

KREY J. (1961) Der Detritus in Meere. *J. Cons. Int. Explor. Mer*, 26, 263–280.

KUHL A. (1962) Zur Physiologie der Speicherung anorganischer Phosphat in *Chlorella*. *Vortr. Gesamtgeb. Botan., hrsg. Deut. Botan. Ges. (N.F.)* 1, 157–166.

KUHL A. and LORENZEN H. (1964) Handling and culturing of *Chlorella*. In: *Methods in Cell Physiology*, edited by D.M. Prescott, Vol. 1, 159–187. Academic Press, New York and London.

KURASAWA H. (1959) Studies on the biological production of fire pools in Tokyo XII. The seasonal changes in the amount of algae attached on the wall of pools. *Misc. Rep. Res. Inst. Nat. Resources*, 51, 15–21.

KUZNEZOV S.I. (1959) *Die Rolle der Mikroorganismen im Stoffkreislauf der Seen*, VEB. Deutscher Verlag der Wiss., Berlin.

KUZNEZOV S.I. and ROMANENKO W.I. (1963) *Microbiological study of inland waters*. Acad. Sci. USSR, Moscow 1–127 (in Russian).

KUZNEZOV S.I. and ROMANENKO W.I. (1966) Produktion der Biomasse heterotropher Bakterien und die Geschwindigkeit ihrer Vermehrung im Rybinsk-Stausee. *Verh. Int. Verein. Limnol.* 16, 1493–1500.

LAESSLE A.M. (1961) A microlimnological study of Jamaican bromeliads. *Ecology*, 12, 199–217.

LACKEY J.B. (1938) The manipulation and counting of river plankton and changes in some organisms due to formalin preservation. *U.S. Public Health Reports*, 53, 2080–2093.

LANDINGHAM VAN J.W. (1960) A note on a stabilised starch indicator for use in iodometric and iodimetric determinations. *Limnol. and Oceanogr.* 5, 343–345.

LANG G. (1964) Vegetations Forschung am Bodensee. *Umschau*, 9, 270–275.

LANG G. (1967) Die Ufervegetation des Westlichen Bodensees. *Arch. Hydrobiol. (Suppl.)*. 32, 437–574.

LINDER A. (1964) *Statistische Methoden für Naturwissenschafter, Mediziner, und Ingenieure.* Verlag Berkhausser, Basel.

LIPIN A.N. and LIPINA N.N. (1939) On methods of hydrobiological work. *Trudy Lab. sapropel. Otlozh.* **1**, 174–180. (English summary, in Russian).

LISON L. (1958) *Statistique Appliquée à la Biologie Expérimentale. La planification de l'expérience et l'analyse des résultats.* Gaulthier Vellons, Paris.

LORENZEN C.J. (1967) Determination of chlorophyll and pheo-pigments: spectrophotometric equations. *Limnol. and Oceanogr.* **12**, 343–346.

LUND J.W.G. (1942) The marginal algae of certain ponds, with special reference to the bottom deposits. *J. Ecol.* **30**, 245–283.

LUND J.W.G. (1949) Studies on *Asterionella formosa* Hass. I. The origin and nature of the cells producing seasonal maxima. *J' Ecol.* **37**, 389–419.

LUND J.W.G. (1950) Studies on *Asterionella formosa* Hass. II. Nutrient depletion and the spring maximum. *J. Ecol.* **38**, 1–35.

LUND J.W.G. (1951) A sedimentation technique for counting algae and other organisms. *Hydrobiologia*, **3**, 390–394.

LUND J.W.G. (1954) The seasonal cycle of the plankton diatom *Melosira italica* subsp. *subarctica* O. Müll. *J. Ecol.* **42**, 151–179.

LUND J.W.G. and TALLING J.F. (1957) Botanical limnological methods with special reference to the algae. *Bot. Rev.* **23**, 489–583.

LUND J.W.G., KIPLING C. and LE CREN E.D. (1958) The inverted microscope method of estimating algal numbers and the statistical basis of estimations by counting. *Hydrobiologia*, **11**, 143–170.

LUND J.W.G. (1959) A simple counting chamber for nannoplankton. *Limnol. and Oceanogr.* **4**, 57–65.

LUND J.W.G. (1964) Primary production and periodicity of phytoplankton. *Verh. Int. Verein. Limnol.* **15**, 37–56.

LUND J.W.G., MACKERETH F.J.H. and MORTIMER C.H. (1963) Changes in depth and time of certain chemical and physical conditions and of the standing crop of *Asterionella formosa* Hass. in the North Basin of Windermere in 1947. *Phil. Trans. B.* **246**, 255–290.

MACFARLANE C. (1952) A survey of certain seaweeds of commercial importance in South-West Nova Scotia. *Canad. J. Bot.* **30**, 78–97.

MADGWICK J.C. (1966) Chromatographic determination of chlorophylls in algal cultures and phytoplankton. *Deep-Sea Res.* **13** (3), 459–466.

MALONEY T.E., DONOVAL E.J. and ROBINSON E.L. (1962) Determination of numbers and sizes of algal cells with an electronic particle counter. *Phycologia*, **2**, 1–8.

MANNING W.M. and JUDAY R.E. (1941) The chlorophyll content and productivity of some lakes in North-Eastern Wisconsin. *Trans. Wisc. Acad. Sci., Arts, Letts.* **33**, 363–393.

MARGALEF R. (1949) A new limnological method for the investigation of thin-layered epilithic communities. *Hydrobiologia*, **1**, 215–216.

MARGALEF R. (1965) Ecological correlations and relationship between primary productivity and community structure. Proc. IBP–PF Symposium. *Mem. Ist. Ital. Idrobiol. (Suppl.)* **18**, 357–364.

MATHEWS C.P. and WESTLAKE D.F. (1969) Estimation of production by populations of higher plants subject to high mortality. *Oikos*, **20** (1).

McALLISTER C.D. (1961) Observations on the variation of planktonic photosynthesis with light intensity using both the O_2 and C-14 methods. *Limnol. and Oceanogr.* **6** (4), 483–484.

McALLISTER C.D., PARSONS T.R., STEPHENS K. and STRICKLAND J.D.H. (1961) Measurements of primary production in coastal seawater using a large plastic sphere. *Limnol. and Oceanogr.* **6**, 237–258.

McALLISTER C.D. and STRICKLAND J.D.H. (1961) Light attenuators for use in phytoplankton photosynthesis studies. *Limnol. and Oceanogr.* **6**, 226–228.

McALLISTER C.D., SHAH N. and STRICKLAND J.D.H. (1964) Marine phytoplankton photosynthesis as a function of light intensity: a comparison of methods. *J. Fish. Res. Bd. Canada*, **21**, 159–181.

McCONNELL W.J. and SIGLER W.F. (1959) Chlorophyll and productivity in a mountain river. *Limnol. and Oceanogr.* **4**, 335–351.

McINTIRE C.D. and PHINNEY H.K. (1965) Laboratory studies of periphyton production and community metabolism in lotic environments. *Ecol. Monogr.* **35**, 237–258.

MILNER C. and HUGHES R.E. (1968) *Methods for the Measurement of the Primary Production of Grassland*—IBP Handbook No. 6. Blackwell Scientific Publications, Oxford.

MONTEITH J.L. (1962) Measurement and interpretation of carbon dioxide fluxes in the field. *Neth. J. Agri. Sci.* **10**, 334–346.

MONTGOMERY H.A.C. (1967). The determination of biochemical oxygen demand by respirometric methods. *Water Res.* **1**, 631–662.

MONTGOMERY H.A.C., THOM N.S. and COCKBURN A. (1964). Determination of dissolved oxygen by the Winkler method and the solubility of oxygen in pure water and seawater. *J. Appl. Chem.* **14**, 280–296.

MOORE J.K. (1963) Refinement of a method for filtering and preserving marine phytoplankton on a membrane filter. *Limnol. and Oceanogr.* **8**, 304–305.

MORTIMER C.H. (1940) An apparatus for obtaining water from different depths for bacteriological examination. *J. Hyg.* **40**, 641–646.

MORTIMER C.H. (1942) The exchange of dissolved substances between mud and water in lakes. III & IV. *J. Ecol.* **30**, 147–201.

MOSS B. (1967a) A spectrophotometric method for the estimation of percentage degradation of chlorophylls to pheo-pigments in extracts of algae. *Limnol. and Oceanogr.* **12**, 335–340.

MOSS B. (1967b) A note on the estimation of chlorophyll *a* in freshwater algal communities. *Limnol. and Oceanogr.* **12**, 340–342.

MULLIN M.M., SLOAN P.R. and EPPLEY R.W. (1966) Relationship between organic carbon content, cell volume, and area in phytoplankton. *Limnol. and Oceanogr.* **11**, 307–311.

MYERS J. (1962) Laboratory cultures. In: *Physiology and Biochemistry of Algae* (edited by R.A. LEWIN), pp. 603–615. Academic Press, New York and London.

NASYROV JU.S., GILLER JU.E., LOGINOV M.A. and LEBEDEV V.N. (1962) The use of C-14 for studying the photosynthetic balance of plant communities. *Bot. Zh. SSSR.* **47**, 1–96.

NAUWERCK A. (1963) Die Beziehungen zwischen Zooplankton und Phytoplankton im See Erken. *Symb. Bot. Upsal.* **17** (5), 1–163.

NYGAARD G. (1958) On the productivity of the bottom vegetation in Lake Grane Langsø *Verh. Intern. Verein. Limnol.* **13**, 144–155.

O'CONNOR D.J. and DOBBINS W.E. (1956) Mechanism of reaeration in natural streams. *J. Sanit. Engng. Div., Am. Soc. Civ. Engrs.* **82**, SA6. Paper 1115.

ODUM E.P., KUENZLER E.J. and BLUNT M.X. (1958) Uptake of P^{32} and primary productivity in marine benthic algae. *Limnol. and Oceanogr.* **3**, 340–348.

ODUM H.T. (1956) Primary production in flowing waters. *Limnol. and Oceanogr.* **1**, 103–117.

ODUM H.T. (1957) Trophic structure and productivity of Silver Springs, Florida. *Ecol. Monogr.* **27**, 55–112.

ODUM H.T. and HOSKIN C.M. (1958) Comparative studies on the metabolism of marine waters. *Publs. Inst. Mar. Sci., Univ. Texas,* **5**, 15–46.

ODUM H.T. and WILSON R.F. (1962) Further studies on reaeration and metabolism of Texas Bays 1958–60. *Publs. Inst. Mar. Sci., Univ. Texas,* **8**, 23–55.

ODUM H.T., SILER W.L., BEYERS R.J. and ARMSTRONG N. (1963) Experiments with engineering of marine ecosystems. *Publs. Inst. Mar. Sci., Univ. Texas,* **9**, 373–403.

OHLE W. (1938) Zur Vervollkommnung der hydrochemischen Analyse. III. Die Phosphorbestimmung. *Angew. Chemie,* **51**, 906–911.

OHLE W. (1958) Diurnal production and destruction rates of phytoplankton in lakes. *Rapp. Cons. Explor. Mer,* **144**, 129–131.

OHLE W. (1961) Tagesrhythmen der Photosynthese von Planktonbiocoenosen. *Verh. Int. Verein. Limnol.* **14**, 113–119.

OMELIJANSKII W.I. (1940) *Manual on Microbiology.* Ed. Acad. Sci. USSR, Moscow (in Russian).

OWEN R.W. (1963) Trailing incubator for studies of C-14 uptake by phytoplankton. *Limnol. and Oceanogr.* **8**, 297–298.

OWENS M., EDWARDS R.W. and GIBBS J.W. (1964) Some reaeration studies in streams. *Int. J. Air Wat. Pollut.* **8**, 469–486.

OWENS M. and MARIS P.J. (1964) Some factors affecting the respiration of some aquatic plants. *Hydrobiologia,* **23**, 533–543.

OWENS M., LEARNER M.A.J. and MARIS P.J.M. (1967) Determination of aquatic plants using an optical method. *J. Ecol.* **55** (3), 671–676.

PAASCHE E. (1960) On the relationship between primary production and standing stock of phytoplankton. *J. Cons: Int. Explor. Mer,* **26**, 33–48.

PAASCHE E. (1963) The adaptation of the C-14 method for the measurement of coccolith production in *Coccolithus huxleyi. Physiol. Plant.* **16**, 186–200.

PAINE R.T. (1966) Endothermy in bomb calorimetry. *Limnol. and Oceanogr.* **11**, 126–129.

PALMER C.M. and MALONEY T.E. (1954) A new counting slide for nannoplankton. *Spec. Publ. Limnol. Oceanogr. Soc. America,* **21**, 1–6.

PARK K., HOOD D.W. and ODUM H.T. (1958) Diurnal pH variation in Texas bays, and its application to primary production estimation. *Publ. Inst. Mar. Sci. Univ. Texas,* **5**, 47–64

PARSONS T.R. (1963) A new method for the microdetermination of chlorophyll *c* in sea water. *J. Mar. Res.* **21**, 164–171.

PARSONS T.R. and STRICKLAND J.D.H. (1962). On the production of particulate organic carbon by heterotrophic processes in sea water. *Deep-Sea Res.* **8**, 211–222.

PARSONS T.R. and STRICKLAND J.D.H. (1963) Discussion of spectrophotometric determination of marine plant pigments, with revised equations for ascertaining chlorophylls and carotenoids. *J. Mar. Res.* **21**, 155–163.

PATTEN B.C., NORCROSS J.J., YOUNG D.K. and RUTHERFORD C.L. (1964) Some experimental characteristics of dark and light bottles. *J. Cons. Int. Explor. Mer*, **28**, 335–353.

PETERSEN C.G.J. (1913) Om Baedeltangens (*Zostera marina*) Aarsproduktion i de danske Farvande. (On the annual production of *Z. marina* in Danish coastal waters—In Danish, English summary). In: *Mindeskr. Japetus Steenstrups. Fødsel.* **1** (9), 20 pp. (edited by H.F.E. JUNGERSEN and E. WARMING). Bianco Lunos Bogtrykkeri, Copenhagen.

PHILLIPSON J. (1964) A miniature bomb calorimeter for small biological samples. *Oikos*, **15**, 131–139.

PIECZYNSKA E. and SPODNIEWSKA I. (1963) Occurrence and colonisation of periphyton organisms in accordance with the type of substrate. *Ekol. Polska, Ser. A.* **11**, 533–545.

PIECZYNSKA E. (1965) Variations in the primary production of plankton and periphyton in the littoral zone of lakes. *Bull. Acad. Polon. Sci. Cl. II.* **13**, 219–225.

PIECZYNSKA E. (1968) Dependence of the primary production of periphyton upon the substrate area suitable for colonization. *Bull. Acad. pol. Sci. Cl. II Sér. Sci. biol.* **16** (3), 165–169.

PIONTELLI R. and TONOLLI V. (1964) Il tempo di residenza delle acque lacustri in relazione ai fenomeni di arricchimento in sostanze immesse, con particolare riguardo al Lago Maggiore. *Mem. Ist. Ital. Idrobiol.* **17**, 247–266.

POMEROY L.R. (1959) Productivity of algae in salt marshes. *Proc. Salt Marsh Conf., Univ. Georgia*, 1958. 88–95.

POOLE H.H. and ATKINS W.R.G. (1926) On the penetration of light into seawater. *J. Mar. Biol. Ass. U.K.* **14**, 177–198.

POOLE H.H. and ATKINS W.R.G. (1929) Photoelectric measurements of submarine illumination throughout the year. *J. Mar. Biol. Ass. U.K.* **16**, 297–324.

POTZGER E. and VAN ENGEL A. (1942) Study of the rooted aquatic vegetation of Weber Lake, Vilas County, Wisconsin. *Trans. Wisconsin Acad. Sci.* **34**, 149–166.

PRATT D.M. and BERKSON H. (1959) Two sources of error in the oxygen light and dark bottle method. *Limnol. and Oceanogr.* **4**, 328–334.

PRINGSHEIM E.G. (1949) *Pure Cultures of Algae, Their Preparation and Maintenance.* Cambridge University Press, London and New York.

PRINGSHEIM E.G., and WIESSNER W. (1960) Photoassimilation of acetate by green organisms. *Nature*, **188**, 919.

PROVASOLI L. (1958) Nutrition and ecology of protozoa and algae. *Ann. Rev. Microbiol.* **12**, 279–308.

PROVASOLI L. and PINTNER I.J. (1960) Artificial media for freshwater algae: problems and suggestions. In: *The Ecology of Algae, The Pymatuning Symposia in Ecology, Spec. Publ.* **2**, 84–96.

QUENOUILLE M.H. (1952) *Associated Measurements.* Butterworth, London; Academic Press, New York.

RACKHAM O. (1966) Radiation, transpiration, and growth in a woodland annual. In: *Light as an Ecological Factor.* (edited by R. BAINBRIDGE, G.C. EVANS and O. RACKHAM) *Symp. Brit. Ecol. Soc.* **6**, 41–51.

RASPOPOV I.M. (1962) On the application of diving apparatus to the study of higher aquatic vegetation of bays of northern Ladogi (Russian). In: *Biology of the Inland*

Waters of the Baltic. Scientific Conference on the Study of the Inland Waters of the Baltic, **7**, 241–244.

RASUMOV A.S. (1947) *Methods of Microbiological Studies of Water.* Ed. of the Inst. WODGEO, Moscow.

REDFIELD A.C., KETCHUM B.H. and RICHARDS F.A. (1963) The influence of organisms on the composition of sea water. In: *The Sea* (edited by M.A. HILL), Vol. 2, pp. 27–79. Interscience, New York.

RICHARDS F.A. and THOMPSON T.G. (1952) The estimation and characterisation of plankton populations by pigment analyses. II. A spectrophotometric method for the estimation of plankton pigments. *J. Mar. Res.* **11**, 156–172.

RICKER W.E. (ed.) (1968) *Methods for the Assessment of Fish Production in Freshwaters—* IBP Handbook No. 3 Blackwell Scientific Publications, Oxford.

RILEY G.A., STOMMEL H. and BUMPUS D.F. (1949) Quantitative ecology of the plankton of the Western North Atlantic. *Bull. Bingham Oceanogr. Coll.* **12** (3), 1–169.

RILEY G.A., VAN HEMERT D. and WANGERSKY P.J. (1965) Organic aggregates in surface and deep waters of the Sargasso Sea. *Limnol. and Oceanogr.* **10**, 354–363.

RIPPEL-BALDES A. (1947) *Grundriss der Mikrobiologie.* Springer-Verlag, Berlin-Göttingen.

RODHE W. (1948) Environmental requirements of freshwater plankton algae. *Symb. Bot. Upsal.* **10**, 1–149.

RODHE W. (1949) The ionic composition of lake waters. *Verh. Int. Verein. Limnol.* **10**, 377–386.

RODHE W. (1958) Primärproduktion und Seetypen. *Verh. Int. Verein. Limnol.* **13**, 121–140.

RODHE W., VOLLENWEIDER R.A. and NAUWERCK A. (1958) The primary production and standing crop of phytoplankton. In: *Perspectives in Marine Biology* (edited by A.A. BUZZATI-TRAVERSO), 299–322. University of California Press.

RODHE W. (1965) Standard correlations between pelagic photosynthesis and light. *Mem. Ist. Ital. Idrobiol. (Suppl.)* **18**, 365–381.

RODINA A.G. (1965) *Methods of Water Microbiology,* pp. 362 (in Russian). Editions 'Nauka' (Science) Moscow.

ROMANENKO W.I. (1964) Heterotrophic assimilation of CO_2 by the aquatic microflora. *Microbiologiia,* **33** (4), 679–683 (in Russian).

ROMANENKO W.I. (1964a) The dependence between the amounts of the O_2 and CO_2 consumed by heterotrophic bacteria. *Dokl. Ac. Sci. USSR.* **157** (1), 178–179) (in Russian).

ROMANENKO W.I. (1965) The relation between the consumption of oxygen and CO_2 by heterotrophic bacteria during the growth in the presence of peptone. *Microbiologiia,* **34** (3), 391–396 (in Russian).

ROUND F.E. (1953) An investigation of two benthic algal communities in Malham Tarn, Yorkshire. *J. Ecol.* **41**, 174–197.

ROUND F.E. (1965) *The Biology of the Algae.* E. Arnold, London.

ROUND F.E. and EATON J.W. (1966) Persistent, vertical-migration rhythms in benthic microflora. III. The rhythm of epipelic algae in a freshwater pond. *J. Ecol.* **54**, 609–615.

RUSSELL E.W. (1961) *Soil Conditions and Plant Growth.* 9th edition. John Wiley, New York.

RUTTNER F. (1948) Die Veränderungen des Äquivalentleitvermögens als Mass der Karbonatassimilation der Wasserpflanzen. *Schweiz. Z. Hydrol.* **11**, 72–89.

204 *References*

RUTTNER F. (1960) Über die Kohlenstoffaufnahme bei Algen aus der Rhodophyceen-Gattung *Batrachospermum*. *Schweiz. Z. Hydrol.* **22**, 280–291.

RYHÄNEN R. (1968) Die Bedeutung der Humussubstanzen im Stoffhaushalt der Gewässer Finnlands. *Mitt. Int. Verein. Limnol.* **14**, 168–178.

RYTHER J.H. (1956) Photosynthesis in the ocean as a function of light intensity. *Limnol. and Oceanogr.* **1**, 61–70.

RYTHER J.H. and YENTSCH C.S. (1957) The estimation of phytoplankton production in the ocean from chlorophyll and light data. *Limnol. and Oceanogr.* **2**, 281–286.

RYTHER J.H. and MENZEL D.W. (1965) Comparison of the C-14 technique with direct measurement of photosynthetic carbon fixation. *Limnol. and Oceanogr.* **10**, 490–492.

SAKAMOTO M. (1966) The chlorophyll amount in the euphotic zone in some Japanese lakes and its significance in the photosynthetic production of phytoplankton community. *Bot. Mag. Tokyo*, **79**, 77–88.

SAUBERER F. (1962) Empfehlungen für die Durchführung von Strahlungsmessungen an und in Gewässern. *Mitt. Int. Verein. Limnol.* **11**, 1–77.

SAUBERER F. and RUTTNER F. (1941) Die Strahlungsverhältnisse der Binnengewässer. In *Probleme Kosm. Phys.* **11**, 1–240.

SAUBERER F. and DIRMHIRN I. (1954) Über den Strahlungshaushalt der Ozeane auf der Nordhalbkugel. *Arch. Meteorol. Geophysik und Bioklimatol.*, Ser. B (6) 1/2, 115–127. :

SAUNDERS G.W. (1961) Investigations in lake metabolism—Bacteria: distribution and activities. *Great Lakes Div. Univ. of Michigan, Ann. Arbor*, publ. **7**, 162–163.

SAUNDERS G.W., TRAMA F.B. and BACHMANN R.W. (1962) Evaluation of a modified C-14 technique for shipboard estimation of photosynthesis in large lakes. *Great Lakes Div. Univ. of Michigan, Ann. Arbor, publ.* **8**, 1–61.

SCHMOLINSKY F. (1954) Einige Ergebnisse vergleichender Lichtmessungen an Seen des Hochschwarzwaldes und der Schweiz. *Arch. Hydrobiol. Suppl.* **20** (Falkau-Schr.), 615–632.

SCHWOERBEL J. (1966) *Methoden der Hydrobiologie*. Franckh'sche Verlagshandlung, Stuttgart.

SEAL H. (1964) *Multivariate Statistical Analysis for Biologists*. Methuen, London.

SEN N. and FOGG G.E. (1966) Effects of glycollate on the growth of a planktonic *Chlorella*. *J. Exp. Bot.* **17**, 417–425.

SERFLING R.E. (1949) Quantitative estimation of plankton from small samples of Sedgwick Rafter cell mounts of concentrate samples. *Trans. Amer. Micr. Soc.* **68**, 185–199.

SIEBURTH J.M. (1963) A simple form of ZoBell bacteriological sampler for shallow water. *Limnol. and Oceanogr.* **8**, 489–492.

SLADEČEK V. and SLADEČKOVA A. (1964) Determination of periphyton production by means of the glass slide method. *Hydrobiologia*, **23**, 125–158.

SLADEČKOVA A. (1962) Limnological investigation methods for the periphyton ('Aufwuchs') community. *Bot. Rev.* **28**, 286–350.

SMIRNOV N.N. (1961) Consumption of emergent plants by insects. *Verh. Int. Verein. Limnol.* **14**, 232–236.

SMITH J.H.C. and BENITEZ A. (1955) Chlorophylls: analysis in plant material. In: *Modern Methods of Plant Analysis* (edited by H. PAECH and M. TRACEY), **4**, 142–196. Springer, Berlin.

SNEDECOR G.W. (1962) *Statistical Methods Applied to Experiments in Agriculture and Biology.* Iowa State University Press, Ames, Iowa.

SOEDER C.J. (1965) Some aspects of phytoplankton growth and activity. *Mem. Ist. Ital. Idrobiol. Suppl.* **18,** 47–59.

SOEDER C.J. (1967) Tagesperiodische Vertikalwanderung bei begeisselten Planktonalgen. *Umschau,* **12,** 338.

SOROKIN Y.I. (1956) The use of radioactive carbon C–14 for studying the production of reservoirs. *Trudy vses. gidrobiol. Obshch.* **7,** 171–186 (in Russian).

SOROKIN Y.I. (1958) Results and prospects of using isotopic carbon for the investigation of carbon cycle in water basins. *Int. Conf. Radioisotopes,* UNESCO, Paris, **4,** 633–648.

SOROKIN Y.I. (1959) Determination of isotopic discrimination by photosynthesis. *Bull. Inst. Biol. Vodokhranil. Ac. Sci. USSR.* **4,** 7–9 (in Russian).

SOROKIN Y.I. (1959a) Determination of the productivity of photosynthesis of phytoplankton in water by C-14. *Fiziol. Rast.* **6,** 118–125 (in Russian).

SOROKIN Y.I. (1959b) Determination of the photosynthetic production of phytoplankton in water, using C-14. *Fiziol. Rast.* **6,** 125–133 (in Russian).

SOROKIN Y.I. (1960a) Vertical distribution of phytoplankton and the primary organic production in the sea. *J. Cons. Int. Explor. Mer,* **24,** 49–56.

SOROKIN Y.I. (1960b) The method of estimation of primary production in the sea by means of C-14. *Trud. vsesoyuz. gidrobiol. Obshch..* **10,** 235–254 (in Russian).

SOROKIN Y.I. (1960c) Bacteriological water bottle. *Byull. Inst. Biol. Vodokhranil. Ac. Sci. USSR.* **6,** 53–54 (in Russian).

SOROKIN Y.I. (1960d) Isotopic discrimination in the determination of chemosynthesis and photosynthesis in water bodies using C-14. *Microbiologiia,* **29** (2), 204–208 (in Russian).

SOROKIN Y.I. (1961) Heterotrophic carbon dioxide assimilation by microorganisms. *Zhurnal Obshchei Biologii,* **22** (4), 265–272 (in Russian).

SOROKIN Y.I. (1962) The estimation of correction coefficients of the self-absorption of the radiation C-14 in the determinations of photosynthesis and chemosynthesis production in water basins. *Microbiologiia,* **31,** 121 (in Russian).

SOROKIN Y.I. (1963) Primary organic production in the Atlantic Ocean. *Hydrobiologia,* **22,** 306–316.

SOROKIN Y.I. (1964) A quantitative study of the microflora in the Central Pacific Ocean. *J. Cons. Int. Explor. Mer,* **29** (1), 25–39.

SOROKIN Y.I. (1964a) On the primary production and bacterial activities in the Black Sea. *J. Cons. Int. Explor. Mer,* **29** (1), 41–60.

SOROKIN Y.I. (1964b) On the trophic role of chemosynthesis in water bodies. *Int. Rev. ges. Hydrobiol.* **49** (2), 307–324.

STAHL E. and WALDI D. (1965) *Thin Layer Chromatography. A laboratory handbook* (edited by EGON STAHL). Academic Press, New York and London.

STEELE J.H. (1962) Environmental control of photosynthesis in the sea. *Limnol. and Oceanogr.* **7,** 137–150.

STEEMANN NIELSEN E. (1951) Measurement of the production of organic matter in the sea. *Nature,* **167,** 684.

STEEMANN NIELSEN E. (1952) The use of radioactive carbon (C-14) for measuring organic production in the sea. *J. Cons. Int. Explor. Mer,* **18,** 117–140.

STEEMANN NIELSEN E. (1954) On organic production in the oceans. *J. Cons. Int. Explor. Mer,* **19** (3), 309–328.

STEEMANN NIELSEN E. (1955) Production of organic matter in the oceans. *J. Mar. Res.* **14** (4), 374–386.

STEEMANN NIELSEN E. (1957) Experimental methods for measuring organic production in the sea. *Rapp. Cons. Explor. Mer,* **144,** 38–45.

STEEMANN NIELSEN E. (1958) Experimental methods for measuring organic production in the sea. *Rapp. Cons. Explor. Mer,* **144,** 38–46.

STEEMANN NIELSEN E. (1963) Productivity, definition and measurement. In: *The Sea,* Vol. 2 (edited by M.N. HILL) 129–164. Interscience, New York.

STEEMANN NIELSEN E. (1964a) Recent advances in measuring and understanding marine primary production. *J. Ecol. (Suppl.),* **52,** 119–130.

STEEMANN NIELSEN E. (1964b) On a complication in marine productivity work due to the influence of ultraviolet light. *J. Cons. Int. Explor. Mer,* **29,** 130–135.

STEEMANN NIELSEN E. and HANSEN U.K. (1959a) Light adaptation in marine phytoplankton and its interrelation with temperature. *Physiol. Plant.* **12,** 353–370.

STEEMANN NIELSEN E. and HANSEN V.K. (1959b) Measurements with the C-14 technique of the respiration rates in natural populations of phytoplankton. *Deep-Sea Res.* **5,** 222–232.

STEEMANN NIELSEN E. and JENSEN H.K. (1957) Primary oceanic production. The autotrophic production of organic matter in the oceans. *Galathea Rep., Sci. Res. of the Danish Deep-Sea Expedition around the World,* **1,** 49–136.

STEEMANN NIELSEN E. (1965) On the determination of the activity in C/14 ampoules for measuring primary production. *Limnol. and Oceanogr.* **10** (Suppl.), R247–R252.

STEEMANN NIELSEN E. and JØRGENSEN E.G. (1962) The physiological background for using chlorophyll measurements in hydrobiology and a theory explaining daily variations in chlorophyll concentration. *Arch. Hydrobiol.* **58,** 349–357.

STEPANEK M. (1961) Der automatische Planktonentnahmeapparat für Talsperren (Hydra). *Verh. Int. Verein. Limnol.* **14,** 955–957.

STEPANEK M. and ZELINKA M.D. (1961) Limnological study of the reservoir Sedlice near Zeliv XVII. The development of phytonannoplankton in silonbags. *Sbornik vys. školy chem.-technol. v Praze,* **5,** 275–323.

STRASKRABA M. (1968) Der Anteil der höheren Pflanzen an der Produktion der Gewässer. *Mitt. Int. Verein. Limnol.* **14,** 212–230.

STREETER H.W. and PHELPS E.B. (1925) A study of the pollution and natural purification of the Ohio River. III. *Publ. Hlth Bull., Washington,* **146,** 75 pp. (reprinted 1958).

STRICKLAND J.D.H. (1958) Solar radiation penetrating the ocean. A review of requirements, data and methods of measurement, with particular reference to photosynthetic productivity. *J. Fish. Res. Bd. Canada,* **15,** 453–493.

STRICKLAND J.D.H. (1960) Measuring the production of marine phytoplankton. *Bull. Fish. Res. Bd. Canada,* **122,** 1–172.

STRICKLAND J.D.H. and PARSONS T.R. (1960) A manual of seawater analysis. *Bull. Fish. Res. Bd. Canada,* **125,** 1–185.

STRICKLAND J.D.H. and PARSONS T.R. (1968) A practical handbook of seawater analysis. *Bull. Fish. Res. Bd. Canada*, **167**, 311 pp.

STRICKLAND J.D.H. and TERHUNE L.D.B. (1961) The study of in situ marine photosynthesis using a large plastic bag. *Limnol. and Oceanogr.* **6**, 93–96.

SZCZEPANSKI A. (1958) Das Streuungsvermögen des Naturalwassers der Masurischen Seenplatte. *Polskie Arch. Hydrobiol.* **5** (1), 25–43.

SZEICZ G. (1966) Field measurements of energy in the 0·4—0·7 micron range. In: *Light as an Ecological Factor* (edited by R. BAINBRIDGE, G.C. EVANS and O. RACKHAM). *Symp. Brit. Ecol. Soc.* **6**, 41–51. Blackwell Scientific Publications, Oxford.

TALLING J.F. (1955) The light relations of phytoplankton populations. *Verh. int. Verein. Limnol.* **12**, 141–142.

TALLING J.F. (1957a) The phytoplankton population as a compound photosynthetic system. *New Phytol.* **56**, 133–149.

TALLING J.F. (1957b) Photosynthetic characteristics of some freshwater plankton diatoms in relation to underwater radiation. *New Phytol.* **56**, 29–50.

TALLING J.F. (1957c) Diurnal changes of stratification and photosynthesis in some tropical African waters. *Proc. R. Soc. B.* **147**, 57–83.

TALLING J.F. (1960) Comparative laboratory and field studies of photosynthesis by a marine planktonic diatom. *Limnol. and Oceanogr.* **5**, 62–77.

TALLING J.F. (1961) Photosynthesis under natural conditions. *Ann. Rev. Pl. Physiol.* **12**, 133–154.

TALLING J.F. (1965) The photosynthetic activity of phytoplankton in East African lakes. *Int. Rev. ges. Hydrobiol.* **50**, 1–32.

TALLING J.F. (1966) Photosynthetic behaviour in stratified and unstratified lake populations of a planktonic diatom. *J. Ecol.* **54**, 99–127.

TALLING J.F. and DRIVER D. (1963) Some problems in the estimation of chlorophyll-*a* in phytoplankton. *Proceedings, Conference of Primary Productivity Measurement, Marine and Freshwater, Hawaii*, 1961. U.S. Atomic Energy Comm. TID–7633, 142–146.

TAYLOR F.J. (1965) The growth of *Pseudococcomyxa adhaerens* in distilled water. *Arch. Mikrobiol.* **50**, 378–381.

THAMS J.C. and WIERZEJEWSKI H. (1958) Messung der Zirkumglobal-strahlung am Alpensüdfuss. *Arch. Meteorol. Geophys. Bioklimatol.* **9** (2), 185–198.

TEAL J.M. (1967) Biological production and distribution of pCO_2 in Woods Hole waters. In: *Estuaries* (edited by G.H. LAUFF). *Amer. Ass. Adv. Sci. Publ.* **83**, 336–340.

TEAL J.M. and KANWISHER J (1966) The use of pCO_2 for the calculation of biological production, with examples from waters off Massachusetts. *J. Mar. Res.* **24**, 4–14.

THOMAS E.A. (1955) Stoffhaushalt und Sedimentation im oligotrophen Aegerisee und im eutrophen Pfäffiker und Greifensee. *Mem. Ist. Ital. Idrobiol. Suppl.* **8**, 357–465.

THOMAS E.A. (1956) Sedimentation und Stoffhaushalt im Turlersee. *Monatsbull. Schweiz. Ver. Gas und Wasserf.* **12**, 1–11.

THOMAS E.A. (1957) Der Zürichsee, sein Wasser und Boden. *Jahrb. v. Zürichsee,* **17**, 173–208. (Verl. Gut, Stäfa & Zürich).

THOMAS E.A. (1959) Das Plankton-Test-Lot, ein Gerät zum Studium des Verhaltens von Planktonorganismen im See. *Monatsbull. Schweiz. Ver. Gas und Wasserf.* 1958, **1**, 3–8.

THOMAS E.A. (1961) Vergleiche über die Planktonproduktion in Flaschen und im Plankton-Test-Lotnach Thomas. *Verh. int. Verein. Limnol.* **14**, 140–146.

THOMAS E.A. (1962) Versuche mit Plankton-Test-Loten im Baldeggersee. II. *Vierteljahrsschr. Naturforsch. Ges. Zürich*, **107**, 155–196.

THOMAS E.A. (1964) Nährstoffexperimente in Plankton-Test-Loten (1958). *Verh. int. Verein. Limnol.* **15**, 342–351.

THOMAS N.A. and O'CONNELL R.L. (1966) A method for measuring primary production by stream benthos. *Limnol. and Oceanogr.* **11**, 386–392.

TRAYLOR T.G. and CRANE R.A. (1961) An inexpensive, very accurate automatic syringe. *Experientia*, **17**, 35–36.

UNESCO (1966) Determination of photosynthetic pigments in seawater. Report of SCOR/UNESCO Working Group 17, which met from 4 to 6 June 1964, UNESCO, Paris: *Monographs on Oceanographic Methodology*, **1**, 69 pp.

U.S. PUBLIC HEALTH SERVICE (1960) *Standard Methods for the Examination of Water and Wastewater.* 11th edition, part IX.

UTERMÖHL H. (1958) Zur Vervollkommnung der quantitativen Phytoplankton-Methodik. *Mitt. int. Verein. Limnol.* **9**, 1–38.

VACCARO R.F. and RYTHER J.H. (1954) The bactericidal effects of sunlight in relation to 'light' and 'dark' bottle photosynthesis experiments. *J. Cons. Int. Explor. Mer,* **20**, 18–24.

VALLENTYNE J.R. and WHITTAKER J.R. (1956) On the presence of free-sugars in filtered lake water. *Science*, **124**, 1026–1027.

VAN NIEL C.B. (1941) The bacterial photosyntheses and their importance for the general problem of photosynthesis. *Adv. Enzymol.* **1**, 263–329.

VERDUIN J. (1952) The volume-based photosynthetic rates of aquatic plants. *Amer. J. Bot.* **39**, 157–159.

VERDUIN J. (1960) Phytoplankton communities of western Lake Erie and the CO_2 and O_2 changes associated with them. *Limnol. and Oceanogr.* **5**, 372–380.

VERNON L.P. (1960) Spectrophotometric determination of chlorophylls and phaeophytins in plant extracts. *Analytical Chem.* **32**, 1144–1150.

VINBERG: *see* WINBERG.

VOLLENWEIDER R.A. (1955) Ein Nomogramm zur Bestimmung des Transmissionskoeffizienten sowie einige Bemerkungen zur Methode seiner Berechnung in der Limnologie. *Schweiz. Z. Hydrol.* **17** (2), 205–216.

VOLLENWEIDER R.A. (1956) Das Strahlungsklima des Lago Maggiore und seine Bedeutung für die Photosynthese des Phytoplanktons. *Mem. Ist. Ital. Idrobiol.* **9**, 293–362.

VOLLENWEIDER R.A. (1958) Sichttiefe und Produktion. *Verh. int. Verein. Limnol.* **13**, 142–143.

VOLLENWEIDER R.A. (1959) Alcune osservazioni sulla dinamica dell' ossigeno nel Lago Maggiore (Bacino di Pallanza). *Mem. Ist. Ital. Idrobiol.* **11**, 241–264.

VOLLENWEIDER R.A. (1960) Beiträge zur Kenntnis optischer Eigenschaften der Gewässer und Primärproduktion. *Mem. Ist. Ital. Idrobiol.* **12**, 201–244.

VOLLENWEIDER R.A. (1961) Photometric studies in inland waters. Relations existing in the spectral extinction of light in water. *Mem. Ist. Ital. Idrobiol.* **13**, 87–113.

VOLLENWEIDER R.A. (1962) Sull'uso di metodi conduttometrici per la titolazione della alcalinità, dei cloruri e dei solfati nelle acque dolci. *Mem. Ist. Ital. Idrobiol.* **15**, 29–42.

VOLLENWEIDER R.A. (1963) Studi sulla situazione attuale del regime chimico e biologico del Lago d'Orta. *Mem. Ist. Ital. Idrobiol.* **16,** 21–125.

VOLLENWEIDER R.A. (1964) Uber oligomiktische Verhältnisse des Lago Maggiore und einiger anderer insubrischer Seen. *Mem. Ist. Ital. Idrobiol.* **17,** 191–206.

VOLLENWEIDER R.A. (1965a) Calculation models of photosynthesis-depth curves and some implications regarding day rate estimates in primary production measurements. *Mem. Ist. Ital. Idrobiol. Suppl.* **18,** 425–457.

VOLLENWEIDER R.A. (1965b) Materiali ed idee per una idrochimica delle acque insubriche. *Mem. Ist. Ital. Idrobiol.* **19,** 213–286.

VOLLENWEIDER R.A. and NAUWERCK A. (1961) Some observations on the C-14 method for measuring primary production. *Verh. int. Ver. Limnol.* **14,** 134–139.

VOLLENWEIDER R.A. and SAMAAN A.A. (1958) A note on the use of C-14 for measuring carbon assimilation in periphyton. *Unpublished manuscript,* 4 pp.

VOLLENWEIDER R.A. and SARACENI C. (1964) Un nuovo terreno nutrizio per la coltivazione di alghe planctoniche d'aqua dolce. *Mem. Ist. Ital. Idrobiol.* **17,** 215–221.

WALKER F.T. (1947) Sublittoral seaweed survey. *J. Ecol.* **35,** 166–185.

WALKER F.T. (1950) Sublittoral seaweed survey of the Orkney Islands. *J. Ecol.* **38,** 139–165.

WALLEN D.G. and GEEN G.H. (1968) Loss of radioactivity during storage of ^{14}C-labelled phytoplankton on membrane filters. *J. Fish. Res. Bd. Canada,* **25,** 2219–2224.

WARREN WILSON J. (1959) Analysis of the distribution of foliage area in grassland. In: *The Measurement of Grassland Productivity,* 51–61. (Edited by J.D. IVENS, University of Nottingham, 6th Easter School in Agricultural Science, 1959.) Butterworths Scientific Publications, London.

WATERS T.F. (1961) Notes on the chlorophyll method of estimating the photosynthetic capacity of stream periphyton. *Limnol. and Oceanogr.* **6,** 486–488.

WATSON D.J. and WATSON M.A. (1953) Comparative physiological studies on the growth of field crops. III. The effect of infection with beet yellows and beet mosaic viruses on the growth and yield of the sugarbeet root crop. *Ann. Appl. Biol.* **40,** 1–37.

WATT W.D. (1965) A convenient apparatus for in situ primary production studies. *Limnol. and Oceanogr.* **10,** 298–300.

WATT W.D. (1965a) Release of dissolved organic material from the cells of phytoplankton populations. *Proc. Roy. Soc. B.* **164,** 521–551.

WELCH P.S. (1948) *Limnological Methods.* Blakiston, Philadelphia.

WESTLAKE D.F. (1963) Comparisons of plant productivity. *Biol. Rev.* **38,** 385–425.

WESTLAKE D.F. (1964) Light extinction, standing crop and photosynthesis within weed beds. *Verh. Intern. Ver. Limnol.* **15,** 415–425.

WESTLAKE D.F. (1965a) Theoretical aspects of the comparability of productivity data. *Mem. Ist. Ital. Idrobiol.* **18,** 313–322.

WESTLAKE D.F. (1965b) Some basic data for investigations of the productivity of aquatic macrophytes. *Mem. Ist. Ital. Idrobiol.* **229**–248.

WESTLAKE D.F. (1965) Some problems in the measurement of radiation under water: A review. *Photochemistry and Photobiology,* **4,** 849–868.

WESTLAKE D.F. (1966a) A model for quantitative studies of photosynthesis by higher plants in streams. *Int. J. Air and Water Pollut.* **10,** 883–896.

WESTLAKE D.F. (1966b) The light climate for plants in rivers. In: *Light as an Ecological Factor*, (edited by G.C. EVANS, R. BAINBRIDGE and O. RACKHAM). *Brit. Ecol. Soc. Symp.* No. **6**, 99–120. Blackwell Scientific Publ.

WESTLAKE D.F. (1966c) The biomass and productivity of *Glyceria maxima I*. Seasonal changes in biomass. *J. Ecol.* **54**, 745–753.

WESTLAKE D.F. (1967) Some effects of low-velocity currents on the metabolism of aquatic macrophytes. *J. Exp. Bot.* **18**, 187–205.

WESTLAKE D.F. (1968) Methods used to determine the annual production of reedswamp plants with extensive rhizomes. In: *Methods of productivity studies in rootsystems and rhizosphere organisms. IBP Root Symposium, Moscow 1968*, 226–234. NAUKA, Moscow

WESTLAKE D.F. (in prep.) The biomass and productivity of *Glyceria maxima II*. Population dynamics. III. Biomass dynamics and productivity estimates.

WETZEL R.G. (1963) Primary productivity of periphyton. *Nature*, **197**, 1026–1027.

WETZEL R.G. (1964) A comparative study of the primary productivity of higher aquatic plants, periphyton and phytoplankton in a large shallow lake. *Int. Rev. ges. Hydrobiol.* **49**, 1–61.

WETZEL R.G. (1965a) Necessity for decontamination of filters in C-14 measured rates of photosynthesis in fresh waters. *Ecology*, **46**, 540–542.

WETZEL R.G. (1965b) Techniques and problems of primary productivity measurements in higher aquatic plants and periphyton. *Mem. Ist. Ital. Idrobiol. Suppl.* 18, 147–165.

WHITFORD L.A. (1960) The current effect and growth of freshwater algae. *Trans. Amer. Microsc. Soc.* **79**, 302–309.

WHITFORD L.A. and SCHUMACHER C.J. (1961) Effect of current on mineral uptake and respiration by a freshwater alga. *Limnol. and Oceanogr.* **6**, 423–425.

WHITNEY L.V. (1938) Continuous solar radiation measurements in Wisconsin lakes. *Trans. Wisc. Acad. Sci., Arts and Lett.* **31**, 175–200.

WHITWER E.E. (1955) Efficiency of finely-divided vs. tape-like aquatic plant leaves. *Ecology*, **36**, 511–512.

WIESSNER W. and GAFFRON H. (1964) Role of photosynthesis in the light-induced assimilation of acetate by *Chlamydobotrys*. *Nature*, **201**, 725–726.

WINBERG G.G. (1955) Significance of photosynthesis for oxygen enrichment of water during self-purification of polluted waters. *Trud. vesoyuz. gidrobiol. Obshch.* **6**, 46–69 (In Russian.)

WINBERG G.G. (1960) *Pervichnaya Produktsiia Voedoemov*. Izd. Akad. Nauk, B.S.S.R. Minsk. *Primary Productivity of Waters*. (In Russian.)

WINBERG G.G. (1963) *The Primary Production of Bodies of Water*. (English translation.) U.S. Atomic Energy Commission, Div. Tech. Inf. AEC-tr-5692 (2 books).

WOOD E.J.F. (1955) Fluorescent microscopy in marine microbiology. *J. Cons. Int. Explor. Mer*, **21**, 6–7.

WOOD E.J.F. (1962) A method for phytoplankton study. *Limnol. and Oceanogr.* **7**, 32–35.

WOOD R.D. (1963) Adapting SCUBA to aquatic plant ecology. *Ecology*, **44**, 416–418.

WOOD K.G. (1964) Gasometric determinations of carbon dioxide in natural waters in relation to pH and to the activities of plants. *Verh. int. Verein. Limnol.* **15**, 322–329.

WRIGHT J.C. (1959) Limnology of Canyon Ferry Reservoir. II. Phytoplankton standing crop and primary production. *Limnol. and Oceanogr.* **4** (3), 235–245.

WRIGHT R.T. (1964) Dynamics of a phytoplankton community in an ice-covered lake *Limnol. and Oceanogr.* **9**, 163–178.

WRIGHT R.T. and HOBBIE J.E. (1965a) The uptake of organic solutes in lake water. *Limno and Oceanogr.* **10**, 22–28.

WRIGHT R.T. and HOBBIE J.E. (1965b) The uptake of organic solutes by planktonic bacteria and algae. Ocean Science and Ocean Engineering 1965. Transactions of conference and exhibit., Wash. D.C., *Am. Soc. Limnol. Oceanog. and Mar. Tech. Soc.* **1**, 116–127.

YENTSCH C.S. (1963) Primary production. *Oceanogr. Mar. Biol. Ann. Rev.* **1**, 157–175.

YENTSCH C.S. and MENZEL D.W. (1963) A method for the determination of phytoplankton chlorophyll and phaeophytin by fluorescence. *Deep-Sea Res.* **10**, 221–231.

YENTSCH C.S. (1966) The relationship between chlorophyll and photosynthetic carbon production with reference to the measurement of decomposition products of chloroplastic pigments. *Mem. Ist. Ital. Idrobiol. Suppl.* **18**, 323–346.

YOUNG O.W. (1945) A limnological investigation of periphyton in Douglas Lake, Michigan. *Trans. Amer. Microsc. Soc.* **64**, 1–20.

ZOBELL C.E. and ANDERSON D.Q. (1936) Observations on the multiplication of bacteria in different volumes of stored sea water and the influence of oxygen tension and solid surfaces. *Biol. Bull.* **71**, 324–342.

ZOBELL C.E. and STADLER J. (1940) The effect of oxygen tension on the oxygen uptake of lake bacteria. *J. Bact.* **39**, 307–322.

ZOBELL C.E. (1946) *Marine Microbiology. Chronica Botanica,* (*Mass.*) **15**, 240 pp.

ZÜLLIG H. (1953) Ein neues Lot zur Untersuchung der obersten Schlammschichten, zur Messung des Sedimentabsatzes und zur Erfassung bodennaher Wasserschichten. *Schweiz. Z. Hydrol.* **15**, 275–284.

ZÜLLIG H. (1959) Eine neue Schöpfflasche mit automatischer Bodenauslösevorrichtung. *Schweiz. Z. Hydrol.* **21**, 109–111.

Index

212